VOLUME TWO

PLANNING THE MODERN CITY

PLANNING THE MODERN CITY

VOLUME ONE

Harold MacLean Lewis

CONSULTING ENGINEER AND CITY PLANNER

JOHN WILEY & SONS, Inc., New York

CHAPMAN & HALL, Ltd., London

Printed in the United States of America

PREFACE

Tremendous strides have been made in city planning throughout the world since the publication of *The Planning of the Modern City*, by the late Nelson P. Lewis, issued in 1916, with a second revised edition in 1922. Much of the progress lies in the wider acceptance of planning as a prerequisite to the orderly and efficient development of both urban and rural areas. Many communities, nevertheless, are still without plans, and much remains to be done in this field.

There has, however, been little change in the general principles governing the theory or the practice of city planning, so that this new book, based on the old one and prepared by the son of the original author, has required little change in the statements regarding these principles. Many references have been replaced with later examples, and statistics have been brought up to date. Chapters have been added dealing with basic information needed, the control of subdivisions, and the problems of parking motor vehicles, the relation of the airport to the city plan, public responsibility for housing, and the redevelopment of blighted areas. New developments and trends in zoning, express highways, and urban transportation have been described.

The present work is presented in two volumes. The first contains a general introduction to city planning, an analysis of its objectives, and a discussion of all the main elements which establish the framework of a master plan for an urban community. The second volume deals with the special physical, social, legal, economic, and administrative problems which should be considered by a city planner and a planning commission.

Nelson P. Lewis wrote with the background of many years spent in municipal work, and his book drew fully on his rich experience as a civil engineer and municipal official. It was recognized as an outstanding engineering contribution to city planning literature. As the first Chief Engineer of the Board of Estimate and Apportionment of the City of New York, a post created in 1902 after the creation of the present city by the consolidation in 1898 of the former city, then comprising only Manhattan Island and The Bronx, with the counties of Kings (including the city of Brooklyn), Queens, and Richmond, Mr. Lewis became one of the outstanding municipal engineers in the United States. He promptly assumed leadership in the city planning field. With his wide knowledge and study of the plans of many other cities, both in this country and abroad, he knew urban problems thoroughly and was active in their solution. His book was frankly written with the idea that the fundamental problems of city planning are, and from their very nature must be, engineering problems. At the same time he fully appreciated that planning is a co-operative process involving the active aid of members of all related professions dealing with design as well as of specialists in economics and sociology.

Cities, large and small, present many urgent planning problems. At the same time, because of the magnitude of their public works programs and their ability to draw on the best technical advisers, they possess great opportunities for benefiting from sound planning. This new book, like the former one, is limited to a discussion of urban planning. Many of the illustrations in the earlier publication were selected to illustrate principles and are retained in the present volumes. Many others were intended as a record of planning accomplishment and have been replaced with later and more timely selections.

I was privileged to have a small part in assisting the original author in the preparation of the second edition of his book. As a son who was fortunate to be associated with his father in some of his later work for the Regional Plan of New York and Its Environs, and as one who has specialized in city planning, I have found the preparation of this new book to be a labor of love. The opinions of the original author have been retained, and nothing has been added which would conflict with these.

HAROLD MacLEAN LEWIS

New York, New York
October 7, 1948

ACKNOWLEDGMENTS

Acknowledgment is made of the assistance received from the published works of others as referred to throughout these volumes. Special acknowledgment is also due to the following: Lloyd F. Rader, Professor of Civil Engineering, University of Wisconsin, and Elisabeth M. Herlihy, Chairman, Massachusetts State Planning Board, for their helpful suggestions and the loan of illustrative material; my office staff members, Charles M. Herrick and Charles L. Austin, who did much of the research work involved in the preparation of new material, Alfred Czanczik, who prepared many of the maps and diagrams, and Grace E. Hutchinson, who, as my secretary, has handled all the secretarial and stenographic work involved; Russell Sage Foundation for permission to use material in the volumes of the Regional Plan of New York and Its Environs; and the many others who have made available photographs and maps used as illustrations.

CONTENTS

Part Three—A Pattern for Land Use

1

PURPOSE AND SCOPE

THE PEOPLES OF THE WORLD HAVE CONGREGATED in cities from time immemorial. Much has been written of their early plans, of their growth, and in some cases of their fall and decay. It may be helpful to explain what is meant by the words "modern" and "city" in the title of this book.

By "modern" is meant the type of city that has resulted from high-speed electric and automotive transportation, the steel-frame building, and the great improvements in long-distance telephone communications—all advancements which have made possible both great concentration for business purposes and great decentralization for residence and industry. They are each typical of the twentieth century. The resultant city still suffers from congestion, which was also present in many of its early counterparts.

By "city" is meant urban, in contrast with rural or agricultural, but with the recognition that many of our urban communities have within their confines substantial areas that are still rural or semi-rural in character and that must be planned as part of the whole.

The term "city planning" has been used in the United States to cover the planning of all types of communities and regions. The term "town planning," as used in Great Britain and its Dominions and on the continent of Europe,

is perhaps a more appropriate one. Herein they are synonymous.

With the increased interest in modern city planning there have been published many books on that general subject and many others dealing with special aspects of the subject, with recent emphasis upon housing and the redevelopment of blighted areas. These are supplemented by a constantly growing collection of reports dealing with specific conditions and localities and affording excellent illustrations of the manner in which city planning problems may be approached and solved. These reports often contain more valuable suggestions than are to be found in books which attempt to cover the entire field and to lay down fundamental principles rather than deal with concrete examples. This being the case, it may be asked, "Why make another contribution to a field so fully covered?"

The answer is that this book, like the earlier one on which it is based, is to be devoted almost entirely to the engineering aspects of city planning, or to city planning as an engineering problem or group of problems. It also will be limited to urban planning and will not attempt to cover either rural or large-scale regional planning. In dedicating the original volume to the municipal engineers of the United States, the author indicated his hope that this group of his co-workers would find its pages of some value in achieving a somewhat keener realization of their part in, and responsibility for, the constructive work of city planning as well as city building. Many other professional groups contribute much to the co-operative task of preparing a city plan, but the civil engineer can and must play an increasing part in solving fundamental urban problems.

Subjects will be discussed that are not generally considered as falling within the scope of the engineer's activities, but they are all subjects with which one who is responsible for the development of the city plan should be familiar. Perhaps the most important characteristic of any design should be its adaptability to altered conditions. If this is true with respect to a building, an industrial plant, a railway or shipping terminal which can be enlarged or replaced or even moved to another location, it is much more important in the ground plan of a city, which cannot be rearranged or transferred to another place. There is no undertaking, therefore, which demands more careful study of what has happened elsewhere, what is likely to happen in a particular place, and the development of tendencies which are sure to result in changes in the methods of living and conducting business, than the working out of the general plan for a city or for the successive additions to an existing city.

The books and periodicals devoted to city planning are not only agreeable reading, but are also instructive and valuable contributions to the literature of the subject. They are profusely illustrated with plans of ancient cities and pictures indicating how they must have appeared in their day, and with numerous views of many of the world's greatest and best-known buildings or groups of buildings, some of which have done duty in nearly every book yet published upon this subject. Such illustrations will be very sparingly used in these volumes. For a study of the history of city planning, both in the United States and abroad, the reader will be referred to books by other authors.

Photographs are used herein, not because they are attractive pictures which would add interest to a book of travel, but in order to illustrate the effect of a certain plan, treatment, or policy discussed in the text. Preference has been given, however, to diagrams and plans which, while they may not make as strong an appeal to the casual reader who turns the pages, will indicate what has more recently been done and what is being planned and executed at the present time, and which will make clearer the purpose of the author and speak more convincingly to those whom he is most desirous of reaching.

The accomplishments of those who built ancient Palmyra, Cyrene, Athens, and Rome are well worthy of admiration and may be an inspiration to the municipal engineers and city planners who are responsible for modern city planning, but it is a mistake to use these ancient cities as models. In many of the cities of antiquity there were superb buildings or groups of buildings, or impressively beautiful and dignified approaches to or connections between them adorned with colonnades and arches which were masterpieces of architectural design, but the plans of the cities themselves were rigidly rectangular, with exceedingly narrow streets, and are examples of the very thing we are now trying to avoid in city planning. The forums of these cities were excellent examples of the effective grouping of temples and public buildings; they were the show places of the city; each was a small unit of the city plan, and as such they were admirable. They were not connected with each other, and each seems to have been located without regard to the general city plan, but rather to have been designed to emphasize the power and glory of a particular period or individual. The model of Imperial Rome in the fourth century, exhibited at the Salon des Artistes Françaises in 1913 by M. Bigot, was much admired and was undoubtedly of great architectural and archaeological value and interest, but it illustrates very forcibly the fact that these units were put down wherever a place could be found for them, and that they were not parts of a general plan for the entire city and could not, therefore, be called good examples of city planning in the modern sense.

Interesting as these old plans and their restoration may be on paper, and profitable as their study may be to the architect, they offer little valuable suggestion to modern city planners unless it is a caution against a concentration of effort to produce a grand climax at the expense of the rest of the city. The conspicuous feature of the twentieth century city and its organization is the consideration given to provision for the health, comfort, convenience, and recreation of all the citizens, the rich and the poor, the dweller in the finest residential district and the inhabitant of the slum, although it is conceded that the modern city should have no slums. In the ancient cities the plans of which are most studied, the number of free citizens whose interests were deemed worthy of consideration was very small in comparison with the slaves who made up the great bulk of the population, but who had no rights and were thought to be entitled to little regard; yet art and architecture flourished. The members of the smaller ruling class thought nothing too fine for their city, and we, in our admiration of the masterpieces they created, forget how the submerged nine-tenths lived and the small consideration shown for them. In view of the vastly different conditions which exist today, when the welfare of the submerged fraction, be it large or small, is one of the chief concerns in city planning and administration, it is obviously unwise to look to the alleged restorations of these ancient cities for illustrations of the fundamental or constructive work of city planning or the work which would naturally be done by the engineer.

Other sources quite generally drawn upon by writers on city planning are the mediaeval cities of Europe, more particularly those of Germany, France, and northern Italy, the chief buildings of which—castles, churches, and town halls—are often effectively grouped about squares or "places" which are now considered masterpieces of city planning. Raymond Unwin observed that the charm of these old towns is not due to the better plan of their streets, but to the dignity and individuality of the buildings. The object seemed to be to do work well and to have it look well when done. Time has mellowed the colors, and sagging beams have relieved the angularity. Compared with the modern suburb with its freedom to do as

each dweller likes, and with the obvious lack of serious effort to adapt each building to its site and surroundings, these old towns are beautiful. But the social conditions prevailing in such towns at the time these much admired "places" or groups were created, while far better than those in the cities of antiquity, were very different from those which must be provided today.

It is true that efficient administration has effected an adaptation of these old plans to modern social conditions, has preserved the old, and has made the new conform with it to such a degree as to preserve the character of the town and the local color, without impairing or curtailing the rights or the enjoyment of the masses other than to the degree necessary to prevent abuse of, or injury to, public or private property. This lesson is little appreciated by those for the betterment of whose condition most writers on city planning appear to be chiefly concerned. This is conspicuously the case in the United States, where citizens of foreign birth and descent, who have some knowledge of the municipal administrative methods and accomplishments in the Old World, are insistent in their demands that the same things be done in American cities. At the same time they are indignantly resentful of the restrictions upon the use of private property or even the improper use and occupation of public streets, parks, and buildings which are so rigidly enforced in the cities of their native lands and upon the enforcement of which the attainment of these results are in large degree dependent.

Although some of the illustrations of the subjects discussed have been drawn from European and South American cities, most of them are taken from those of the United States, and it may be thought that New York and other eastern cities are given undue prominence. This does not mean that conspicuous progress in the solution of city planning problems has not been made in other cities. In fact, some of the most notable undertakings and accomplishments of this kind have been in the smaller towns of the interior, where the people appear to be more ready to appreciate a new idea, to realize a change in conditions, and to adopt and carry out plans for readjustment than in the more conservative towns along the Atlantic Coast. In recent years planning for municipalities, both large and small, has been particularly active in the Pacific Coast states. While most of the literature of the subject, even that produced by American writers, abounds in references to and illustrations of the cities of the Old World, and although some of these writers appear to believe that these are the only models worthy of being followed and that American cities can best be used as examples of what should be avoided, the author is convinced that the cities and towns of the Western World afford very many examples of sane and reasonable planning as well as of the things that should not be done.

Perhaps more of the text and illustrations would have been devoted to the cities of Europe had it not been for the interruptions in the execution of new projects as a result of the two World Wars. It was a great loss to the world when countries which had contributed so much that is admirable and worthy of imitation in city planning and especially in city administration abandoned their constructive work to engage in destruction, with the result that many of the public squares which had been much praised and freely drawn upon for illustrations were, together with the imposing buildings, churches, libraries, universities, and town halls, reduced to ruins. After World War I France and Belgium made great strides in rebuilding not only public squares and buildings but whole towns which had been almost entirely demolished. In many cases advantage was taken of the opportunity to avoid some of the congestion and inconveniences resulting from the old plans, while the picturesque effects which have added so much to the charm of those countries were maintained. Tremendously greater devastation was caused by World War II, and Poland, England, Russia, Italy, Germany, France, and other countries faced difficult problems of reconstruction and, in many cases, economic problems rendering construction difficult. But new city plans were under way even before the fighting ceased and should result in better adaptation to modern methods of living and doing business.

While it would be unfair and misleading to say that much which has been written on the subject of city planning is inaccurate, it is true that much has been presented on hearsay, and statistics have frequently been given that are obviously, although inadvertently, incorrect or at least misleading. Some writers have indulged in savage criticism of what they have observed or been told about conditions in other countries or cities, much of which is due to misunderstanding or misinformation, yet some of these conditions and practices, while at variance with the ideas of the critic, may be fully justified by the circumstances.

Much information must be secured at second hand or by correspondence. When inquiries are addressed to foreign cities, either they or the replies to them are frequently misunderstood, but, after making an effort to secure pertinent information, the temptation to use whatever is obtained, even though one is not entirely satisfied as to its complete accuracy, is very strong. It is not improbable that some of the data given in the following chapters may be found to be somewhat incomplete or defective, but the author has made every effort to insure their accuracy; where believed to be doubtful, statistics which it was desired to include have been omitted. An effort has been made to distinguish between facts and opinions, and, where opinions are given, they are not presented as conclusions which settle questions under discussion.

Where the opinions or conclusions of others or data compiled from them are used, the authority for them has been stated. In going over the literature of any subject, however, it frequently may happen that the opinions or conclusions encountered coincide with those which one has already formed, and the expression of them may conform so closely with the language used by others that the reader may think them appropriated without credit. If such instances occur in these volumes, it is the hope of the author that they will be attributed to the influence which the master exercises upon the student and not to a disposition to put forward the ideas of others as his own.

Questions

1. What professions have contributed most to the technique of city planning?
2. Describe the main characteristics of the plans of ancient cities.
3. What useful lesson can be learned from a study of such plans?
4. What were conspicuous new objectives in city planning of the twentieth century?
5. What feature is largely responsible for the charm of the mediaeval cities of Europe?
6. How have the two World Wars contributed indirectly to the advancement of city planning?

2

THE CITY PLANNING MOVEMENT

THE WIDE INTEREST IN CITY PLANNING ALL OVER Europe and America indicates quite clearly that it is a subject in which the people generally are concerned; not only those who live in large cities, which may undertake some costly and pretentious schemes of improvement, but also dwellers in the small towns and even villages are eager for information upon the subject and are ready to devote their time and energy to the study of plans to make their communities more orderly and attractive. Conferences and exhibits are frequent and largely attended, whether in Europe or America, books and magazine articles upon the subject appear at short intervals, and several periodicals regularly feature material on this subject. National planning conferences have been held annually in the United States since 1909 and have brought together large numbers of interested officials and laymen. The professional city planners, through such groups as the American Institute of Planners (originally the American City Planning Institute) and the Town Planning Institutes of Great Britain and Canada, give more intensive study to the technical problems involved, and all publish a journal at regular intervals.

A great international town planning conference was held in London in 1910 and was followed by several others in European cities. An international city and regional planning conference was held in New York City in 1925. Both a world engineering congress held in Tokyo in 1929 and an international technical congress held in Paris in 1946 featured papers on city planning.

At the Congress of Cities in Ghent in 1913 much attention was given to the subject, and a special exhibition of town planning, organized by Professor Patrick Geddes of Edinburgh, was a conspicuous feature of the exposition held in that city during the same year, although both the congress and the exhibition were devoted chiefly to the sociological aspects of the subject. An excellent exhibition was also held in New York at the close of 1913, the amount of material furnished far exceeding the space available for its display. Other exhibitions followed at the international conferences referred to above and are a regular feature of the national planning conferences in the United States. Exhibitions are also being used more and more by city planning commissions in bringing their proposals to the attention of the citizenry and obtaining constructive discussion thereon. For example, the City Planning Commission of Philadelphia, in co-operation with a local department store, staged a comprehensive exhibit in the fall of 1947, at which plans, sketches and models illustrating its proposals were presented.

The meetings of the International Congress for Housing and Town Planning, suspended during World War II, were revived in October, 1946, by a meeting at Hastings, England, at which 23 countries were represented by 1,257 persons. Replanning of the centers of cities, decentralization, housing, and methods of implementing plans were the general subjects featured at the sessions. Much interest was expressed in the views of the American delegates.

A large exhibition of plans was one of the popular features.

Definitions of City Planning

Notwithstanding all these meetings and discussions and the great amount that has been written and said, there is still more or less uncertainty as to just what city planning or town planning means. Some appear to consider it the designing of spectacular effects in the grouping of public buildings and the establishment of civic centers, the creation of imposing open spaces, the cutting through of broad avenues or the straightening and widening of existing streets, the reorganization and rearrangement of transit facilities and terminals—in short, the rebuilding or making over of cities and towns. These activities might more properly be called the correction of mistakes or the remedying of defects due to a lack of proper planning, rather than the more fundamental work of city planning, which should have as its chief object the avoidance of the necessity of costly reconstruction. What, then, is city planning? Many definitions have been written, some long and some short, some emphasizing the architectural and artistic side and others laying chief stress upon the social aspects, but few of them appear to recognize city planning as an engineering problem.

George McAneny, who has rendered distinguished service as President of the Borough of Manhattan, as President of the Board of Aldermen and Comptroller of New York City, and as President and, later, Chairman of the Board of the Regional Plan Association, said:

City planning simply means getting ready for the future in city growth. It is the guidance into proper channels of a community's impulses towards a larger and broader life. On the face it has to do with things physical—the laying out of streets and parks and rapid-transit lines. But its real significance is far deeper; a proper city plan has a powerful influence for good upon the mental and moral development of the people. It is the firm base for the building of a healthy and happy community.

James Ford defined city planning as follows:

City planning is a science and an art concerned primarily with the city's ever-changing pattern. As a pure science it examines causes (history, etiology) and reciprocal influences of man and environment (urban geography and ecology). As applied science it synthesizes these findings with those of the economic, sociological, and political sciences, as well as the technological branches of statistics, civil and sanitary engineering, architecture, landscape architecture, and all other pertinent branches of human knowledge, in an attempt thoroughly to understand conditions and their contexts and trends. As an art it utilizes these materials, instructs or organizes citizens, molds events, and thwarts or guides trends to bring about the changes in city design which it contemplates.[1]

Thomas Adams said:

City and town planning is a science, an art, and a movement of policy concerned with the shaping and guiding of the physical growth and arrangement of towns in harmony with their social and economic needs. We pursue it as a science to obtain knowledge of urban structure and services and the relation of its constituent parts and processes of circulation; as an art to determine the layout of the ground, the arrangement of land uses and ways of communication and the design of the buildings on principles that will secure order, health, and efficiency in development; and as a movement of policy to give effect to our principles.[2]

Earle S. Draper described city planning as follows:

Planning consists of a great number of things. Careful surveys and inventories of resources are necessarily the first requirement. The deliberative process which we call planning consists of an analysis of the facts, of an appraisal of the situation, and of the resulting considered opinion which comes forth as a plan presented in the proper garb, whether it be pictures, charts, maps, verbal descriptions, or a combination of all these.

A brief definition frequently used by Nelson P. Lewis is:

City planning is simply the exercise of such foresight as will promote the orderly and sightly development of a city and its environs along rational lines with due regard for health, amenity, and convenience and for its commercial and industrial advancement.

A simple definition of a different type appears in the following statement by Edward M. Bassett, an attorney eminent in planning and zoning law:

City planning subjects are streets, parks, public reservations, sites for public buildings, harbor lines,

[1] *Slums and Housing,* by James Ford, Harvard University Press, Cambridge, Mass., 1936, page 490.
[2] *Outline of Town and City Planning,* by Thomas Adams, Russell Sage Foundation, New York, 1935, page 21.

locations for transportation facilities, and zoning regulations. There may be others, but I think not. When these are stamped by law on the land, there you have the city plan.

The expanding scope of city planning is indicated by the statement of purposes in the constitution of the American Institute of Planners, as amended in 1946. It reads:

Its particular sphere of activity shall be the planning of the unified development of urban communities and their environs, and of states, regions, and the nation, as expressed through determination of the comprehensive arrangement of land uses and land occupancy and the regulation thereof.

Varying Emphasis in Different Countries

While the inhabitants of any country are usually inclined to think their own institutions and customs far better than, and to be somewhat intolerant of, those of other countries, there appears to be a disposition to attribute peculiar merit to the planning of the cities in other lands. The English, for instance, greatly admire the wide streets and the effective grouping of buildings in German cities, while the Germans are charmed with the garden villages attached to some of the great manufacturing plants in England, although nowhere, perhaps, have more attractive homes been made for artisans, or have these homes been arranged in a more pleasing manner than in the several colonies established in connection with the Krupp works at Essen. American writers on city planning have been extravagant in their praise of the planning and arrangement of Old World cities and are constantly comparing them with their own towns to the great disadvantage of the latter. Such unfavorable comparisons are too frequently justified, and yet some admirable planning has been and is being done in the cities of the United States.

Can this tendency be attributable to a sort of national modesty, which prompts the people of one country to admire and praise what has been done in another country? Probably not, as national modesty is a quality rarely, if ever, manifested. It seems to be due, rather, to an almost universal disposition to be attracted by and to admire effects with which one is unfamiliar, provided they do not too violently offend certain customs and standards which are so ingrained as to have become habits. When tall buildings were first erected in American cities, they were declared to be monstrosities, not only by visitors from abroad, but by most Americans as well. The architects, except those who were fortunate enough to secure commissions to design one or more of them, were especially offended, as they were held to violate the most sacred architectural traditions. As the character of their design improved, and some really beautiful effects were produced, the American architects were still severely critical, and it was not until foreigners began to admit that many of these buildings were really beautiful that Americans began to realize that they had produced something admirable. (See Figures 2·1 and 2·3.) That the erection of buildings twenty, thirty, and forty stories high, close together along streets of ordinary width has had a very serious effect upon traffic and other conditions, that they have injuriously affected each other as far as light and air are concerned (Figure 2·2), and that they have seriously impaired the land values is only too evident. As a result New York and other cities have been forced to control the height, bulk, and arrangement of buildings, as will be told in a later chapter. The tall buildings themselves, so far as their appearance is concerned, are not altogether condemned. One well-known architect has enumerated three points in their favor—their beauty in the aggregate is most impressive, they represent a distinctive type of national architecture, and they have become the artistic expression of a commercial necessity.

Patrick Abercrombie made a number of interesting comments in 1913 on the achievements and salient points of city planning in different countries. They are still pertinent, many years later, and some are briefly abstracted below.[3]

Sweden was, perhaps, the first country (1874) to enact a comprehensive town planning law, which appears to be based upon the assumption that a plan is requisite for every town. The results ob-

[3] "International Contributions to the Study of Town Planning and City Organization," by Patrick Abercrombie, *Town Planning Review*, Vol. IV, No. 2 (July, 1913), University of Liverpool, pages 98–117.

tained through the application of this act may be subject to criticism in that the insistence upon wide streets has tended towards a monotonous gridiron type, which in some cases has been forced upon the old and irregular parts of the cities.

Germany has, perhaps, achieved more modern town planning than any other country. If judged by legislation, the German municipalities appear to possess very limited powers, but in Germany town planning is a tradition, and the desirability of it is never questioned. Conspicuous features of German

bears the name of a distinguished municipal officer of a German city.[4]

Austria is essentially German in its treatment of town planning problems, but Vienna, the Austrian capital, is a city in its own class. Its Ringstrasse, located on ground formerly devoted to the inner fortifications, is one of the most notable streets in the world. A second ring street has been provided on the line of the outer fortifications, and there is again a ring of meadow and beyond that a ring of wooded hills.

Photo by Brown Brothers. Courtesy, Regional Plan Association, Inc.

Photo by William Frange. Courtesy, Regional Plan Association, Inc.

Photo by Brown Brothers. Courtesy, American Scenic and Historic Preservation Society.

FIGURE 2·1. THE CHANGING SKY LINE OF LOWER MANHATTAN ISLAND, NEW YORK CITY

The result is an ultimate composition of tall buildings, both striking and beautiful. Upper view is in 1876 from Brooklyn tower of the Brooklyn Bridge, then under construction; the lower views are from Governor's Island, at the left about 1927 and at the right as the sky line appeared in 1947.

planning are: zoning, by which the erection of lofty tenements has been restricted; the practice of converting old fortifications into wide circumferential streets, as in Bremen and Cologne (this has been conspicuously neglected in Berlin); the careful preservation of the ancient centers of the city, as in Frankfort and Nuremberg; and the acquisition of large tracts of land outside the city, which in Strassburg was said to be equivalent to a plot 57 feet square to each inhabitant, in Ulm to 60 per cent of the total area of the city and its immediate suburbs, and in Berlin to three times the area of the city. The "Lex Adickes" gives the municipal authorities power to redistribute land which, as originally divided, may have been rendered practically useless by the adoption of a street system, the land remaining after providing for streets and open spaces being redistributed in usable portions. This law, which appears to meet a difficult situation long recognized in other countries, was devised by and

France has paid more attention to the physical construction of its cities than to their organization, and has laid more stress upon the monumental and architectural aspects of the street plan than upon picturesque effects. No other city has provided as well as Paris for direct exits from and approaches to the city, although several of her great boulevards were originally constructed as private drives for royalty. Perhaps the Avenue de l'Opera is one of the most notable achievements of city planning by the construction of a new street furnishing an impressive vista. Traffic planning has claimed a large share of the attention of students of city planning in France.

England has been very backward in what is known as modern town planning, particularly in its monumental aspects. Scarcely a single great building

[4] This matter is discussed further in Volume II, Chapter 23.

Photo by Office of President, Borough of Manhattan.

Photo by Office of President, Borough of Manhattan.

Rotary Photograph Series.

FIGURE 2·2. EXAMPLES OF INTENSIVE DEVELOPMENT, MAKING STREET WIDENING IMPOSSIBLE ON
ACCOUNT OF EXPENSE INVOLVED

Illustrated by typical views in the downtown financial and office centers in the borough of Manhattan,
New York City.

has been provided with an adequate site and approach, and failure to provide for traffic needs has been most conspicuous. It is the English individual home, which has been religiously protected for generations, which appears to be the moving spirit in most of the modern town planning.

In Belgium the strong individuality of the different towns, such as Brussels, Antwerp, Ghent, and Bruges, is conspicuous. Plans for the improvement of Brussels, however, appear to have derived their inspiration from Paris.

Italy has not been behind its neighboring countries in city planning or in legislation directed to that end. The Italian cities possess powers of expropriation which have been found to be exceedingly valuable, and these powers have been exercised in a wise fashion, enabling the authorities to recoup a large proportion of the cost of new public works.

In America four conspicuous features of town planning were emphasized by Professor Abercrombie:

First, the devotion to the gridiron plan, which was described as a scientific nightmare in which squares are carried over the whole country irrespective of natural zones and contours and in comparison with which the lack of planning which formerly prevailed in England was admirable. Second, the current craze for the development of civic centers and other colossal schemes of monumental magnificence, largely inspired by the first Chicago World's Fair. Washington, the national capital, represents the climax of this phase, but Cleveland, Chicago, Philadelphia, and St. Louis are scarcely less ambitious. Many such projects include practical traffic improvements. Third, the scientific provision for recreation which has lately been made in many American cities. Fourth, an astonishing number of excellent reports, many prepared by private agencies or firms. The earlier reports were largely pictorial and monumental, Chicago standing first in this respect, but the later ones, in many cases, indicate a more practical approach to a solution of planning problems.

In the South American cities of Rio de Janeiro and Buenos Aires some ambitious projects have been carried out, particularly the cutting through of new streets and the creation of great boulevards along the waterfront, which have made these cities among the most notable in the world.

While it is interesting to note the characteristics of city planning in various countries, as interpreted by students of the subject, it must not be forgotten that the fundamental principles underlying the planning of all cities are practically the same, although the method of their expression may differ. Such method may be the result of habit or of local tradition rather than of painstaking investigation; it is frequently admired because it is somewhat different from that to which we are accustomed, but, as A. T. Edwards has observed, "Parochial art is invariably second rate." He further remarked, "While there is town planning in England, town planning in Germany, town planning in France, there is no such thing as English, German, or French town planning any more than there are English, German, or French sciences of arithmetic."

Perhaps it may fairly be said that much of the city planning in America has been chiefly confined to projects covering very restricted areas, the designs for which are usually made by a single man or a small group of men, architects, landscape architects, and engineers being associated together. The gradual development of a beautiful city, like some of the old towns of Europe, through the painstaking work of many individuals of successive generations, all with an intense pride in their city, is practically unknown. The spirit which produced the old towns so frequently found on the Continent appears to be lost. Wages are standardized and are paid for so many hours of work without regard to quantity or quality. Without the idea of work for work's sake, the devotional feeling of the workman who carved the pillar of a church or created some beautiful detail not noticed by the casual observer, it is doubtful that the fine old towns of Continental Europe could have been produced.

There is a deplorable lack of originality in many of the city planning schemes which are constantly being advocated. The designers are too prone to try to reproduce some public square or "grand place" which may arouse well-merited admiration in the town in which it is located, but which may be entirely incongruous in a modern American city. Most of the towns which are so greatly admired owe their peculiar attraction to some special quality closely related to their history and environment, to the nature of the scenery about them, to the customs of their people, to the type of their industries, or even to the color of their building material. In the gray old English towns a bit of brilliant color appears incongruous. The "rose-red town of Inverness" has

FIGURE 2·3. TYPICAL AMERICAN SKYSCRAPER BUILDINGS WITH AMPLE LIGHT AND AIR AROUND THEM

Upper view shows the Nebraska State Capitol at Lincoln; lower left, the Los Angeles City Hall; lower right, the RCA Building in Rockefeller Center, New York City.

a peculiar charm due to the color of the stone so generally used in the construction of its buildings. Now that any town can draw upon the building materials of an entire country or even of foreign countries, that consistent harmony of color no longer exists. An attempt to transplant a picturesque bit of Rothenburg to the plains of Long Island or to the prairies of the Mississippi Valley would be absurd; a Venetian "piazza" in Pittsburgh or Omaha would be grotesque. "Don't copy Europe" is the advice given to American city planners by no less an authority than Werner Hegemann of Berlin.

A rational city plan is inevitably of slow growth, and, while there seems to be a passionate desire at the present time to correct at once such obvious defects as are to be found in the plans of most of the cities of Great Britain and the United States, and from which those of Continental Europe are by no means free, the task is too great for any one man or group of men, or even for any one generation. Consequently there is danger that, recognizing the futility of the attempt, and staggered by the magnitude of the undertaking, we will lose interest and go on repeating our old mistakes. As Professor Eberstadt said, "Town planning rushed at too hurriedly or pursued inadvisedly may turn out to be an instrument of greater danger than a mere leaving to chance the growth of our cities."

Much was accomplished before people began to talk about such a thing as city planning. It was realized that conditions were bad, that cities were ugly, and that the cost of conducting business, both public and private, was needlessly great; and there were insistent demands for the improvement of these conditions, both with respect to the physical plan of the city and the administration of its public business. We often fail to realize what great progress has been made, and that the object lessons thus afforded have been the greatest stimulus to demands for something still better. Perhaps there are New Yorkers who regret the passing of the old days before the advent of the tall building, and think that the city must then have been far more picturesque and interesting. Let us see what the principal street of New York

looked like in those days. In 1847 there was published under the title "New York in Slices" a collection of sketches which had appeared from time to time in the columns of the *New York Tribune*. In one of these will be found the following description of Broadway:

Broadway narrowly escapes being the most magnificent street in the world. If the money expended upon it architecturally had been guided by half a grain of true taste or common sense the effect would have been perfectly glorious. As it is we have the chaotic elements of a noble avenue, the contemplation of which gives us more pain than pleasure. . . . A few really fine structures here and there meet the eye, but they appear like exhalations from an incredible extent of rubbish. A long, low row of unmeaning outlines and angles that geometry would blush to own; here a brick schoolhouse, there a clapboard barn; now a penitentiary, and then a pound; now stumbling over a rotten cellar door, and anon walking through an obtrusive plate-glass window, stuffed with gaudy cashmeres and mildewed muslins: this is the external appearance of Broadway. You search in vain for even some faint acknowledgment of the line of proportion and continuation, and involuntarily wish for darkness to conceal the jagged and unfinished upper story of magnificent Broadway. . . . But notwithstanding these glaring defects of taste, Broadway is, as times go, a very noble street, altogether the most showy, the most crowded and the richest fashionable thoroughfare on the continent, and surpassed by not more than three or four in Europe.

Speaking of the early morning on Broadway, the writer said:

You look around with a feeling of almost uneasiness. It does not seem that this is the noisy, rattling, bustling, flashing, joyous Broadway to which your steps are accustomed. Soon, however, the sidewalks begin to fill with the clerks and early workers trudging downtown to begin their day. The awakened swine gallop furiously downward to have the first cut of the new garbage which, despite the City Fathers, is sure to have been deposited in the gutters. In an hour or two the great thoroughfare will be alive and the whole city will go surging and thundering through it.

Although due allowance must be made for the extravagance of the writer of special articles for newspapers, the picture drawn by him was doubtless reasonably accurate, and the improvement in the physical aspect of Broadway will be readily acknowledged, an improvement which took place long before city planning, as we now understand it, was heard of.

The city planning movement, as it is now generally understood in America, may be said to date from 1893, when the "white city," created by the genius of Daniel H. Burnham and an able group of associates for the international exposition held that year in Chicago, made a profound impression upon all who saw it. It is safe to say that such effective grouping of a series of monumental buildings of harmonious design had never before been accomplished or even attempted; and, while the buildings themselves were temporary, the effect which they produced was permanent, and the influence of the general plan is quite evident in most of the ambitious projects for the creation of civic centers which have since been put forward. In every great exposition which has since been held this effective grouping of the buildings has been followed to a greater or less degree, and with the introduction of lagoons and canals and the wonderful improvements in electric lighting, the results have been so beautiful that they have given a new impetus to what is commonly called city planning.

The British, who have developed great enthusiasm over town planning, appear to have acquired a more fundamental conception of what planning really means, in that, except for the rebuilding of urban areas devastated by the bombing and rocket attacks of World War II, they are devoting their attention chiefly to the territory not yet developed. Rather than trying to make their towns over, or, when that is found to be impossible, to create one or two beauty spots or show places and stop there, they are trying to save the unspoiled places. If too much attention is devoted to costly schemes of reconstruction, fresh mistakes will be made elsewhere, as too often happens in the United States. The town planning legislation of Great Britain, the underlying principles of these acts and what has been accomplished under them, are discussed at some length in other chapters.

Planning versus Administration

There are many who believe that the chief purposes of city planning are social, that problems of housing, the provision of recreation and amusement for the people, the control and

even the ownership and operation of all public utilities, the establishment and conduct of public markets, the collection and disposal of wastes, the protection of public health, the building of hospitals, the care of paupers, criminals, and the insane, and the many other activities of the modern city are all a part of city planning. All of these, however, are matters of administration rather than of planning in the sense in which it will be considered in these volumes. Although some of them will be referred to in the succeeding chapters, the author's intent is to do so only as they are related to the more fundamental problems of so planning a city that the necessary buildings or the space required for them may be provided without the destruction of improvements already made or a recasting of the plan. Thus good sanitation, decent housing and all that makes a city a better place to live in will be made easy rather than difficult. While the author is in hearty sympathy with all movements that will promote better living, a finer citizenship, and greater culture and that will give every citizen an equal chance to enjoy the advantages which may be provided, the chief emphasis will be placed upon the initial work of planning which will make all these goals easier of attainment.

Trends in Urban Growth

There have been times when the opinion quite generally prevailed that the city was a necessary evil, that it was an unnatural and unwholesome thing for large numbers of people to be gathered together within the confines of a city. Walter E. Weyl, writing in *Harper's Magazine* for April, 1915, said that to "the fathers" the very conception of the city had in it something unwholesome. It was in their opinion

. . . a dwelling place of turbulent, impious, impudent mobs, of a congregation of "unproductive" artizans, wastrels, criminals, Sabbath-breakers. It was a blister on the social body; a tumor which absorbed the healthy juices. The city was vaguely associated with royalties, courts, armies, beggars, and tattered, insolent, rascally mobs; the country was the cradle of republican virtue and democratic simplicity. Jefferson, having in mind the squalid agglomerations of the old countries, congratulated America on being rural. . . .

For the most part the ancient city, whether great or small, lived parasitically on the country. It was the abode of exploiters, princes, landlords. Rome rendered nothing to Egypt for the corn which it took from Egypt. The modern city renders service commensurate with the service rendered to it. It fashions in its factories the products of the country and redistributes them to a wide nation, economically dependent.

Under modern social conditions with the subdivision of labor and a high degree of special-

nomical and desirable to combine in the carrying out of certain enterprises which are metropolitan in their nature, such as water supply, main drainage, policing, and the protection of public health.

In 1820 but one person in every twenty in the United States lived in cities of 8,000 or over. In 1850 this proportion had increased to one in eight, in 1870 to one in five, in 1900 to very nearly one in three, and in 1920 to one in two and three-tenths. The drift to the towns

TABLE 1

RATE OF INCREASE OF URBAN AND RURAL POPULATION IN THE UNITED STATES BETWEEN 1900 AND 1940

Class of Towns, by Population	Number of Towns			Total Population			Per Cent of Increase	
	1900	1920	1940	1900	1920	1940	1900–1920	1920–1940
1,000,000 or more	3	3	5	6,429,474	10,145,532	15,910,866	57.8	56.8
500,000 to 1,000,000	3	9	9	1,645,087	6,223,769	6,456,959	271.6	3.8
250,000 to 500,000	9	13	23	2,861,296	4,540,838	7,827,514	58.7	72.4
100,000 to 250,000	23	43	55	3,272,490	6,519,187	7,792,650	99.2	19.5
50,000 to 100,000	40	76	107	2,709,338	5,265,408	7,343,917	94.3	39.5
25,000 to 50,000	82	143	213	2,800,627	5,075,041	7,417,093	108.8	46.2
10,000 to 25,000	280	465	665	4,338,250	7,034,668	9,966,898	62.2	41.7
5,000 to 10,000	465	715	965	3,204,195	4,967,625	6,681,894	55.0	31.5
2,500 to 5,000	832	1,255	1,422	2,899,164	4,385,905	5,025,911	51.3	14.6
Total urban population	1,737	2,722	3,464	30,159,921	54,157,973	74,423,702	79.6	37.4
Rural population	.....	.....	.....	45,834,654	51,552,647	57,245,573	12.5	11.0
Total population of the United States	.....	.....	.....	75,994,575	105,710,620	131,669,275	39.1	24.6

ization, each individual doing one thing fairly well, if not expertly, and depending upon others for the things he does not do himself, urban living is a natural condition. Whether the very large cities will continue to increase as they have during the recent past may be doubted, and estimates of future population, based upon such increase, may be very misleading. That the percentage of urban population will continue to increase is probable, if not certain, but that the very large urban units will ever again increase at the sensational rates which occurred over the several decades preceding 1930 is unlikely. Decentralization has been taking place in metropolitan areas. This trend is desirable where it results in more towns of moderate size and proportionately few very large cities, even though some of the towns may be so near together as to make it eco-

has been very decided, but is continuing at a decreasing rate, as is shown in Table 1, the data for which are taken from the United States Census of 1940. It will be seen that, while the percentage of increase in the urban population from 1900 to 1920 was nearly 6.5 times that in the rural population, the percentage of increase in the urban population from 1920 to 1940 was only 3.4 times that in the rural population. In 1920 a little over one-half of the total population was living in towns of 2,500 or over. In 1940 56.5 per cent of the total population was living in such towns. The only population group that showed a larger growth from 1920 to 1940 than from 1900 to 1920 was the cities with populations of 250,000 to 500,000.

It should be remembered that a uniform rate of growth in both rural and urban communities would result in a constant passage of certain communities from the rural to the urban class and from each urban class to the one next above, but the census figures show that the rate of increase in the population of the rural territory has remained fairly constant.

In 1940 the Federal Census showed that, of the 13,479,142 people in New York State, 55.5 per cent lived in the single city of New York and no less than 82.8 per cent lived in munici-

and do not include any of the great capitals. Up to 1900 the greater growth of the German cities was very decided. Since then all the cities have experienced slower rates of growth, the German cities having been retarded by World War I. But at the end of the period each German city still had a greater population than its American counterpart. Some of the newer American cities which were still quite

TABLE 2

THE INCREASE IN POPULATION OF SIX GERMAN AND SIX AMERICAN CITIES FROM 1880 TO 1940

Cities	Population						Per Cent of Increase		
	1880	1890	1900	1910	1920 [a]	1940 [b]	1880 to 1900	1900 to 1920	1920 to 1940
Cincinnati	255,139	296,309	325,902	363,591	401,247	455,610	27.7	23.1	13.5
Breslau	272,900	335,200	422,728	510,929	528,260	615,006	54.9	25.0	16.4
Buffalo	155,000	255,664	352,387	423,715	506,775	575,901	127.3	43.8	27.7
Cologne	144,800	281,800	372,229	513,491	633,904	768,426	156.1	70.3	21.2
New Orleans	216,000	242,039	287,104	339,075	387,219	494,537	32.9	34.5	27.7
Dresden	220,800	276,500	395,394	546,822	529,326	625,174	79.1	33.9	18.1
Louisville	123,758	161,005	204,731	223,928	234,891	319,077	65.4	14.7	35.8
Hanover	122,800	163,600	235,666	302,384	310,431	472,527	91.9	31.7	52.2
Providence	104,850	132,099	175,597	224,326	237,595	253,504	67.5	35.3	6.7
Nuremberg	99,519	142,523	261,022	332,539	352,675	430,851	162.4	35.1	22.2
Rochester	89,366	133,896	162,608	218,149	295,750	324,975	82.0	81.9	9.9
Chemnitz	85,000	138,955	206,584	286,455	303,775	334,563	143.0	95.5	10.1

[a] Populations for German cities in 1920 are from *Statesman's Year Book* for 1921 and are as of Oct. 9, 1919.

[b] Populations for German cities in 1940 are from *Statesman's Year Book* for 1944 and are as of May 17, 1939.

palities of 2,500 or over; and the same conditions, though in somewhat less degree, existed in other eastern states of the United States.

Great increases in urban population have not been confined to North America. On January 1, 1945, Buenos Aires had a population of 2,620,827,[5] and Rio de Janeiro was estimated to have 1,941,700; both have been increasing at a considerably greater rate than Chicago, Berlin, or Vienna.

Table 2 shows a comparison of the relative rates of growth from 1880 to 1940 of six pairs of cities, one American and one German, which had approximately the same population in 1880. The places selected are believed to be typical

[5] From *Statesman's Year Book*, The Macmillan Company, New York, 1946.

small in 1880 have shown much greater rates of growth, an outstanding example being Los Angeles, which grew, largely through annexation, from 11,182 to 1,504,277, or over 134 times.[6] The extent to which the German figures may be further affected by World War II is indicated by an estimate of Professor Heinz Sauermann of Frankfort University, released November 16, 1946, that 50 years from then there would be only half as many Germans as there were in 1939—35,000,000 instead of 70,000,000.

It is quite apparent that the need of proper city planning is not confined to the very large cities, but that it is equally important in smaller cities and towns, which also present

[6] See pages 85 and 86.

greater opportunities. The small manufacturing town of today may be the great industrial city of tomorrow. What is now a small city

Courtesy, Boston City Planning Board.
Airphoto by Fairchild Aerial Surveys.

FIGURE 2·4. CHANGES IN THE FORT HILL SECTION OF BOSTON

Top view, as an early residential neighborhood; center view, being leveled off about 1870; bottom view, as a part of Boston's main business district in 1929.

may be the center of a metropolitan district during the next generation. In some cases such growth and development may be predicted with considerable confidence, and planning on a large scale would be justified.

An interesting example of the unpredictable changes that may come with urban growth is shown in Figure 2·4. The site is one of the hills on which the city of Boston was located. The building of a fort on this site in 1632 gave it the name of Fort Hill, although it had previously been called Corn Hill, being one of the early planting grounds of the colonists. This hill, of which the only trace remaining today is its name, rose to a height of 80 feet above the level of the sea, and to the strangers sailing up the harbor was one of the most prominent features of the town. As the years went on, the top of the hill was developed as one of the most desirable residential sections of the city, as indicated by the top view. About 1870 it was decided to level off the hill to make way for progress in the development of the city's business section, and today it is the site of many 125-foot buildings, as shown in the air view (bottom of Figure 2·4).

Objectives of Sound Planning

Whatever the plan may be, such reasonable foresight can be exercised as will permit it to be adapted to new conditions with as little disturbance and destruction of improvements as possible. The important thing is that the work of planning be entrusted to men of vision as well as technical training and experience. But this is not all that is necessary; a reasonable plan, once decided upon, should be adhered to in its essential features notwithstanding the opposition and the insistent demands for a departure from it which are likely to be encountered from those who are actuated by selfish interest or who are unable to look beyond their own limited horizon. President Taft, speaking of the plan of Washington, said:

Washington's appointment of L'Enfant, an educated French army engineer, to lay out the Capital City was a most lucky circumstance in our history. L'Enfant's plan in a way resembles the Federal Constitution. That great instrument of government has proven itself adaptable to a change of conditions that even the most clear-sighted man of affairs could not have anticipated. The simple comprehensiveness of its broad lines under the statesmanlike interpretation of Marshall has proved equal to the greatest emergencies and the most radical crises that could possibly confront a nation. So Washington and L'Enfant and Jefferson in their planning for Washington have left a framework for its development that the ablest architects and artists, now more than a hundred years after the plan was drawn and its execution begun, have confessed themselves unable to improve. The plan has been departed from in two or more notable instances through the obstinacy of men in power who could not appreciate its admirable qualities. Instead, however, of manifesting regret at these we should be grateful that they are so few in number, and that we are still able to carry out the plan and to make what its complete execution will make of Washington—the most beautiful city in the world. The reason why this is possible is because it has never been a center for business or manufacture, because its *raison d'être* is only to provide a seat for government activities and a home for public servants who carry them on. It is thus singularly free in its opportunity to devote its energies to enhancing its own stateliness and acquiring a dignity appropriate to the heart of our national sovereignty. . . . In its history Washington city has had to live through the day of small things. The plan of L'Enfant met the obstinacy and lack of artistic sense of certain legislators who closed the vista between the White House and the Capitol by insisting upon the erection of the Treasury across the line of Pennsylvania Avenue. Then later on, when Congress seemed determined to minimize everything national, it retroceded to Virginia the part of the ten miles square on the south side of the Potomac River and furnished substantial proof of its contracted view of Washington's future.

What is the dominant idea behind the city planning movement as we see it in the United States today? What are the ideals which the average city planner has in mind, and what the models which he strives to emulate? Beauty has heretofore been his chief aim, as was clearly shown by the frequent use of the term "the city beautiful," which was formerly so much in evidence but which happily is now more seldom heard. His ideals were obtained from brief visits to the show places of foreign cities, and his models were the imposing open spaces, the broad streets, the well-designed façades, and the fine vistas so frequently found in them. Beautiful indeed they are; but behind these attractive façades, and as the price paid for them and the wide streets on which they front, most distressing living conditions are frequently found. Werner Hegemann points out that in remodeling some of the European cities, the charms of which dazzle so many Americans, only beauty and elegance were sought and that

. . . to the production of this metropolitan elegance the most refined thought was given, but this thought benefited mainly the central sections of these capitals (the parts near the castles) and the exterior façades of the tenement houses. Behind these good-looking façades miserable crowding, lack of house gardens, and the choking of the next generation were permitted. This kind of city planning did not attempt to make comprehensive, preconceived plans, covering all branches of city growth, but touching only one or two aspects (mainly artistic), exaggerated their importance and did nearly as much harm as no planning at all.

Seldom does the peripatetic student of European city planning look for anything except these particular beauty spots. He is familiar with the unsightly parts of his own home city, the memory of the bare ugliness of which is particularly unpleasant when he looks upon the most notable achievements of the builders of Old World cities. He forgets the newness of everything at home. He does not look forward to the day when the open and unimproved spaces between the scattered groups of modest dwellings will be completely improved. These modest dwellings, though commonplace in appearance and monotonous in design, house the families of men who are working for a daily wage in a degree of comfort unknown to those of the same class who live behind the pretentious fronts which line many European streets.

The contrast between the appearance of the more important business thoroughfares and the unpaved and somewhat ragged streets characteristic of the outlying parts of some American cities is a rather painful memory, but the comforts which are found in the dwellings more than compensate for their less impressive exteriors. The cheapness of wood in America, the rapidity with which frame buildings can be erected, and the tolerance of the use of combustible building material have resulted in the erection of a large number of wooden buildings in the suburbs of American cities. This wooden construction, with the stock plans so frequently used and the obtrusive ugliness of scroll-saw applications, formerly resorted to in order to relieve the monotony of the design, has given these buildings a cheap and temporary appearance which compares unfavorably with the more substantial look of the stone and brick dwellings generally found in Great Britain and on the Continent. It is true that those who are responsible for the planning of American cities have been slow to realize the importance of an orderly arrangement of the fundamental ground plan or of the system of main streets will facilitate easy movement between different parts of the city, and a heavy penalty must some day be paid for this oversight in costly street widenings and cutting through of new connections, but this has been characteristic of city planning the world over.

Another thing that must be borne in mind when considering the pleasing effects of the centers of the European capitals is that they were planned by princes to whose courts were attracted the greatest architects and artists of the time; their services were at the command of their royal masters, who themselves were men of cultivated tastes and large ideas, and were ambitious to create a capital worthy of their own importance in the world. If they could also secure a minister of finance who had the genius to devise a means to wring from their subjects the money to carry out these plans, the thing was done. When the people themselves are called upon to decide whether they will furnish the funds to carry out such ambitious schemes, they are likely to hesitate a long time. Only as a result of a campaign of education which will convince them that a proposed improvement will bring them a direct return through increased business or in some other material way can they be induced to undertake such a project. When once undertaken, its execution must be entrusted to the duly authorized city officials, or a special commission must be created for the purpose. The former course is obviously the proper one, but the limited periods during which such officials hold office in American cities and the disposition of a new man or group of men to make changes, which may be prompted in some cases by considerations of economy and in others by a desire to impress their own individuality upon the scheme, often justify resort to a special commission.

It does not follow that a plan once adopted should never be changed in any respect. We call these plans comprehensive and final. If really comprehensive, they should be adaptable to changing conditions with little, if any, interference with the general scheme; but final in all details they never can be. President Taft noted the unfortunate results of some modifications of the L'Enfant plan for Washington, but the plan was so simple, yet so comprehensive, in its main features that it could not be spoiled. No greater tribute to its excellence could be paid than the action of the committee of Congress to which was referred the question of the improvement of the capital city in recommending that, in most of the cases where the l'Enfant plan had been departed from, it should be restored.

Postwar Planning Abroad

Much has been written in the United States during recent years, and considerable, but not nearly enough, has been done about postwar planning. In the devastated countries of Europe and the Far East, however, the problem has been more urgent, and therefore its attack has met with wider public support. The rebuilding of large sections of the cities destroyed in World War II has been an urgent necessity, while in America such projects are still more in the nature of things one would like to do. This chapter would not be complete without some reference to these proposals for rebuilding cities abroad.

The British have shown great originality and daring in planning for the rebuilding of devastated areas and have published some elaborate reports, in the preparation of which Patrick Abercrombie, whose earlier comments on planning have been abstracted in a preceding section of this chapter, has played a leading part. The first of this series of reports was the County of London Plan, prepared for the London County Council by J. H. Forshaw and Professor Abercrombie in 1943. This was far more than a plan for revamping destroyed areas —it was an attempt to reorganize the 117 square miles of the county of London, which had a prewar population of about 4,100,000. It contemplated the reconstruction and decentralization of the congested areas, recommending three density zones, averaging 200 persons per acre in residential districts in the central area, 136 persons per acre in a subcentral area, and 100 persons per acre or less in the outer area. An elaborate scheme of ring roads and arterial roads, many of them express, was co-ordinated with improvements in rail lines and terminals and new market locations. Reconstruction areas were based on existing communities, which would be grouped within natural borders, surrounded by new open belts and subdivided into neighborhood units, each grouped around the elementary school serving it. Plans for reconstruction along the banks of the Thames, use and height zones, relocation of industry, housing, and architectural control were all included. Some of the features will be discussed in later chapters.

Tied in with this plan was a later report (1944) for reconstruction in the city of London, dealing with the approximately one square mile which forms the commercial core of the London region.[7] It included proposals for distribution of land uses, heights of buildings, new street improvements, and land acquisition. The street proposals included a new "ring route" with a northern arm from Holborn Circus to Aldersgate Street and a southern arm by continuing the Victoria Embankment to Tower Hill. New vistas of St. Paul's Cathedral and more open space around it were featured in the report.

Postwar plans have also been published for Coventry, Manchester, Plymouth, Exeter, and other British cities, the first two of which may be taken as examples. It was found that the damage in Coventry was confined to a relatively small section, the city center, an area which urgently needed replanning before. Property lines are ignored in planning the redevelopment, but the accustomed centers of business, recreation, and shopping are retained as nearly as possible in their previous positions, so that the people would not have to change their habits. The railroad and motor-bus stations are combined at the location of the old railroad station. Mass transportation and parking are controlling features of the plan. All of this has been tied in with prewar plans for radial and ring streets.

The various units which contribute to the life of Coventry have been grouped together. The new shopping center is envisioned as two main blocks flanking a shopping avenue from which only pedestrians would have access to the arcades grouped around pedestrian cul-de-sacs. Service roads and parking areas are planned at the backs of the shopping blocks and off the main thoroughfares. The new recreation center, consisting of cinemas and theatres, is co-ordinated to take its place in and contribute to the design as a whole.

The plan for Manchester is more comparable to the type of plan needed for an American city, as Manchester suffered relatively little war damage, and its problems are similar to those faced by the older cities in the United States. It looks forward 50 years and, as in the London Plan, provides for a series of ring roads and radial highways with passenger and freight terminals relocated along an inner ring. The land use plan would unscramble mixed areas of homes and industry, set aside new industrial sites, and provide wedges of open areas.

The housing program has been carefully worked out. New homes to be provided during the first 30 years would reduce by 50 per cent the present densities of the central areas. The total proposed reduction in the population of the entire city is much greater in proportion than that proposed for London and calls for the creation of new communities outside the present city. The planners have resisted the temptation, often yielded to in this country, to redevelop central areas at higher densities to avoid a loss of population. Neighborhood units are based on a population of 10,000, five such neighborhoods making up a planning district.[8]

In France, under a Ministry of Reconstruction, the emphasis has been on the need of replacing destroyed housing, it being pointed out

[7] *Report of the Improvements and Town Planning Committee to the Lord Mayor, Aldermen and Commons of the City of London,* 1944. Plan by F. J. Forty, City Engineer.

[8] *City of Manchester Plan,* by R. Nicholas, Jarrold & Sons, Ltd., Norwich and London, 1945. See review by G. Holmes Perkins, *Journal of the American Institute of Planners,* Vol. XII, No. 2 (April–May–June), 1946, page 32.

that nearly 2,000,000 dwellings were destroyed in World War II, twice as many as in World War I. The planners have been seeking far more efficient construction methods. That city planning has been active is shown by the fact that, by the end of 1946, of the 1,600 French communities declared in need of reconstruction, 524 had projects and plans under consideration, and 283 had been approved by all governmental units concerned, including the national committee.[9]

In Poland the planning effort has concentrated around rebuilding the capital city of Warsaw. In the nineteenth century Warsaw experienced a period of prosperity and development because of the industrialization of the country, but its growth was haphazard. Within a single block factories, schools, apartment houses, and churches were often built. In some sections of the city there were as many as 550 inhabitants per acre. In the 1930's an active planning commission was making plans for the amelioration of these conditions.

In 1939 Warsaw had a population of 1,300,-000. During six years of German occupation 90 per cent of the central business and industrial section of the city and 50 to 60 per cent of the residential sections were destroyed. Three months after liberation 400,000 people had returned to the ruins of the city.

To accomplish the reconstruction, three bodies have been organized: (1) the Supreme Council of Warsaw Reconstruction, presided over by the President of Poland and including representatives of social, scientific, artistic, political, professional, and other organizations, with the task of establishing general principles and standards; (2) the Reconstruction Committee, consisting of representatives of ministries and municipalities with the task of coordinating the work of those agencies; (3) the Warsaw Reconstruction Office, headed by the Deputy Mayor, responsible for the economic, social, and physical plans and also for issuing orders for the work and supervising their realization.

Before the planning work of each development is begun, a public hearing is held; every-

[9] *News Letter*, American Society of Planning Officials, January, 1946, page 10.

one concerned is invited to give his suggestions on planning, and the completed plan has to be displayed for public inspection. All the objections and suggestions have to be either complied with in the ultimate plan or pre-

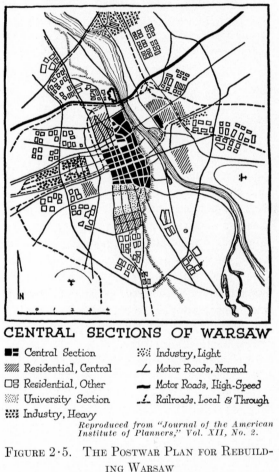

ORDER EMERGES

CENTRAL SECTIONS OF WARSAW

■⊟ Central Section ░░ Industry, Light
▨▨ Residential, Central ∠ Motor Roads, Normal
⊡⊟ Residential, Other ━ Motor Roads, High-Speed
░░ University Section ⌐ Railroads, Local & Through
░░ Industry, Heavy

Reproduced from "Journal of the American Institute of Planners," Vol. XII, No. 2.

FIGURE 2·5. THE POSTWAR PLAN FOR REBUILD-ING WARSAW

sented to the higher authority along with the plan.

The new plan will be for a region instead of just the area of the old city. The boundaries of this region will be determined by the time needed for travel from the most remote point to the center of the city. This, it has been decided, should not exceed 30 minutes, using the most modern means of transportation. A general land use plan has been made for this area, locating the central business area in the most accessible spot, placing the heavy and light industries in places related to the business and residential districts without being objectionable, and laying out residential districts of controlled densities in healthful locations with parks, schools, and other services. This avoids the heterogeneous conglomeration of uses and unhealthful densities of the old city. With these features established, the main traffic streets and other traffic facilities can be designed to fit the probable ultimate needs. (See Figure 2·5.) Because of the almost complete destruction of the old city the new plan is an attainable ideal, while the plan made in the thirties was an unattainable and unsatisfactory compromise.

In the Netherlands the national government has assumed the leadership for postwar replanning under the Ministry of Public Works and Reconstruction. In the vast areas that were devastated through flooding and other enemy action each municipality was required to prepare a detailed redevelopment plan, a panel of qualified city planners was established, and the fees to be paid them by the municipalities were fixed. Contributions for war damage are paid from national funds, but the rebuilding scheme must be approved by a committee of the Ministry.

In Czechoslovakia a Central Planning Commission has emphasized means of restoring and extending agricultural and industrial production but has also studied problems of transportation, housing, and resettlement.

Replanning of Berlin was started promptly after the termination of hostilities through a Building and Housing Department. The planning office of this department has, among others, sections on master plan, planning studies, and open-space planning. Their plans are based on an assumption that certain standards will have to remain low, or be lowered, under the economy dictated by the Potsdam Agreement, and contemplate an organically decentralized metropolis by 1975. For example, the density of the inner communities will be reduced from 350 to 100 persons per gross acre. Garden city principles will be applied to the suburban residential communities. His-toric streets and places such as Unter den Linden are to be restored.[10]

China has a Central Planning Board which co-ordinates planning programs through political, economic, financial, and social divisions.

It is proposed that Tokyo, with a prewar population of 7,000,000, be rebuilt to house a maximum population of 3,500,000.

Thus World War II, while it led to wholesale destruction and set back for many years effective progress in city planning, ended with a more general realization of what better city and town planning can do in giving the citizens of countries all over the world communities more efficient and more attractive, with higher standards of housing, open spaces, recreation, and health, with improved systems of transportation, and with a better relation between sites of business, industry, and residence.

Selected References

ADAMS, THOMAS: *Outline of Town and City Planning,* Russell Sage Foundation, New York, 1935.

BLACK, RUSSELL VAN NEST: *Planning for the Small American City,* Public Administration Service, Chicago, 1933.

County of London Plan (prepared for the London County Council by J. H. FORSHAW and PATRICK ABERCROMBIE), The Macmillan Company, Ltd., London, 1943.

HEGEMANN, WERNER: *City Planning—Housing,* Vol. III: *A Graphic Review of Civic Art, 1922–1937* (edited by WILLIAM W. FORSTER and ROBERT C. WEINBERG), Architectural Book Publishing Company, Inc., New York, 1938.

HUBBARD, T. K., and H. V. HUBBARD: *Our Cities, To-day and To-morrow,* Harvard University Press, Cambridge, Mass., 1929.

JUSTEMENT, LOUIS: *New Cities for Old,* McGraw-Hill Book Company, New York, 1946.

Our Cities—Their Role in the National Economy (report of the Urbanism Committee), National Resources Committee, Washington, D. C., 1937.

Report of the Urban Planning Conferences at Evergreen House, Johns Hopkins Press, Baltimore, 1944.

SAARINEN, ELIEL: *The City, Its Growth, Its Decay, Its Future,* Reinhold Publishing Corporation, New York, 1946.

SERT, J. L.: *Can Our Cities Survive?* Harvard University Press, Cambridge, Mass., 1942.

[10] "Report on Berlin, 1945," by T. J. Kent, *Journal of the American Institute of Planners,* Vol. XII, No. 1, pages 5–17, and No. 2, pages 18–27.

SITTE, CAMILLO: *The Art of Building Cities,* Reinhold Publishing Corporation, New York, 1946.

The Problems of a Changing Population (report of the Committee on Population Problems), National Resources Committee, Washington, D. C., May, 1938.

PERIODICALS

American Planning and Civic Annual, 1929 to the present, American Planning and Civic Association, Washington, D. C.

Journal (Quarterly) of the American Institute of Planners (until 1944 *The Planners' Journal*), 1935 to the present, 77 Massachusetts Avenue, Cambridge, Mass.

Proceedings (Annual) of the American Society of Planning Officials, 1935 to the present, 1313 East 60th Street, Chicago.

Proceedings (Annual) of the National Conference on City Planning, 1910–1934.

Questions

1. What are the principal objectives of city planning as revealed by its definition by leaders in that field?

2. How has the scope of city planning expanded in the twentieth century?

3. What are some of the disadvantages and the justifications for tall buildings as developed in American cities?

4. Describe the variations in emphasis in the planning of cities in the different countries of Europe.

5. Describe some of the conspicuous features of American town planning in the period just before World War I.

6. How did the Chicago Exposition of 1893 influence city planning in the United States?

7. How has the usual approach to town planning in Great Britain differed from that in the United States?

8. In what municipal activities do problems of administration and city planning overlap?

9. What were the relative trends in growth of urban and rural population in the United States in the first four decades of the twentieth century? What new influences contributed to these trends?

10. What factors have led to the drab appearance of the outlying parts of many American cities?

11. To what extent should a city plan be adhered to without change?

12. What were the outstanding features of postwar plans for cities in Great Britain?

13. In what way were countries on the European continent accelerating urban planning in the postwar period?

3

THE CORRECTION OF MISTAKES

IT IS NOT UNFAIR TO SAY THAT A LARGE PART OF city planning, too large a part in fact, consists of the correction of mistakes. This is not unnatural, since it is the realization of the blunders that have been made through lack of foresight or appreciation of the unsuitability of a plan under changed conditions that has rendered the need of better planning obvious. Often conditions due to these mistakes or misfits become intolerable. Obstruction of free movement creates both public inconvenience and actual financial loss from delays. Ugliness follows disorderliness. Eventually there arises an insistent demand for correction and a willingness to pay the price, however great it may be. Most of what are called city planning projects are of this kind. Serious attempts to avoid the same mistakes in parts of the city where improvements have not gone so far as to forbid readjustment of the plan without great expense, or to profit by past experience in the development of plans for the portions not yet mapped, or to save the unspoiled places, appear to have been afterthoughts.

In some cases correction has involved stupendous plans for improvements on a city-wide basis; in others, it has involved only revamping of the street system in central areas; in still others, local adjustments have improved or remedied small-scale, but nevertheless serious, ills. Examples of each of these types will be given.

Large-scale Corrections

Perhaps the most spectacular of all the large-scale projects for correcting city-wide mistakes

was the construction of the great boulevard system of Paris under the direction of Baron Haussmann. (See Figure 3·1.) Undertaken in 1853, partly for reasons of military strategy but also to beautify the city, many of the various projects were carried out within a relatively short time, considering their magnitude, and were financed by an imperial government with little delay and debate. The Boulevard Haussmann, one of the major proposals, was, however, not completed until 1929, and many others are still in the planning stage.

Naples also has carried out some great improvements by the cutting of broad avenues through districts where narrow, tortuous streets did not provide sufficient light and air to make business profitable or living tolerable. Vienna made itself one of the world's most beautiful cities, not by correcting mistakes due to poor planning or to lack of planning, but by availing itself of an opportunity to use lands formerly devoted to defensive works which were useless under modern conditions. (See Figure 8·15, page 130.)

One of the most ambitious schemes for correcting the defects of a great city is the Chicago Plan, developed by Daniel H. Burnham in 1909 under the auspices of the Commercial Club of that city. A phenomenally rapid growth had brought about within a generation conditions which it was desired to correct, the city having been so intent upon its physical and material development that little thought was given to the manner of its growth and the embarrassments to which its faulty plan would lead.

The plan has been so often and so fully described, illustrated, and discussed that it is scarcely necessary to refer to it at length. It included not only the widening of many of the existing streets, but also the creation of a great number of diagonals to cut through many blocks of intensively developed property. Perhaps its most spectacular feature is the great

though the city already possessed an unusually complete park system, and an outer parkway circuit swinging around the city about 30 miles from the downtown center. The lake front proposals, involving the extension of Grant Park into Lake Michigan and the construction of a series of lagoons bordered by an outer drive, have been largely completed and pro-

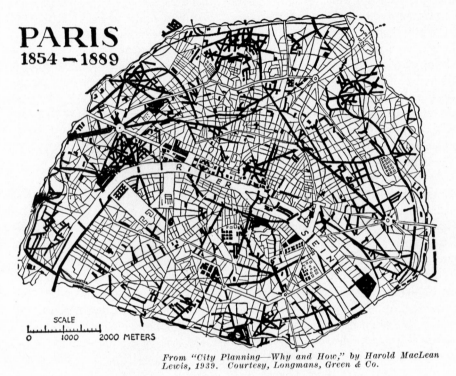

PARIS
1854 — 1889

SCALE
0   1000   2000 METERS

From "City Planning—Why and How," by Harold MacLean Lewis, 1939. Courtesy, Longmans, Green & Co.

FIGURE 3·1. THE HAUSSMANN PLAN OF PARIS

The heavy lines show new streets and arteries.

boulevard which sweeps on a circular curve through or about the district to be rearranged with an imposing civic center midway, or at the point of the curve farthest from the lake front. In the Preliminary Comprehensive City Plan of Chicago, published by the City Planning Commission in 1946, a modern expressway loop ringing the downtown area, with radials reaching out into the suburbs, superseded some of the earlier highway proposals, and the relocation of the civic center has been shelved.

Other striking features of the Burnham Plan were an ambitious scheme for the development of the lake front by the improvement of existing parks and the creation of new ones, al-

vided a site for the Chicago World's Fair of 1932. The Forest Preserve District of Cook County has acquired many thousands of acres of lands along the outer circuit, looking forward to a parkway or forest way from 200 to 600 feet in width.

The entire project of reconstruction, if carried out as planned, will require many years and will involve the expenditure of scores of millions of dollars. Its serious consideration and the actual commencement of the work offer evidence of a courageous optimism and faith in the future of their city on the part of the people of Chicago, and a devotion to the public interest on the part of the aggressive organization which put forward the plans, which may bring about their substantial realization, stupendous as they are.

New York, or at least the borough of Manhattan, continued until the last few decades to grow in accordance with the plan prepared for it a century or more ago without a realization of the defects of that plan. Now some modifications, the need of which is quite apparent, are rendered prohibitively costly on account of the building damage which would result, although some radical changes have been and are being carried out.

Difficult and costly as the correction of the defects in the plans of European towns has been, it is vastly more so in cities like New York or Chicago, where, as the result of a lack of reasonable restrictions governing the height and arrangement of buildings, great and costly structures have been erected on narrow streets to such an extent that widening streets or cutting through new ones would involve so great an expense that they are out of the question. Perhaps the fundamental mistake was the failure to impose limitations of height and bulk which would in the first place have prevented the overtaxing of the streets and yet would have diminished the cost of widening them should it become necessary. For example, a structure like the downtown Equitable Building in New York, constructed just before zoning restrictions were adopted and occupying a block approximately 160 by 308 feet in size, one of the four bounding streets of which has a width of 75 feet, another 45 feet, and the other two 35 feet, could be built to a height of 38 stories, or 536 feet, at a cost of $20,000,000 for the building and land, converting each of the adjacent streets into a narrow canyon where direct sunlight is almost unknown. Now modern zoning ordinances regulating the use of land and the types of buildings (see pages 259 to 268) prevent such recurrences, but in many cases the harm has already been done.

Efforts to bring about improvements in existing conditions or to correct mistakes frequently fail for the reason that they are too ambitious or attempt to do too much at the same time. Official commissions and unofficial committees have been appointed, and have made many plans for the correction of all the defects they could discover, but by reason of their failure to concentrate their efforts on one or two details of unquestionable importance, their labors have been fruitless. Such a commission was created in New York City in 1904, and three years later presented a report, accompanied by a great number of plans involving radical changes. Some of them were admirable, particularly a few which related to the provision of a system of parks and parkways for a part of the city which was still undeveloped and for which there was no adopted street plan. Attention and interest were diverted from these, however, by a number of more spectacular projects for the cutting through of new streets and the widening of existing ones and the creation of plazas, the cost of acquiring the land for which, with the damage to existing buildings, but with no allowance for construction, was estimated to be nearly $100,000,000. One or two of the projects have been or are in process of being carried out, but the agitation for them began before this commission was created and was persistently kept up until actual results were obtained.

Faced with the need of substantial rebuilding to repair the damages of World War II, both the city and the surrounding county of London have developed elaborate plans for not only the revamping of their street systems and rearrangement of terminals but also the redistribution of land uses and a substantial decentralization of population.

Time and Patience Required

It is obvious that long-time programs are required to carry out plans to revise large areas of a city. Much time and patience are also required before specific projects forming part of such a plan may advance from plan to reality. The New York metropolitan area provides several examples to illustrate this point: for the Holland Vehicular Tunnel beneath the Hudson River the period required between the initiation of the project and its completion was 21 years (1906–1927); for the George Washington Bridge, crossing the Hudson River a few miles further north, it was 17 years (1914–1931); for the rebuilding of the New York Central Railroad tracks on the west side of Manhattan to eliminate grade crossings and carry Riverside Park over the railroad to the waterfront, it was 21 years (1916–1937).

In such cases many of the conditions which it has been necessary to remedy have been of very slow growth, and the agitation which has finally resulted in their improvement has continued for many years. A conspicuous example in which the time required was much greater than the projects referred to above is the Strand-to-Holborn Improvement in London. Its history will be described in some detail.[1]

This proposal involves one of the oldest parts of the city, where in the course of centuries a series of narrow, crooked, and unrelated streets and lanes had grown up. The original conditions in this area and the highway proposal finally adopted to remedy them are shown in Figure 3·2. High Holborn, of fairly generous but very irregular width, bounded this area on the north, and the Strand, narrower and equally irregular in width and lines, lay to the south. Drury Lane made an attempt to connect the two thoroughfares, but seemed to give up the idea and was shunted off into narrow Wych Street before reaching the Strand.

In the eastern part of the district and about 300 feet south of High Holborn lay Lincoln's Inn Fields, an open space which gave the public authorities much concern for generations. At one time it was the place for the execution of criminals, and, although parts of it were bordered by "dwellings of noblemen and gentlemen of qualitie," it had a bad name. Conditions became so objectionable that in 1735 Parliament passed an act "to enable the present and future proprietors and inhabitants of the houses in Lincoln's Inn Fields in the County of Middlesex to make a rate on themselves for

[1] The agitation leading up to this improvement and the conditions which it was designed to remedy are described in detail by Charles Gordon in *Old Time Aldwych, Kingsway and Neighbourhood,* from which and from official reports of the construction and opening of the new thoroughfares the following information has been obtained. A fuller description was included in *The Planning of the Modern City,* by Nelson P. Lewis (pages 28–34).

raising money sufficient to enclose, clean, and adorn the said fields."

Lincoln's Inn Fields was finally redeemed and became an attractive park of some six or seven acres in addition to its bounding streets, but it was so hidden away in a maze of narrow lanes that one not familiar with its location would be unlikely to discover it. Even today the visitor to London might pass along Kingsway within 50 yards or along High Holborn within 100 yards of this little park without suspecting its existence unless his attention were directed to it by a guidebook. (See Figure 3·2.) Its improvement was of little more than local benefit; the delays and inconvenience to traffic in its vicinity were in nowise abated; and the need of a direct connection between the Strand, somewhere near the Church of Saint Mary le Strand or the Church of Saint Clement Danes, and High Holborn in the neighborhood of this open space was more and more obvious.

The first plan was laid before the Select Committees on Metropolitan Improvements in 1836 and again in 1838. It provided for two new streets each 50 feet wide. One connected Holborn with the northwest corner of Lincoln's Inn Fields, and the other extended from the southwest corner of the field to the Strand at point A on Figure 3·2, following in part the line of Newcastle Street. These two new streets were joined by the existing street along the westerly side of the fields.

This plan, which from present-day standards would obviously have been entirely inadequate, was not adopted because of difficulty of financing and because other improvements were given precedence. In 1847 a somewhat similar scheme, but with the new thoroughfare entering the Strand near Wellington Street (B in Figure 3·2), was submitted to a commission which had been appointed "to consider the most effectual means of improving the metropolis." Again nothing was accomplished.

In 1855 the same plan, with many others, was brought before a new Metropolitan Board of Works. There was frequent discussion, and in 1883 this board applied to Parliament for the necessary powers to construct such a street and also to widen the Strand. At that time the plan called for a street 60 feet wide to enter the Strand to the north of Saint Clement Danes Church. Parliament did not grant the authority requested.

provements Committee and to the Committee on the Housing of the Working Classes, because it was believed that not only did the require-

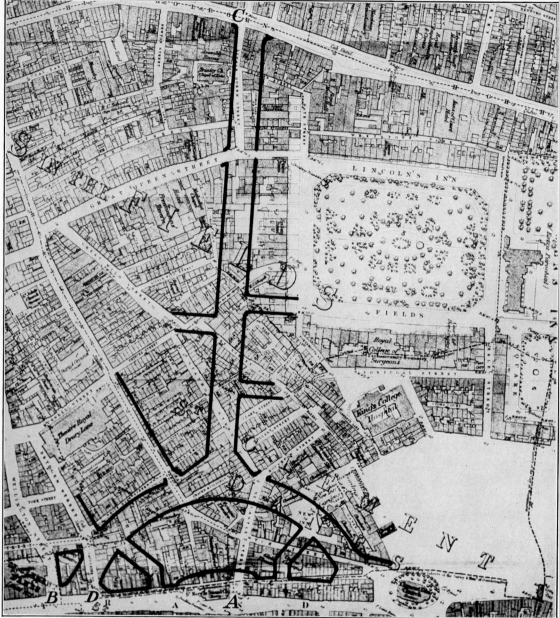

From "Old Time Aldwych, Kingsway and Neighbourhood," by Charles Gordon. Courtesy, E. P. Dutton and Company.

FIGURE 3·2. PLAN OF STRAND-TO-HOLBORN IMPROVEMENT, LONDON

This plan was finally carried out nearly seventy years after it was first proposed.

It was not until 1889, when the London County Council superseded the Metropolitan Board of Works, that real progress was made. The Council referred the project to the Im-

ments of traffic demand this new means of communication between Holborn and the Strand, but also that the building of such a street would cut through an area which would be greatly improved by its construction. As a result there was submitted to the Council a plan for the construction of a new street from Holborn at Southampton Row (*C* on plan) in an almost direct line to Catherine Street at the Strand (*D* on plan), with a spur from the new street running from a point about 500 feet north of the Strand to the latter street at Saint Clement Danes Church. Again it was resolved to postpone this or any other large improvements until some satisfactory provision could be made for an equitable distribution of the expense.

In 1892 the Committee submitted a modified plan which provided a new street 100 feet wide with a circus some 200 feet in diameter about midway between its termini. They recommended that the owners of the property benefited should contribute to the cost. Although the Council adopted the recommendations, they did not receive the approval of Parliament. The net cost, after deducting recoupment by the disposal of surplus land, was then estimated at $11,230,000. In 1896 the Council concluded that it was necessary to proceed with the widening of the Strand, and a year later with the widening of Southampton Row north of Holborn.

When these improvements were carried out, it became quite apparent that the only logical plan for the new Strand-to-Holborn thoroughfare would be that which was suggested in 1892 or such a modification of it as would result in a direct connection with the widened Southampton Row. In 1898, after careful consideration of a variety of competing plans, it was decided that the scheme of 1892, providing a direct route from Holborn at Southampton Row to the Strand, but modified in accordance with some suggestions made by the Royal Institute of British Architects, and with some alterations proposed by the Committee, was the one to be carried out, together with a further widening of the Strand to the north of Saint Mary's Church. The plan also provided for the acquisition of the whole site within the area bounded by the Strand and the two branch streets, as well as a considerable area of land which would front on the new streets.

There was some difference of opinion as to whether these new streets should be made 90 or 100 feet wide. It was found that exactly the same properties would have to be acquired for the 90-foot as for the 100-foot street; and while there would result from the wider street a smaller amount of surplus land, it was believed that the increased width of the street would enhance the value of this land to an amount greater than the value of the 10-foot strip to be added to the thoroughfare. This plan having been decided upon, it was submitted to Parliament, and was the largest scheme of town improvement ever undertaken in London.

The bill authorizing the improvement became a law in 1899, although it was opposed by forty or more powerful and influential companies and persons. Among the criticisms were: that the Council should not take more property than was actually required for the improvement; that, if it took such excess property, it should not have the power to impose a special assessment; and that the owners of property to be taken were entitled to reinstatement upon some other convenient site. In its final form the total estimate of the gross cost of the completed scheme was about $30,600,000; it was estimated that about $21,800,000 would be realized from the sale of surplus land. The new street was constructed and formally opened on October 18, 1905, and it is interesting to note that the gross cost of property taken was just about $1,000,000 less than had been estimated. The extent of the recoupment through the sale of the surplus land is indicated in Chapter 23, "Financing a City Plan," Volume II.

London's experience in securing this great improvement has been recited at considerable length for the purpose of showing for what long periods many defective street plans have existed, how the defects become emphasized as the city grows, and what long and persistent effort and agitation are required before their correction is undertaken. Those who have struggled to bring about some similar improvements in their own city and have become discouraged at the repeated failure of their efforts may take heart when they realize that the Strand-to-Holborn Improvement was first advocated no less than 69 years before it was physically completed.

There may be scant satisfaction in the thought that those of a succeeding generation will see the fruition of one's efforts, but plans for betterment which are really worth while and are intelligently and persistently advocated may be realized with fair promptness when their importance is generally appreciated. The people of a self-governed city seem to have a strong desire to talk over and debate any question relating to a municipal improvement, and this disposition is especially marked in the cities of Great Britain. The need of the improvement may be generally recognized, but the manner in which it is to be carried out must be thoroughly discussed, not by experts, but by the people themselves before they are ready to undertake it. When an unexpected opportunity to correct a defective condition at a minimum of expense is presented, it is rarely availed of, owing to this passion for full and free discussion. W. E. Riley, Architect of the London County Council, in a paper presented at the London Town Planning Conference of 1910, noted that in the great fire of London in 1666 an area of 436 acres was burned over, and, although Wren and Evelyn promptly put forward their plans for the rebuilding of these areas (Figures 8·8 and 8·9, page 124) "select committees and royal commissions have met and reported with frequency and perseverance during the last century." This illustrates the unwillingness of the people to act upon the suggestions even of one who had done so much to make London notable as had Sir Christopher Wren, without ample opportunity for full and free discussion, which became so protracted that the city adjusted itself to the conditions brought about by the fire and the old defects in the plan were perpetuated in the rebuilding.

Typical American Examples of Downtown Street Changes

The extension of Seventh Avenue and the widening of Varick Street in the borough of Manhattan, New York City (Figure 3·3), provide a typical example of a correction of a downtown street system. This project was completed in 1919. Old Greenwich Village had an irregular street plan with no continuous and adequate north-and-south artery of traffic. The plan adopted in 1811 with its series of broad north-and-south avenues adjoined Greenwich on the north. The new Pennsylvania Station was located on Seventh Avenue between Thirty-first and Thirty-third streets, while the

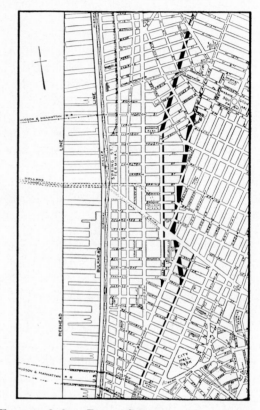

FIGURE 3·3. PLAN SHOWING THE CUTTING THROUGH OF NEW STREETS AND THE WIDENING OF EXISTING STREETS TO FORM TRAFFIC ARTERIES 100 FEET WIDE IN NEW YORK CITY

building of the new Chelsea Docks along the Hudson River just west of the northerly part of Greenwich resulted in an increase of street traffic which had no adequate outlet to the south. A new four-track, rapid-transit subway was planned for the west side of lower Manhattan, but there was no available street which would afford a direct route for this transit line. A southerly extension of Seventh Avenue, together with a widening of Varick Street to West Broadway, appeared to offer a solution of the difficulty. After considerable discussion, which seemed brief in comparison with that devoted to the Strand-to-Holborn Improvement, the street was laid out, title acquired, the four-track, rapid-transit railway constructed in it, and the roadway substantially paved; and this part of the city has shown the vitalizing

An example of a change which affected a considerable area is the removal of "the hump" in Pittsburgh, where the street grades over an area of 18½ acres in the heart of the office district were lowered varying amounts up to

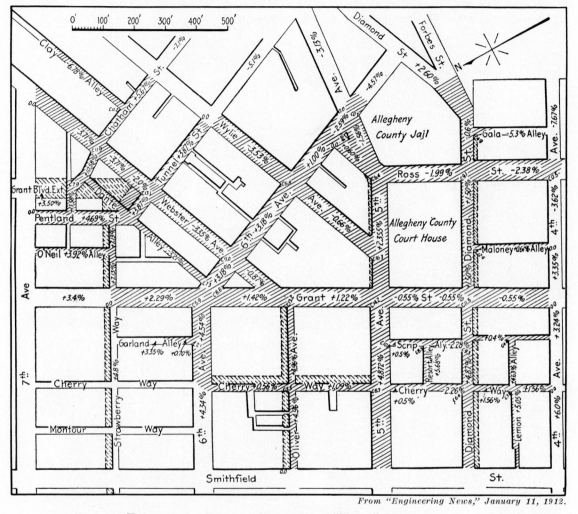

From "Engineering News," January 11, 1912.

FIGURE 3·4. PLAN OF PITTSBURGH "HUMP" REMOVAL

Full-line hatching shows existing streets on which grades were changed; broken-line hatching shows new or widened streets.

effect of a new traffic artery, conspicuously lacking in the old plan. The cost of acquiring the property, exclusive of the physical improvement, was more than $8,200,000.

Eleven years later this improvement was paralleled by the extension of Sixth Avenue, again to permit the construction of a new rapid-transit subway, from its southerly terminus at Carmine Street to a widened Church Street south of Canal Street.

a little over 16 feet, buildings of over 20 stories being underpinned and carried down to the new grades and their façades being remodeled to conform with the new conditions. The extent of this improvement is shown by Figure 3·4. The gradient of the principal thoroughfare traversing the district was reduced from 7.6 per cent to 4.87 per cent, and at one point this street was lowered nearly 15 feet. The value of the property affected was over $56,-

TRAFFIC RELIEF PROJECTS
TO BE ACCOMPLISHED THROUGH
BOSTON REGIONAL BRIDGE & TUNNEL AUTHORITY
AS RECOMMENDED BY
STATE PLANNING BOARD
UNDER
HOUSE DOCUMENTS 96 & 98
1947
LEGEND
1 MYSTIC RIVER BRIDGE
2 SUMNER TRAFFIC TUNNEL
3 SECOND TRAFFIC TUBE
4 CENTRAL ARTERY

Photo by Fairchild Aerial Surveys. Courtesy, Massachusetts State Planning Board.

FIGURE 3·5

000,000, and waivers of damages were secured on property representing more than 77 per cent of this valuation. The cost of the improvement was estimated to be $3,141,000, of which about $763,000 was for the physical work of changing the street grades, with the readjustment of sewers and water mains, the remainder of the sum being for damages, against which there were offset assessments for benefit amounting to about $909,000. These figures do not include the expense imposed upon the

city is proposing to develop a system of downtown expressways. A proposal submitted to the Massachusetts 1947 Legislature, which the State Planning Board recommended be carried out by a Boston Regional Bridge and Tunnel Authority, is illustrated in Figure 3·5.

Minor Corrections

Such corrections are not often on so vast a scale. Many have been carried out, and many

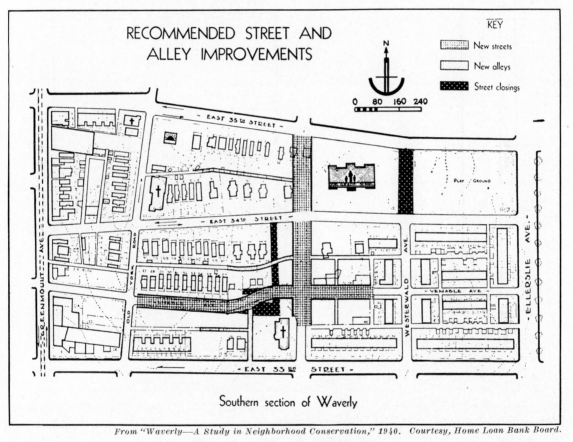

From "Waverly—A Study in Neighborhood Conservation," 1940. Courtesy, Home Loan Bank Board.

FIGURE 3·6. STREET CHANGES RECOMMENDED IN PORTION OF WAVERLY SECTION OF BALTIMORE AS PART OF A REHABILITATION PROGRAM

public service corporations in the removal and reconstruction of their surface and subsurface structures, nor that incurred by property owners who waived damages and reconstructed and adjusted their buildings at their own expense.

Boston is renowned for the narrow and crooked streets in its downtown area. On the basis of a comprehensive thoroughfare plan prepared by its City Planning Board in 1930, the

more have been proposed which, while covering a limited area and involving comparatively little expense, have redeemed the neighborhood by the removal of a blight which has grown up as the result of an inadequate street system. More open spaces, in the form of streets or parks, have let in the sunlight and revitalized an area. An example of this kind which has attracted a good deal of interest is the redevelopment plan prepared for the Waverly area in Baltimore (Figure 3·6).[2]

With the development of large-scale housing, public or private, old street layouts have often needed revision in the opposite direction—the provision of larger instead of smaller blocks. This will probably continue to be true in the

Figure 3·8. This section of the city was laid out in 1845 with lots 20 feet by 45 feet, facing on streets 30 feet wide. During the eighties the one-family dwellings were replaced by four- and five-story tenements with no setbacks and excessive land coverage. These factors, combined with poor drainage and unprotected

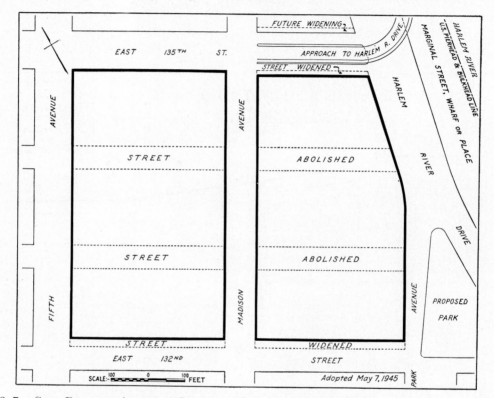

FIG. 3·7. SITE PLAN OF ABRAHAM LINCOLN HOUSES, ONE OF THE POSTWAR PUBLIC HOUSING
————————PROJECTS IN NEW YORK CITY

The plan shows the street changes involved.

redevelopment of blighted areas where only large-scale projects can do the job. Figure 3·7 provides an example of this kind, where a public housing project in New York City required the consolidation of six old blocks into two new ones and both street closings and street widenings.

A proposed redesign of both the street system and lot layout in a blighted area in the South End Section of Boston, as proposed by the Boston City Planning Board, is shown in

foundation piling, resulted in a blighted area. The proposed plan would replace all but one row of existing buildings, close several streets, provide ample recreation areas under city ownership or control, and reduce the building coverage from 44.5 per cent to 20.9 per cent, with a reduction of only 4½ per cent in the population to be housed in this 17½-acre area.[3]

Another Boston example is presented in Figure 3·9, which shows a block in the North End in 1814, in 1914, and as proposed for redevelopment. Initially this block was developed with

[2] *Waverly—A Study in Neighborhood Conservation,* Federal Home Loan Bank Board, Washington, D. C., 1940.

[3] *Rehabilitation in Boston,* Vol. II, Boston City Planning Board, May, 1943.

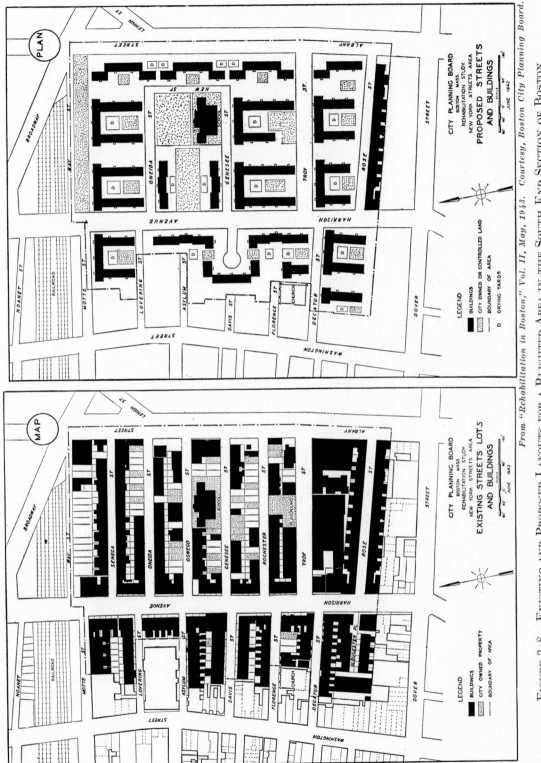

From "Rehabilitation in Boston," Vol. II, May, 1943. Courtesy, Boston City Planning Board.

FIGURE 3·8. EXISTING AND PROPOSED LAYOUTS FOR A BLIGHTED AREA IN THE SOUTH END SECTION OF BOSTON

dwellings close to the streets, with ample space in the rear for barns, stables, and vegetable gardens. But, as time went on, the large lots

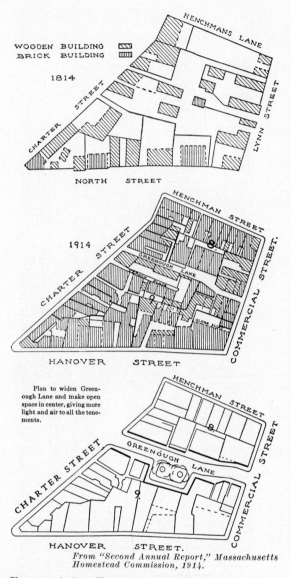

WOODEN BUILDING ☒
BRICK BUILDING ▥

From "Second Annual Report," Massachusetts Homestead Commission, 1914.

Plan to widen Greenough Lane and make open space in center, giving more light and air to all the tenements.

FIGURE 3·9. EXCESSIVE DEVELOPMENT OF A BLOCK IN THE NORTH END OF BOSTON LEADS TO A PLAN FOR READJUSTMENT OF THE STREET SYSTEM

encouraged rear dwellings, and by 1914, in spite of a narrow interior lane, the block was almost covered with structures crowded together so as to permit little light or air. The lower plan indicates a proposal to correct the mistakes of lack of planning and control.

The overdevelopment of the land between wide and attractive streets where the block dimensions are such as to permit the erection of interior dwellings is illustrated in Figure 8·34 (page 151), which shows a small section of Charlottenburg. The restrictive ordinances enacted by German cities do not appear to have prevented the development of conditions such as these, which are frequently found immediately back of the imposing buildings which line the streets so much admired by casual visitors. It is true that liberal provision has been made for the recreation and amusement of the people of these cities, but their lives might be more wholesome and comfortable if they were given more light and air in their homes, even at the cost of some curtailment of their free entertainment.

Many more instances might be given of corrections which, while less spectacular and attracting less attention than the creation of civic centers or new boulevards, are fully as important and will as vitally affect the districts in which they are located. They are called city or town planning, and no exception can well be taken to their description as such, yet it must be admitted that the necessity for them is due to a lack of far-sighted planning in the beginning and that they are really the correction of mistakes.

Changing Land Use Patterns

One of the most serious corrective problems facing nearly all large cities and many small ones today is to find some way of using outmoded, obsolete, and blighted areas which have resulted from shifts in land use. Residential areas have moved outward, encouraged by improved transportation facilities; shopping centers have found old quarters too cramped and congested and have shifted to other locations; some industries have left central areas and moved to suburban sites. City fathers cannot be blamed for having failed to foresee such tremendous changes as have taken place in our metropolitan areas, but the failure to stabilize business, residential, and industrial districts by providing them with sound neighborhood plans and protecting them against overbuilding and invasion by alien uses poses difficult problems for the city planner.

Imperial Capital of India. A commission was appointed to recommend a site for the new city. Here was a case where a very old city had to

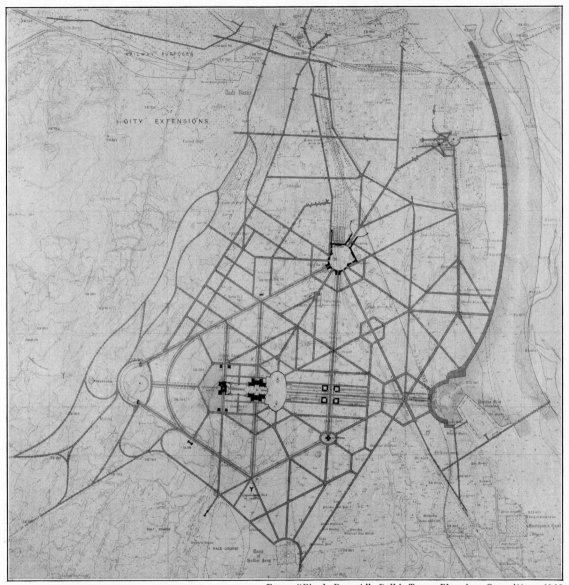

From "Final Report," Delhi Town Planning Committee, 1913.

FIGURE 3·10. GENERAL FEATURES OF THE PLAN FOR THE INDIAN CAPITAL AT DELHI

There may be occasional instances where not only the use to which the land in a particular neighborhood is devoted may so change as to require a recasting of its plan, but even an entire city may undergo a radical change in character. This is what happened when it was decided that the city of Delhi, which in 1911 had a population of 232,837, should become the

be adapted to new conditions, or a new city had to be created which would be a part of or merged with the old town. The latter course was followed, and the manner in which the problem was solved and the general features of the plan which was recommended by the commission are shown in Figure 3·10. The final report of the Delhi Town Planning Committee,

made in March, 1913, with the two which preceded it, furnishes an interesting record of the
problem presented, the manner in which it was
attacked, and the various considerations which
determined the final choice. The new Delhi,
located southwest of the old city, was formally
opened in 1930 and by 1937 already contained
80,000 people, while the old city had continued
to grow to about 350,000.

Selected References

*Final Report of the Delhi Town Planning Committee
Regarding the Selected Site* (with plan and two
maps), His Majesty's Stationery Office, Edinburgh,
1913.

GORDON, CHARLES: *Old Time Aldwych, Kingsway and
Neighbourhood,* E. P. Dutton and Company, New
York. (Gives history of Strand-to-Holborn Im-
provement in London.)

Plan of Chicago (prepared by DANIEL H. BURNHAM
and EDWARD H. BENNETT, Architects; edited by
CHARLES MOORE), Commercial Club of Chicago, 1909.

Rehabilitation in Boston, Vol. II, May, 1943, and Vol.
III, January, 1946, Boston City Planning Board.

*Report of the New York City Improvement Com-
mission* to the Honorable George B. McClellan,
Mayor of the City of New York, and to the Honorable Board of Aldermen of the City of New York,
1907.

Waverly—A Study in Neighborhood Conservation,
Federal Home Loan Bank Board, Washington, D. C.,
1940.

Questions

1. What types of mistakes in city building have
   led to the adoption of city planning procedures?
2. Describe two examples of large-scale city replanning to correct past mistakes.
3. What was the fundamental mistake which permitted an overconcentration of building, with
   resulting congestion, in large American cities?
4. Give examples of the great length of time that
   often elapses between the planning of a major
   project and its execution.
5. What cities have succeeded in making major
   changes in their downtown street systems?
   Describe two examples.
6. Describe some of the types of minor corrections
   in the street plan of a city that may be developed as part of a city plan.
7. How may changes in the pattern of land use
   require important alterations in the city plan?

4

BASIC INFORMATION NEEDED

BEFORE GETTING DOWN TO THE FORMULATION OF a city or town plan, some time must be spent on the collection of basic information. Here the planner faces a two-horned dilemma—will he gather a lot of useless facts and thereby waste time and money, or will his data be so scant that he will be led astray when he comes to estimate future needs and to determine the location, type, and extent of the various elements in the plan? He must try to find a middle ground, but it is better to err on the side of some excess, rather than a deficiency, in information. Municipal officials should recognize that the trained and experienced planner will, like a doctor with similar qualifications, diagnose a situation more surely and expeditiously than a layman. But in each case the diagnosis must be based on a careful examination and will be greatly helped by the co-operative assistance of the patient in explaining his symptoms.

Certain types of information are of general use in almost all parts of the city plan; others are special types applying to only one or more elements, and their collection can be deferred until that phase of the plan is taken up. These latter types will be discussed in Volume II, which deals with special subjects.

Base Maps

The first requirement is a suitable base map of the community, upon which the planner can plot the various special kinds of information he needs and over which he can sketch and study different proposals. As time goes on, the planner should find this particular basic information available in more complete and usable form, but in many communities available maps have been woefully inadequate, even for a starting point in planning, and the planner has found it necessary to prepare his own map from such scattered sources as are available. This inadequacy may lie in accuracy, completeness, or scale, or, in some cases, in all three.

The accuracy need not be that required for the preparation of a contract drawing for the construction of a building, bridge, or other structure. Although dimensions are not needed, the streets should be drawn to scale, and it should be possible to scale dimensions of blocks or other distances to within a few feet of their actual value. The street system, shore lines, political boundaries, railroads, and other features shown should be up to date.

In many communities the only map available is a street map, and this frequently does not show the difference between public and private streets, nor include those streets in filed, but undeveloped, subdivisions; the planner needs to know about all of these. Other features needed to give the base map reasonable completeness are:

1. Location of public buildings, such as city hall, public schools, fire houses.
2. Watercourses.
3. Boundaries of all property devoted to public use and designation of use, such as parks, playgrounds, school sites, hospital sites, sewage treatment plant.
4. Topography, shown by contours at 5-, 10-, or 20-foot intervals, depending on the steepness of the slopes.

5. Railroad stations and tracks, including industrial sidings.
6. Pierhead and bulkhead lines on navigable waterways.
7. Easements for public utilities.

The scale of the base map will vary with the size of the community, but, in general, a scale of 100 to 400 feet to the inch has been found suitable. The scale should be large enough for group discussions and exhibits, but small enough to reproduce the maps in printed reports. The author has found it expedient in some cases to use a base map at relatively large scale suitable for conferences, and then to reduce it by a photo-lithoprint process to about half the original scale for the preparation of final drawings to be used in a printed report. For cities of large area it is often desirable to have the base map drawn in sections and to have printed copies available at different scales.

It is also helpful to have an outline map of the municipality at a smaller scale which will show only the main highways, railroads, and any large public parks. Such a map will be found very useful in the presentation of various statistical information concerning the community.

It is desirable to supplement these municipal base maps with a map of the larger area tributary to the city or town. This may be in less detail, showing only the principal highways and larger public areas, railroad lines, waterways, and political boundaries. Its scale may vary from 400 to 2,000 feet to the inch, depending upon the size of the area to be shown.

Natural Resources

The modern city should be so planned as to conserve its resources, both natural and man-made. Thus the collection of basic information should include a survey of the community's natural resources, including both character and location.

Waterways and watercourses are obvious resources and, as already explained, should be shown on the base map. In addition, the waterways and their shores should be classified as suitable for commerce, manufacturing, residence, or recreation; existing sources of pollu-tion from either sewage or industrial wastes should be plotted. Potable water supplies, developed or undeveloped, are part of the water resources.

Lying below the surface of the ground are such resources as sand, gravel, brick clay, building stone, and deposits of metallic minerals. The planner should know of these so as to plan for their conservation or development. In the form of surface resources are fertile soils, forests, and lakes suitable for recreation. Wooded areas and steep slopes (such as those with grades of over 15 per cent) can advantageously be plotted on one of the base maps; such areas are potential park sites or at least are unsuitable for intensive development.

The character of the soil is of interest from the standpoint of the adaptability of an area for buildings, airports, and other uses where drainage or suitable foundations are of importance. The soil surveys (pedological) and the resulting soil maps made by the United States Department of Agriculture generally include a classification by adequacy of drainage as well as by fertility of soil. The geologic maps made by federal and state agencies provide useful information about underground conditions. Local records of borings have in some cities been compiled in the form of maps showing the depth of bedrock, a matter of concern in locating both surface and underground structures.

Climate affects the city plan in various ways. Temperature determines the growing season for crops and the depth to which water pipes must be laid to avoid freezing. Snowfall may affect the design of highways and parking facilities. Prevailing wind directions influence the suitability of sites for airports and industry.

Economic Resources

More and more attention is being given in city planning to the economic base upon which the city is built. One-industry towns have flourished and died. Employment is necessary to maintain an urban community. There is a place in metropolitan areas for suburban residential communities and towns with specialized functions, but in central cities a broad economic base is the best guaranty of permanence. In such cities information should be gathered on the location and kinds of manufacturing industries and on all types of employment. Many of these data are available in the reports of the Bureau of the Census and the Bureau of Labor Statistics, both under the United States Department of Commerce. Local directories of manufacturing establishments are also usually available.

But it is not enough to know of what exists today; some knowledge of industrial trends is also essential if one is to plan for the future. This becomes either a regional or a national problem, and the planner of the city should be able to turn to a regional or state planning agency for guidance. For example, in New York State, one would find a report called *Trends in Important Manufacturing Industries in New York, 1929–1939* and other current publications of the State Department of Commerce comparing state and national trends. The report of the National Resources Board, *Industrial Location and National Resources*, published in December, 1942, would prove a valuable source of reference.

The first volume published by the Committee on a Regional Plan for New York and Its Environs was a report on a survey of economic and industrial conditions.[1] As a basis for planning for the postwar era, the Regional Plan Association carried these studies further in 1944.[2] The following quotations from this later report indicate the importance of a city's economic background:

Every city grows from its inception to a certain population size as a result of one fundamental force —its economic background. It is obvious that the urban site must possess certain advantages, natural or man-made, which enable it to give employment to people in fabricating goods, in trading, transportation, or other activities. . . . A city cannot live on itself. . . . Every person employed in a basic industry will normally require the services of one or more additional persons in the service lines. . . .

[1] *Major Economic Factors in Metropolitan Growth and Arrangement*, Vol. I, Regional Survey of New York and Its Environs, 1927.

[2] *The Economic Status of the New York Metropolitan Region in 1944*, Regional Plan Association, Inc., New York.

The rate of improvement in technical efficiency varies from industry to industry, and in a few industries an increasing amount of labor is required to produce the same quantity of goods. The extent to which employment will decline in any industrial area, as a result of the improvement in the technical efficiency of labor, depends upon the type of industries in that city.[3]

Population Distribution and Trends

Basic to all parts of a city plan is some information about the number and distribution of the people who live in the community and some estimate of the future population to be provided for. Any estimate of the future requires some study of past trends, but the planner may be led far astray if he assumes that these same trends will continue, unchanged, in the future.

There are two ways of showing the distribution of population. One is the dot map, where each dot represents a certain number of people (Figure 4·1), and the other is a density map, where ranges of density, generally expressed as persons per gross area in acres, are shown by patterns of hatchings, the darker patterns representing the higher densities (Figure 4·2). The first method gives the more accurate picture, but where the variation in density is great, as in a large city, the second method may prove more practical. Either gives at a glance a picture of the extent of vacant or nonresidential areas and the location of population centers and subcenters. Necessary data are generally available in the United States Census reports but may be supplemented by local directories, as was the case in the preparation of Figure 4·1.

A series of dot maps or density maps showing the population at various dates will be useful as an indication of population trends in both the city as a whole and its various sections. Most large cities have suffered extensive population losses in their older, central areas during recent decades. The losses on the Lower East Side of Manhattan in a single decade are strikingly shown by Figure 4·2. Hatchings may also be used effectively to show losses or gains in a single map, as in Figure 4·3, which

[3] *Ibid.*, pages 1, 3, and 41.

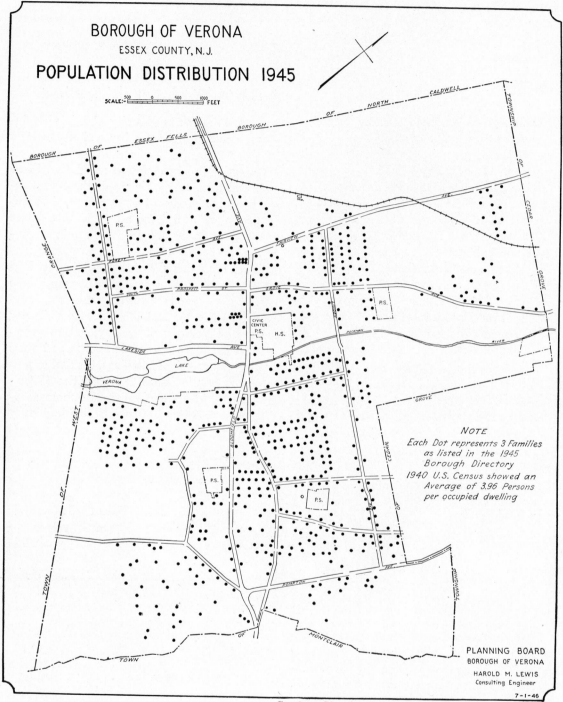

FIGURE 4·1. A POPULATION DOT MAP FOR A MUNICIPALITY OF ABOUT 9,000 POPULATION

shows both continuing and changing trends over a 20-year period in Providence, Rhode Island. The study from which this was taken predicted that "the population of Providence will probably be smaller in 1960 possibly by 1950, than it was in 1940." [4]

think that far ahead in some features of the city plan—most such estimates have proved to be overoptimistic and have promoted extravagant, rather than practical, plans. It should, however, be possible to make fairly accurate estimates for a 15- or 20-year period, recogniz-

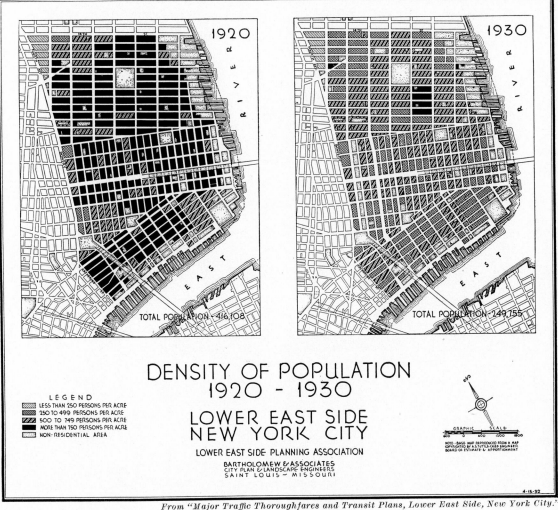

From "Major Traffic Thoroughfares and Transit Plans, Lower East Side, New York City."

FIGURE 4·2. POPULATION DENSITY MAPS USED TO SHOW CHANGES IN POPULATION DISTRIBUTION

After the collection of both graphic and statistical data on past trends in population, the planner is ready to make an estimate of the future trends. While a few estimates have been made with remarkable accuracy for periods of 25 to 50 years—and the planner should

ing that any projections beyond such a period may require later revision. The more self-contained and the larger a community is, the more accurate an estimate is likely to be. Population estimates are particularly difficult on the edge of a metropolitan area within which population shifts will be affected by new transportation facilities and by the competition between municipalities and land developers in

[4] *The Future Population of Providence*, the City Plan Commission of Providence, R. I., October, 1945, pages 5 and 10.

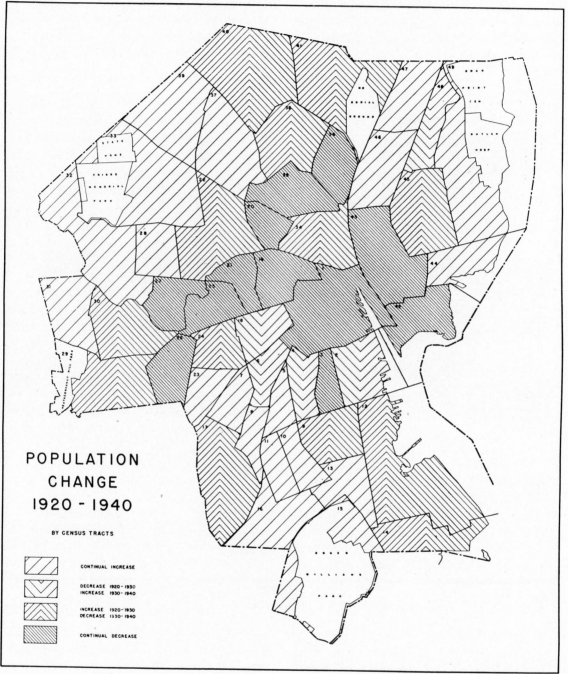

POPULATION
CHANGE
1920 - 1940

BY CENSUS TRACTS

CONTINUAL INCREASE

DECREASE 1920-1930
INCREASE 1930-1940

INCREASE 1920-1930
DECREASE 1930-1940

CONTINUAL DECREASE

Courtesy, Providence City Plan Commission

FIGURE 4·3.   USE OF HATCHINGS TO SHOW POPULATION CHANGES

Illustration is a study of Providence, Rhode Island.

providing attractive sites and facilities for residents.

Where graphic methods are used, a logarithmic scale for plotting population is frequently employed. On such a scale, a uniform rate of growth is represented by a straight line; the steeper the slope of the line, the higher the rate, and figures varying from a few to a million may be plotted on a single sheet. A comparison of the use of arithmetic and logarithmic

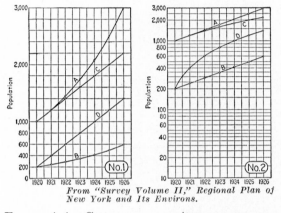

From "Survey Volume II," Regional Plan of New York and Its Environs.

FIGURE 4·4. COMPARISON OF ARITHMETIC AND LOGARITHMIC SCALES

Diagram No. 2 shows at a logarithmic vertical scale the same curves as are plotted at an arithmetic scale in diagram No. 1.

scales is shown in the two diagrams in Figure 4·4. Four series of figures are plotted on each diagram, the curves marked with the same letter being plotted from the same figures. Curves A and B show constant and equal percentage increases in growth, and curves C and D show constant and equal numerical increases.

A typical population estimate made by a projection at logarithmic scale is shown in Figure 4·5, which also illustrates the presentation of alternative estimates, including a maximum and minimum curve. These estimates were made, however, before the nation-wide trend of stabilization of urban areas, discussed in Chapter 2 (pages 14 to 17), became evident, and in 1940 Knoxville had a population of only 111,580, less than the minimum predicted. For a small community the arithmetic scale may prove most useful. The use of such a scale in estimating for a suburban community

comprised almost entirely of one-family homes on quite large lots, and based on the maintenance of its present character, is shown in Figure 4·6. This also includes a curve for annual population increases, which showed a striking reversal in trend and the projection of which provided the basis for the middle population estimate.

The United States Census figures provide useful information on age groups and trends and these figures should be analyzed, as they have a direct bearing on such features of the city plan as parks, playgrounds, and public schools. Declining birth rates in the 1920's and 1930's and during World War II, coupled with medical advances to lengthen the life span, have resulted in a much greater average age and a greater proportion of population in the older age groups. Since the end of the war, birth rates have suddenly risen, but it is too early to tell whether or not this is a purely temporary trend. The declining birth rates were followed by substantial reductions in school registrations, appearing first in the elementary schools but later evident in the high schools. These age changes, coupled with an outward movement from the central cities, have called for major revisions in the school plant in many cities. The planner should be alert to gather information of this sort.

Land Use Survey

The distribution of existing land uses is of particular importance to such phases of the city plan as zoning and control of land subdivision, but is also of interest in most other parts of the plan. In the community that has grown without a plan, it will be found that manufacturing, business, and residence have become badly scrambled. Land use maps will provide the basic information needed for developing a more orderly pattern.

There should be shown on a single map the areas predominantly devoted to industry, business, or residence, public properties, and undeveloped lands. These can be shown most effectively in colors but may be rendered in black and white for reproduction in reports. An example of the latter is shown in Figure 4·7. In many communities, it will be found that a substantial portion of the area is in public or semi-public lands of one kind or another. In such a

munity is shown in Figure 4·9. This subject is discussed further in later chapters.[5]

From such data the city planner will be able to determine the best use to which the various parts of the community should be put—in other

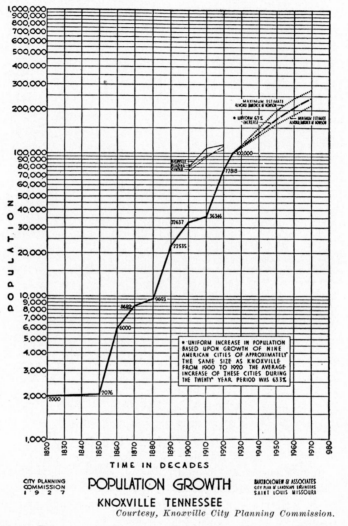

FIGURE 4·5. A TYPICAL POPULATION ESTIMATE BASED ON A GRAPHIC STUDY OF PAST TRENDS AT LOGARITHMIC SCALE

case, a separate map might well break down the public lands into parks and playgrounds, school sites, public building sites, sites of public institutions, and lands acquired through tax delinquencies. (See Figure 4·8.)

A quantitative study of these uses will help to bring out the general character of the community. A graphic presentation of such a study for a predominantly residential com-

words, to develop a master plan of land use. This will be somewhat diagrammatic and will represent an ideal toward which to strive and should not be confused with the building zone ordinance and map, which prescribe minimum standards adopted and enforced through a leg-

[5] See discussion of shopping areas, page 245, and figures for urban land uses in typical communities, page 263.

islative process and described in Chapter 12 (see page 254). As a basis for zoning, more detailed data as to types of residence, business, or industrial uses, location of structures on a lot, and heights of buildings are required.

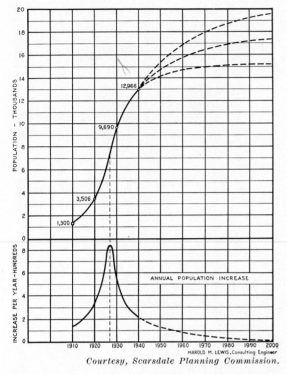

Courtesy, Scarsdale Planning Commission.

FIGURE 4·6. POPULATION TRENDS, VILLAGE OF SCARSDALE, NEW YORK

Showing estimates, at arithmetic scale, based on maintenance of the present character of a suburban community.

Use of Aerial Photography

Aerial maps and oblique airphotos have greatly facilitated the collection of basic data for city planning. The inaccuracy and incompleteness of available ground maps have, as already pointed out, frequently complicated the task of the planner and required him to spend much time and effort in preparing his own base maps for master plan studies.

Effective use has been made of aerial maps for preliminary location plans for highways and other utilities. They are invaluable in the collection of data concerning the existing uses of land for zoning, and for the selection of suit-able areas for parks, playgrounds, and other open types of use. Oblique views are particularly useful for the presentation of proposals, whether these involve routes of highways or other communication facilities, uses of land, or structures such as bridges, public buildings, or housing.

Methods have been developed for making accurate topographic maps from aerial maps taken with special cameras. While this process has been used principally as an aid in surveys of large inaccessible areas, it has possibilities in regional and urban planning in cases where no accurate topography is available from ground surveys.

Airphotos and aerial maps have been found of great value in soil surveys, the use of which has already been mentioned. The color pattern of soils and numerous other features giving evidence of both surface and subsurface conditions are clearly recorded on such photos, but require expert interpretation. The form of gullies and terraces, the colors of weathered profiles where there has been erosion or excavation, and the extent and form of surface drainage are among these features. These airphoto techniques are especially valuable in engineering studies for the selection of an airport site of predetermined size and class, and reveal vital information affecting the cost and stability of proposed runways and the extent of drainage required. The method is most useful where some ground information on soils is also available to supplement that obtained from the air.[6]

Even if photographs are not taken, a survey from the air is most useful to the planner in providing him with a vantage point for observing both the problems and the possibilities of

[6] See "The Engineering Significance of Soil Patterns," by Donald J. Belcher, Research Engineer, Purdue University, *Proceedings, 23rd Annual Meeting,* Highway Research Board, National Research Council, 1943, pages 569–598; also "The Origin, Distribution and Airphoto Identification of United States Soils, with special reference to Airport and Highway Engineering," *Technical Development Bulletin* 52, Civil Aeronautics Administration, U. S. Department of Commerce, May, 1946.

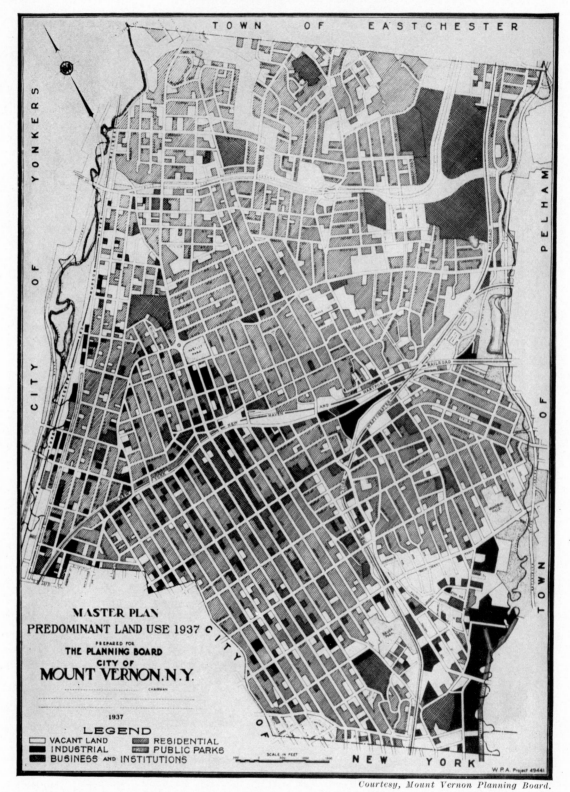

Courtesy, Mount Vernon Planning Board.

FIGURE 4·7. A TYPICAL MAP OF EXISTING LAND USES IN AN URBAN COMMUNITY

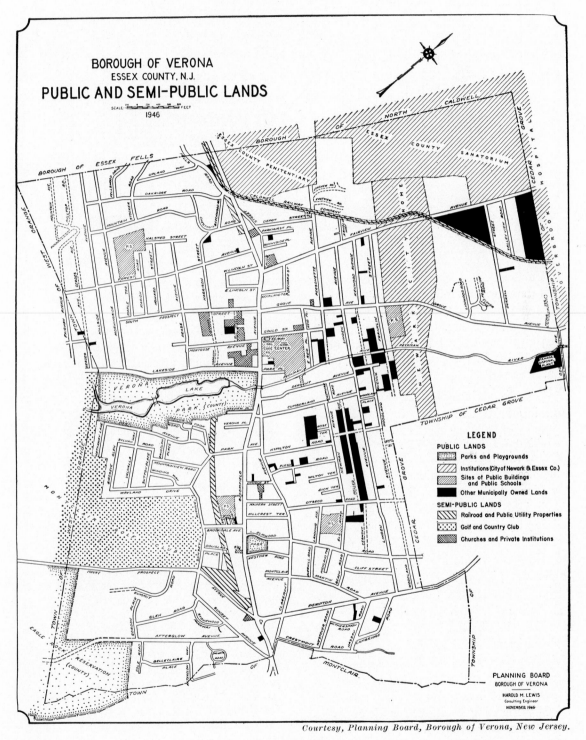

BOROUGH OF VERONA
ESSEX COUNTY, N.J.
PUBLIC AND SEMI-PUBLIC LANDS
SCALE
1946

LEGEND

PUBLIC LANDS
Parks and Playgrounds
Institutions (City of Newark & Essex Co.)
Sites of Public Buildings and Public Schools
Other Municipally Owned Lands

SEMI-PUBLIC LANDS
Railroad and Public Utility Properties
Golf and Country Club
Churches and Private Institutions

PLANNING BOARD
BOROUGH OF VERONA
HAROLD M. LEWIS
Consulting Engineer
NOVEMBER 1946

Courtesy, Planning Board, Borough of Verona, New Jersey.

FIGURE 4·8

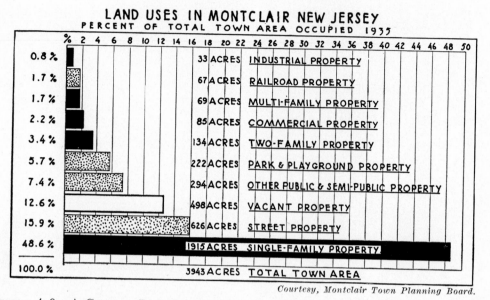

FIGURE 4·9. A GRAPHIC PRESENTATION OF LAND USES IN PERCENTAGES OF TOTAL AREA
Illustrating conditions in a high-class, suburban, residential community of about 40,000 population.

the area under study. An hour or two spent in an airplane over a large city might well be the first step in the preparation of a master plan.

Planning Principles

Many early city planning reports have devoted considerable space to the development of principles governing various elements of the city plan. This involved time-consuming research into many physical, social, economic, and legal problems. Today much of this research is available through published reports of the National Resources Committee and its predecessors; the eight Survey Volumes of the Regional Plan of New York and Its Environs, and the bulletins of its successor, the Regional Plan Association; the Proceedings of the Annual Conferences of the American Planning and Civic Association and the American Society of Planning Officials; the *Journal of the American Institute of Planners;* papers by members of the City Planning Division, American Society of Civil Engineers, to be found in the society's publications; and other sources.

It is also hoped that this volume will set forth in convenient form the principles and standards to be followed in urban planning. The reader must remember, however, that these cannot be applied arbitrarily to a community but must be fitted to its own particular needs. The city or town which has charm as well as efficiency and maintains its own individuality will, in the long run, be one that can rightly claim to be well planned.

Selected References

"Action for Cities—A Guide for Community Planning," *Publication* 86, Public Administration Service, Chicago.

LEWIS, HAROLD M.: "Basic Information Needed for a Regional Plan" (with discussion), *Transactions of the American Society of Civil Engineers,* Vol. 92 (1928), pages 1056–97.

Major Economic Factors in Metropolitan Growth and Arrangement, Vol. I, Regional Survey of New York and Its Environs, by ROBERT MURRAY HAIG in consultation with ROSWELL C. MCCREA, 1927. Distributed by Regional Plan Association, Inc., New York.

MORROW, C. EARL: *Planning Your Community,* Regional Plan Association, Inc., New York, 1945.

Population Statistics: 3. Urban Data, National Resources Committee, October, 1937.

Suggested Symbols for Plans, Maps and Charts, National Resources Committee, Washington, D. C., revised April, 1937.

The Economic Status of the New York Metropolitan Region in 1944, Regional Plan Association, Inc., New York.

Questions

1. What types of information should be shown on a base map suitable for city-wide planning studies?
2. At what scales should base maps be drawn for a typical city of 200,000 population? For a typical municipality of 5,000 population?
3. What natural resources are of interest to the city planner, and why?
4. What types of census statistics should be gathered and analyzed as a basis for a city plan?
5. What is the importance of population studies? How are such studies shown graphically?
6. Describe the types of information concerning land use that should be collected.
7. How can aerial photography be of help in planning studies?

5

ELEMENTS OF A CITY PLAN

WHAT IS THIS THING THAT WE SPEAK OF AS A city plan? The idea most commonly conveyed by the term is a map showing the boundaries of the city, the street system which already exists, and such streets as have been laid out for future development. Actually it is much more than that. It includes both the map legislated by the governing body of the municipality and the master plan for the future city prepared by its planning commission.

The first of these maps is generally designated the "official map" in the planning laws of the states and in city charters.[1] As first adopted, it is generally merely an "as is" map to which are added, from time to time, proposals for new streets or parks adopted by the legislative body and to the acquisition and construction of which it is therefore committed. The original charter of the city of New York called such a map the city "plan" and described it as a permanent map "showing the parks, streets, bridges, and tunnels, and approaches to bridges and tunnels as heretofore laid out, adopted, and established pursuant to law, and the maps and profiles included in or accompanying the same showing the grades of such streets duly fixed, adopted, and established." The preparation of such a plan is little more than surveying; more or less precise surveying, it may be, but it may involve little study of the needs of the community, little sympathy with the traditions and ideals of its people, little exercise of imagination as to its future

development and requirements. It is chiefly a record of what has already been done and cannot be changed without great expense; a record of the mistakes which have been made through lack of foresight and imagination. Not that such mistakes were necessarily due to stupidity, for a generation or two ago no one could have foreseen the marvelous development of our cities or the great social and economic changes brought about by recent inventions which have so greatly facilitated transit and other means of communication.

The real "city plan" need not be so minute as to details but must consider, primarily, the city as a whole, not only as it is, but as it will be. Referred to at first as a "comprehensive city plan," it is now generally called the "master plan," the term used in most state planning acts and also provided for in the new charter for the city of New York, effective January 1, 1938. This comprehensive, or master, plan shows the general system of arterial streets and transportation lines by which the different sections of the existing and the future city will be connected with each other and with centers of population outside the city limits; parks and open spaces and other resorts for recreation and amusement; the existing water-front development and the space needed for its further increase; existing public and semi-public buildings and sites for those which may be required in the future; and includes such public controls over private development as are found in a zoning ordinance. Such a plan will control future development, stimulating it or retarding it as the case may

[1] These are described in more detail in Chapter 20, "City Planning Legislation," Volume II.

require. It supplies something to which the city may grow, not something to which it must be restricted or within which it must be confined as in a straitjacket, as was too often the effect of the official map, particularly as it was arbitrarily extended over the undeveloped portions of a city.

The economic considerations which should control city planning are precisely those which should prevail in the design of a house, shop, railway terminal, or water-supply system; namely, adaptation to probable or possible increase in demand and capacity to supply that demand. If a factory or railway is foreordained to failure, the less expended upon it the better. There are a few towns which were laid out during "boom" periods on lines which were fancied to be those of a future metropolis, where the broad streets are grass-grown, where the public buildings are but half occupied, and where everything speaks of a splendid ambition which resulted in grotesque failure. When a city, occupying a strategic position, has begun a natural development which causes growing pains indicative of a misfit in its general plan, it is time to look toward the future, to adjust the plan to new conditions, and to provide for still further growth. To tear down and enlarge is very costly, especially when there is no room for enlargement without the purchase of additional land which has become far more valuable than when the original enterprise was begun. This is constantly being done by individuals and corporations whose domestic or business requirements make it necessary. In any case it involves a distinct loss which may be justified by the means of indulging in a luxury or by the prospect of increased profit.

Cannot the city, it may be asked, instead of trying to provide for the remote future, well afford the expense of reconstruction to adapt itself to its growing needs, especially when it has the power, through its ability to levy taxes and assessments, to impose a part or all of the cost of the necessary changes upon the property which will be chiefly benefited? No expense involving the destruction of property can be justified if it can be avoided by the exercise of reasonable forethought, and the taxing power of the city should not be used

unnecessarily. The requirements of the modern city are so great that the burden of taxation will inevitably be heavy. Improvements in the city plan may increase values to such a degree that they would be cheap at almost any price, but if the plan had been so made as to avoid the need of costly changes, both the city at large and the individual property owner would have been the gainers. To defer the correction of mistakes which are quite apparent in well-developed sections of the city or to put off the adoption of a broader policy for those in process of development because land is expensive and costly improvements would be destroyed is not unnatural, even though unwise. To fail to take advantage of such object lessons in parts of the city where there are few, if any, improvements or where the street plan has not yet been definitely fixed is the height of folly.

Scope of the Comprehensive Plan

Several writers on city planning have attempted to define the elements of a comprehensive plan. Some have laid special emphasis upon the organization and administration of the city, particularly its social activities, and their list is a long one. Others have defined the several districts or quarters of a city which require special treatment, and their list is shorter. An American architect has given twelve heads under which significant facts should be collected and classified in a study of city planning, namely: streets; transportation of people; transportation of goods; factories and warehouses; food supply and markets; water supply and sanitation; housing; recreation; parks, boulevards and tree planting; architecture; laws; and financing. A French writer gives four divisions of the city which require special study and treatment: the business, the industrial, the administrative, and the residential quarters.[2] He also notes that "the climatic conditions of each country must necessarily determine the type of dwellings

[2] A paper, "The Growth and Development of Towns," by A.-Augustin Rey, presented at the London Town Planning Conference, 1910.

selected by the inhabitants." In 1874 the
United Society of German Architects and Engineers laid down the fundamental principles
of city planning as follows:

The basic principles of enlarging a city, considered from the technical, the economical, and the
administrative points of view, are:

1. The scope of city planning consists principally
in fixing the base lines of all traffic movements and
transit facilities, viz.: streets, street cars, railroads,
and canals, which must be treated liberally and sys-
tematically.

2. The street net should contain the main streets,
with the existing streets taken duly into consideration; the auxiliary streets which are fixed by local
conditions, and in addition, other subordinate streets,
treated in accordance with the necessities of the
immediate future, or having their development
placed in the hands of interested property owners.

3. The grouping of the parts of the city should
be effected in accordance with their location and
individual characteristics, subject to such modifications as may be demanded by sanitary considerations and the exigencies of commerce and industry.

4. The duty of the building department is to determine the rights and privileges of tenant and
neighbor and house owner. Such rights and privileges are related to fire protection, freedom from
interference, health, and safety of buildings, and
all aesthetic considerations must be secondary
thereto.

5. It is desirable that expropriation and impro-
priation be facilitated by legal measures, and of
still more importance is the creation of a law providing for the regulation of the contour of new or
reconstructed blocks to be built upon.

6. The city should be reimbursed by property
holders directly benefited by improvements for
funds advanced by the city for such purposes, and
it is advisable to have the amount stipulated before
the work is begun and a normal cost per front foot
fixed.

7. The activities of interested property owners'
associations, in regard to the improvement of certain sections, should be subject to municipal supervision.

8. Land upon which it is imperative to make
improvements should only be built upon under
reservations for its subsequent use by the city.

Edward M. Bassett has listed the following
seven elements of community land planning:
streets, parks, sites for public buildings, public
reservations, zoning districts, routes for public
utilities, pierhead and bulkhead lines. He
pointed out that "a master plan cannot take the
place of the official map, although it may help
to co-ordinate items in that instrument." [3]

[3] *The Master Plan*, by Edward M. Bassett, Russell
Sage Foundation, New York, 1938, pages 11–44 and 69.

Six Principal Elements

City planning is often held to include many
things besides the physical city and to embrace
the various functions, the efficient performance
of which will depend to a large degree upon
the skill and foresight with which the ground-
work for the physical plan is laid. As this
volume will deal for the most part with the
engineering aspects of the problem, consideration will be given chiefly to the physical city.
Without regard, therefore, to the various municipal activities and administrative details,
the convenience and attractiveness of a city
will depend chiefly upon the following six features of its plan:

1. The transportation system for the movement of persons, freight, and other goods in
and out of the city, including the necessary
terminals and means of interchange. In a
water-front city this includes port development;
in all cases it covers transport by rail, water,
highway, and air where such facilities are available.

2. Public facilities for the quick movement
of passengers and freight from one part of the
municipality to another. This may be called
the intraurban transit system. It is obvious
that such needs cannot be accurately foreseen,
but provision should be made for improving
and extending the facilities when needed. Part
of such transit facilities will always be in the
streets themselves.

3. The street system in and through which
the daily business is done and by which the
people gain access to their homes and pass
from these homes to their work, recreation, and
amusement. A street system once adopted and
developed must remain indefinitely. While
some streets may be widened and an occasional new street may be cut through existing
improvements, the general street plan, once
established and constructed, is fastened upon
the city as long as the city itself lasts. A
catastrophe such as the great fire of London
in 1666, the San Francisco fire in 1906, or the
devastations of war may afford an opportunity
for a recasting of the plan for a considerable
area, but it is seldom availed of.

4. The park and recreation facilities upon which the comfort and health of the community are to a large degree dependent. It is true that a lack of proper parks may be remedied at any time, even when the spaces to be devoted to that purpose shall have been built upon and when the cost of their acquisition will be greatly enhanced. A park system, however, can be most economically and satisfactorily established in advance of other improvements, and facility of access to the park units and proper connections between the different ones will depend upon the street system, so that it is desirable that the park plan be worked out in connection with the street plan.

5. The location of public buildings, which may render the conduct of public business convenient or difficult and may give a favorable or unfavorable impression to visitors. Public buildings like business buildings can be changed in location as necessity and convenience may require, but the suitability of their sites, whether they are convenient and commanding or awkward and unprepossessing, will depend upon the streets about them and leading to them, so that the location of these buildings should receive the most careful study in the preparation of the general plan of the city.

6. The pattern of land uses, to be effectuated primarily through comprehensive zoning. Such a pattern should specify not only the kind of use but also the character and density of its development. The need for correlating communication facilities with the uses of the land they will serve is obvious. The stability of commercial and residential centers is dependent on a city plan which considers land uses both qualitatively and quantitatively.

While there are other elements which go to make up the complex organism called the modern city, those enumerated above are the ones likely to give the town its character, to make it convenient or inconvenient, dignified or commonplace. Upon the skill and foresight exercised in providing for them will depend to a large degree the orderliness of the city's growth, and the facility with which individual and corporate activities can be carried on. These six features of a city plan will be discussed in some detail in the seven succeeding chapters, two of which are devoted to the street system—one dealing with the street pattern and one with highway traffic and design problems.

Every town has its traffic problems, and the street plan should not only provide sufficient capacity for the types of vehicles which will wish to use the streets but should be correlated with a system of traffic regulation. The plan should permit existing facilities to be used to their fullest capacity, avoiding in many cases costly changes which may be deemed necessary to accommodate unregulated traffic, when by the introduction of better system and control the desired results can be secured by ordinance instead of by bond issues or assessments. It may be said that this is a matter of administration rather than of planning, but if the city planner can point out how conditions can be improved by so simple and inexpensive a method as regulation instead of a replanning to meet changed conditions, it is surely within his province and it is his duty to do so.

Amenity, or pleasantness of surroundings, requires good design of the streets and their details. Good proportion, the obvious adaptability of means to ends, and the repression of garish and obtrusive signs and hideous noises will accomplish more than the introduction of fountains, statues, and other highly decorative features. The convenience and comfort of those using the streets are sacrificed if private owners are permitted to encumber the sidewalks by projecting portions of buildings or by temporary occupation for the display of goods. Street capacity, which may be ample if the abutting buildings are of moderate height, may be seriously congested if buildings are allowed to be carried to any height which the owners may find profitable. Healthy living may be rendered impossible by overintensive development, failure to provide sufficient light and air through the absence of adequate courts and back yards, and the lack of restrictions on the height to which buildings may be erected. Even though the framework of a city is intelligently planned, its main objectives may fail of realization if there is a lack of such control over the development of private property as will insure amenity, convenience, and health.

While the original ground plan has chiefly to do with the street system, the provision of suitable sites for public and semi-public buildings should be kept in mind. Although the precise location of such buildings cannot be designated far in advance, the general plan should be such that a special site need not be created for each building when the time arrives for its erection, streets being widened and new streets cut through in order to provide access to it or to enable it to be seen to advantage. If, for the sake of public convenience and in order to secure a good architectural effect, the important public buildings can be so grouped as to create a civic center, it should not be necessary to recast the street plan in order to do so. Not only should suitable sites be provided for the buildings which are erected by the city and used for its public business, but those of a semi-public character, such as railway stations, private educational institutions, churches, and places of amusement, will, if properly designed and advantageously located, add character and distinction to the city and are entitled to consideration in the preparation of the original plan.

Certain parts of the city will be peculiarly adapted to specific uses, depending upon the topography, accessibility to transportation lines, and other considerations. There will be business districts, industrial districts, high-class residential districts, and those where workmen can find cheap homes or low-rent dwellings convenient to the places where they are to be employed. Zoning and other controls can assure a reasonable and efficient pattern for future growth.

Other Phases of Planning

Some of the other parts of the physical city plan are discussed in Volume II.

Three of these deal essentially with the community as part of the city, and involve both the planning of new areas and the replanning of obsolete ones. Neighborhood features should be created and maintained through planned residential communities as part of the city plan; the general problems of housing, both public and private, are of vital concern to the town planner; and the prevention and cure of blighted areas are essential to stability of use and values.

Other special planning problems to be discussed in Volume II are the relation of the airport to a city plan, a problem combining the elements of communications and land use discussed in this volume; the parking of passenger cars and the loading and unloading of commercial vehicles in commercial and retail areas; the possibilities of decentralization of both industry and residence; and the importance of extending the plan beyond the corporate limits of the municipality.

The air age followed World War II, and any city is remiss that neglects the potentialities of air transportation, both public and private, in its city plan. The parking problem is no respecter of communities—it attacks them all, and few have yet found an adequate solution.

Special developments on the order of the so-called garden cities, either for the accommodation of those employed in the business districts or in connection with industrial plants, will be undertaken if there are places available for them. In order that this may be possible without going miles beyond the city limits, considerable areas may well be left undivided, in order that such developers may have a rather free hand in carrying out such plans, provided always that there is a competent authority who has full power to control the general plan and whose approval should be required before it can be carried out.

Careful study may be given to, and skill shown in, the orderly planning of a city or even of the entire area within the city limits, and yet, when the boundary line between the city and the adjacent towns is passed, the roads may be of inadequate capacity or without proper articulation. Approaches to a city may be shabby and uninteresting, and the only available roads leading to the neighboring towns may be tortuous in their course and may pass through the meanest parts of both, giving the traveler a very unfavorable impression. The environs of the city should, therefore, be studied in connection with and in relation to the plan of the city itself.

Related Legal, Economic, and Administrative Problems

The final section of Volume II deals with those legal, economic, and administrative problems which, while not parts of a physical plan and not capable of expression on a map, are nonetheless essential in the planning process.

American cities generally have little power of initiative. Legislative action is commonly required to permit them to do constructive work themselves or to enable them properly to control improvements undertaken by private individuals or corporations. Laws permitting them to do, to allow others to do, or to forbid others from doing, seem therefore to be necessary, and the framing of wise legislation to this end is an important part of a city planning program. Most of the municipal planning in the United States is now being done under enabling legislation adopted by the various state legislatures, or through the grant of such powers to cities through municipal charters. Other features of control, such as the control of land subdivision design, may be delegated directly to the local planning commission.

Among the recognized objectives of city planning are the maintenance of values and, where possible, the improvement of values. This means that sound planning can lead to direct economic advantages for the citizens at large. The preparation of the plan may well include an intelligent program for carrying it out progressively. Such a program requires plans for the sane financing of these improvements in order that the burden of cost will be distributed as equitably as possible, that the few will not be enriched at the expense of the many, and that the city's credit will not be recklessly used.

European cities are often large landowners and frequently indulge in land speculation, from the profits of which many of their social activities are financed. The adoption of and consistent adherence to a wise and prudent land policy are therefore necessary. Frequent changes of administration and reversal of policies have made state legislative bodies reluctant to give much power of self-government to American cities, and public opinion appears to incline to this view. Intelligent city planning and the orderly execution of a plan depend to so large a degree upon municipal prudence and self-restraint and upon continuity of policy and purpose that municipal officers will have to show that they are capable of exercising such restraint and of working out and adhering to wise and prudent, as well as progressive, policies before they will be given that degree of self-government obviously needed at the present time.

No one individual can hope to master all the problems involved in planning the modern city, but all should command the sympathetic interest of the man or group of men who may be responsible for planning for the further growth or development of a city or town. They must not only be thoroughly familiar with the technical subjects involved, but should also have some knowledge of the legal and economic questions which will arise and of the methods whereby these have been solved in other cities, while social and humanitarian considerations should be given proper weight. The planners and builders of our modern cities are confronted with problems which are not only highly technical, but which are unsurpassed in their intensely human interest.

Selected References

A *City Planning Primer* (prepared by the Advisory Committee on Zoning), U. S. Department of Commerce, Government Printing Office, Washington, D. C., 1928.

BASSETT, EDWARD M.: *The Master Plan*, Russell Sage Foundation, New York, 1938.

LEWIS, HAROLD MacLEAN: *City Planning—Why and How*, Longmans Green and Company, New York, 1939.

LOHMANN, KARL B.: *Principles of City Planning*, McGraw-Hill Book Company, New York, 1931.

NOLEN, JOHN, ed.: *City Planning: A Series of Papers Presenting the Essential Elements of a City Plan*, D. Appleton and Company, New York, Second Edition, 1929.

Questions

1. What is the essential difference between an "official map" and a "master plan"? What agency is responsible for each?

2. List the principal items which make up a "master plan."
3. What are the seven elements of land planning as listed by Edward M. Bassett?
4. What are the six principal elements of the comprehensive physical city plan as described in this volume?
5. List some of the other related parts of the physical plan.
6. What legal problems are involved in city planning?
7. How do questions of economics and administration enter into the city planning process?

Part Two

Communications Master Plan

6

TRANSPORTATION AND PORT DEVELOPMENT

THE MODERN CITY OWES, IN MOST CASES ITS genesis, and in all cases its growth and prosperity, to its facilities for internal communication and for easy access to its sources of supply and to markets for the disposal of its manufactured products. A globe trotter who had developed greater powers of observation than of thought is said to have remarked that during his travels he had noticed that, by some wise provision of Providence, wherever there was a great center of population or industry, there was usually a navigable river or an arm of the sea and advantageous locations for railways to connect it with other parts of the country. Though this is conspicuously true of industrial towns, it is true to an equal extent of all great centers of population. The need of giving the fullest consideration to the general problem of transportation in the original planning of a city or its various additions has been emphasized in the preceding chapter, but the most that can be accomplished by such study will be to render it possible to provide for the expansion of transportation facilities as required with a minimum of disturbance of the general city plan.

The kind of transportation dealt with in this chapter is intercity, as against intracity, movement; intracity movement, for which the term "local transit" is generally used, will be discussed in the succeeding chapter. The larger a city

grows, the more difficult it is to discuss separately these two types of movement because the local area becomes both the central city and its surrounding suburban areas. In a small community the intercity transportation problem is primarily one of locating terminals to fit in with the city plan, but in a large city the routes to and from terminals and provision for easy interchange between terminals for different kinds of movement—such as by rail, water, highway, and air—and for different kinds of commodities require careful study. Industry and general business will prosper only if adequate provision is made for getting both passengers and goods into and out of the city. The special problems of air-transport terminals are discussed in Chapter 16, Volume II.

A port city, serving waterborne commerce as well as commerce by land and air, brings special problems to the planner. The port areas must have room for expected expansion and must be so laid out as to handle goods and passengers at reasonable cost. The economic welfare and stability of the port activities of such a city are of vital importance to the city as a whole, as many of its business and industrial activities will be closely linked to its port functions.

A city is fortunate if its general ground plan has been laid out with due regard for the entry into it of trunk-line railroads with ample terminal facilities, for such connecting lines as will provide for the economical and expeditious handling of freight, and for spurs to serve industrial plants; and if, in the case of a port city, the water front has also been so planned as to provide for the convenience of shipping and for ready intercommunication between rail and water traffic. The needed facilities can then be provided, as the demand for them grows, with a minimum of expense and disturbance of ordinary business. In the English-speaking countries the trunk-line railways are still owned and operated by private corporations, but there is a growing tendency toward the municipal control and in some cases the construction and ownership of terminals, the facilities of which are open to all railroads and ships on equal terms.

Seaport cities have been slow to appreciate the need of the proper correlation, if not the unification, of rail and water terminals. They appear to have proceeded under the idea that the material brought into the city is for home consumption, or is to be transformed into manufactured products before it is transshipped to interior points, and have not appreciated the importance of their functions as distributing centers. Railroad terminals are often planned as if there were no other means of transportation. Shipping terminals are likewise designed as though railroad connections were of little or no importance. Only recently has the problem of port organization attracted the attention which it deserves.

There is not infrequently a feeling that residence outside the city limits by those whose daily occupation is within the city should be discouraged and that the growth of towns beyond the city lines is detrimental to the best interests of the city, for the reason that everyone who derives his income from the city's activities should contribute, through taxation and the trade resulting from his domestic establishment, toward the expense of the municipal government and the business of the city shops. This feeling is due to a lack of appreciation of the extent to which every town and hamlet outside an important urban district stimulates

its growth and ministers to its prosperity. Ample facilities to enter and leave a city are as important as those for intercommunication between the different parts of the same city.

The Railroad Network

The railroad as a means of intercity transportation and the important part which it plays in the development and growth of a city are generally recognized. Essential as it is to the prosperity of a city, it presents serious physical problems and often great difficulties in the development of a convenient and adequate street system. The different railway lines entering a city cannot be permitted to divide it into sections which are isolated, one from another. The streets cannot be abruptly stopped at the railroad tracks but must be carried across them, even though to do so involves danger or large expense. When towns or districts of an existing town are being rapidly developed into important manufacturing, commercial, or distributing centers, the railroads are eagerly welcomed, the more of them the better, in the belief that competition will reduce transportation rates. They are not only allowed to locate their terminals wherever they can secure the cheapest property for the purpose, but they are permitted to reach these terminals by such routes as they please without regard to the location of tracks of other railroads, which they may cross at grade if the state laws permit. The result is often such a condition as has grown up in Chicago (Figure 6·1), though usually on a much smaller scale.

In a report made on the local railroad situation by the civic committee of the City Club of Chicago, from which Figures 6·1, 6·7, and 6·8 are reproduced, the jumble of railroad lines entering the city was described as follows: "The criss-crossing of railway lines—each line an independent enterprise and welcomed as such by a land-speculating public—which began so conspicuously in the fifties, has continued and grown until we have our present network of steam railroads, one of the most remarkable examples of chaos ever produced by human activity."[1] Many of these must have had a serious effect upon the adjacent property, condemning it to a type of occupancy and character of improvement which have contributed to the extensive blighted areas which Chicago is now striving to replan and rebuild.

ket, and in these pockets are found the worst tenements and slums."

The most serious congestion of rail traffic, either passengers or freight, is generally found at terminals; but in metropolitan areas, particularly where natural routes are limited in

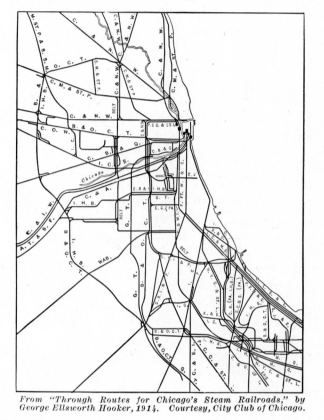

From "Through Routes for Chicago's Steam Railroads," by George Ellsworth Hooker, 1914. Courtesy, City Club of Chicago.

FIGURE 6·1. TRUNK-LINE RAILROADS ENTERING THE CITY OF CHICAGO

Each railroad has its own right of way.

Railroad approaches to any large city are notoriously unattractive. Where the land is not in demand for industry, the adjoining areas are likely to be shabby and unsightly, frequently given over to the poorer class of homes. Edward H. Bennett observed that "where many railroads radiate from the city in different directions, the triangular-shaped areas lying between them for a considerable distance out from the center of the city are reduced to a low level of utility, even though they may have comparatively high values in the real estate mar-

number, it may also occur on radial lines. The extent to which passenger traffic builds up as one approaches New York City is shown in Figure 6·2. In most cities today, available low-gradient routes have already been preempted by the railroad companies, and any need for increased facilities must be taken care of by enlarging the track facilities of existing routes.

In a port city served by different railroad systems there will be a considerable movement of interchange freight which enters the port on one railroad only to leave it on a different one. Likewise, much freight coming in on one railroad will be destined to a local destination

[1] *Through Routes for Chicago's Steam Railroads,* by George Ellsworth Hooker, the City Club of Chicago, 1914.

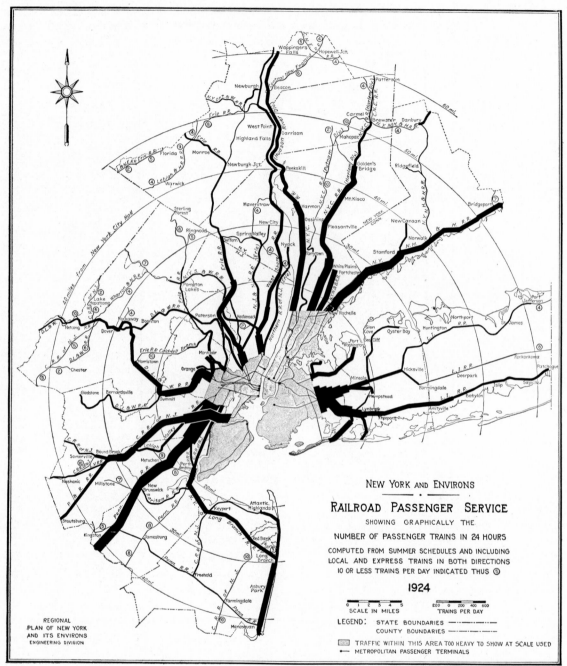

From "Survey Volume IV," Regional Plan of New York and Its Environs.

FIGURE 6·2

on another one in the port district. Outbound freight moves similarly in the reverse direction. Such movements will be greatly facilitated if a belt line is provided encircling the principal one owing to the natural obstacles to their proper connection. The great navigable waterways which give this city and the district tributary to it a commanding position as a com-

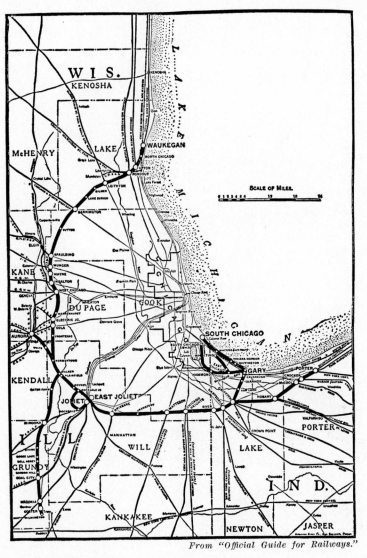

From "Official Guide for Railways."

FIGURE 6·3. THE CHICAGO OUTER BELT LINE

Operated by the Elgin, Joliet, and Eastern Railway Company.

port and industrial areas and connecting with all the radial lines entering the city. Through such a line local freight can reach its destination directly, and through freight can be bypassed around the city and its terminals. The Chicago outer belt line is a good example of such a facility (Figure 6·3).

The problem of co-ordinating the railroad lines serving New York is an especially serious mercial and manufacturing center render the problem peculiarly difficult of solution. But one trunk-line railroad, the New York Central, has direct rail connection between the great center of population on Manhattan Island and other parts of the country for the handling of freight, and this system reaches only the northeastern portion of the United States by way of the Hudson River Valley. The New York, New

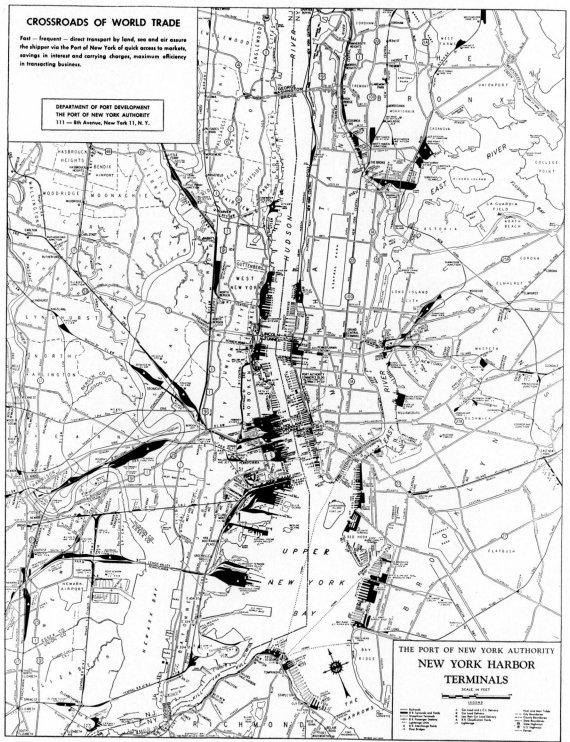

FIGURE 6·4

Courtesy, Port of New York Authority.

Haven, & Hartford, serving New England, stops at the Harlem River. All the other lines have their rail termini on the west side of the Hudson in the state of New Jersey and transfer their freight cars across the river by means of floats (Figure 6·4). The Pennsylvania Railroad has, at enormous expense, brought its pas-

mous bridge across the East River with long viaduct approaches. (See Figure 6·5.)

The comprehensive plan prepared by the Port of New York Authority and approved February, 1922, by the state legislatures of New York and New Jersey (Figure 6·6) makes the New York Connecting Railway a part of

Courtesy, Triborough Bridge Authority.

FIGURE 6·5. HELL GATE BRIDGE OVER THE EAST RIVER AND ITS APPROACHES, AS PART OF THE NEW YORK CONNECTING RAILWAY

The railroad bridge appears beyond and parallel to the Triborough Bridge, a link in the city's expressway system.

senger business to Manhattan Island by two tracks in a tunnel under the Hudson. It has four tracks under the East River to reach its passenger terminal yard on Long Island, where it connects with the Long Island railroad system, which it controls, but it is not allowed, under the terms of its franchise, to use these tracks for freight business. It has established a great freight terminal on the New Jersey side of the Upper Bay at Greenville, and opposite this, in Brooklyn, is the terminus of the New York Connecting Railway which swings around through the boroughs of Brooklyn and Queens and connects with the New York, New Haven, & Hartford and with New England by an enor-

a middle belt freight line which connects at Greenville (ultimately by a tunnel under the Upper Bay, but temporarily by carfloats) with all the railroads terminating in New Jersey, and at Mott Haven in The Bronx with the New York Central Railroad. The plan also includes an outer belt line and a series of marginal railroads; the only one of these which has been constructed is marginal railroad No. 13, operating as a belt line about 16½ miles in length along the westerly side of the Hudson River and Upper New York Bay. Many of the Port of New York Authority's efforts have been devoted to improving highway communication between the two sides of the port by the construction of interstate bridges and tunnels and to providing adequate terminals (see pages 68 to 69).

ably the most conspicuous instance, and when nearly all these lines have their termini in this city, it is quite likely that each will have estab-

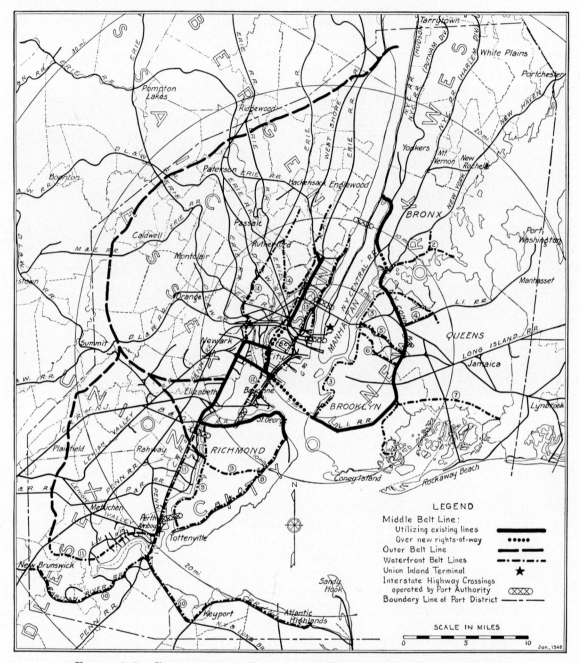

FIGURE 6·6.   COMPREHENSIVE PLAN OF THE PORT OF NEW YORK AUTHORITY

Rail Terminals

When a city is served by a great number of trunk-line railroads, of which Chicago is prob-

lished its terminal independently of the others, and that subsequent connections between them will be difficult and costly.   There will be a great number of terminals, those for passengers often having commodious and handsome stations, while those for freight are, as a rule, unsightly and exercise a blighting influence upon the parts of the city in which they are located. Chicago has six separate passenger terminals (Figure 6·7) within the limited area known as the "loop district," and, while the

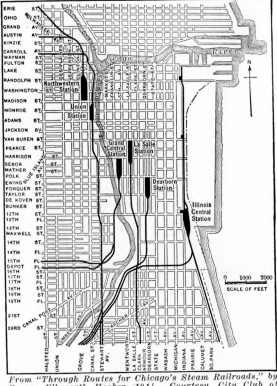

From "Through Routes for Chicago's Steam Railroads," by George Ellsworth Hooker, 1914. Courtesy, City Club of Chicago.

FIGURE 6·7. LOCATION OF THE SIX PASSENGER RAILWAY TERMINALS OF CHICAGO

extraordinary growth of the city could not have been anticipated when the original city and its successive additions were planned, the problem of so connecting the various lines as to reduce the number of separate terminals and the cost of transferring freight and passengers differs only in magnitude from that presented in any other railroad center.

Although some of these Chicago terminals occupy beautiful stations with every device for the convenience and comfort of passengers, and some of them are used by several lines, through passengers are compelled to traverse the streets from one station to another unless the outgoing

line happens to use the same station as does the line by which they arrive.

A study was made for the City Club of Chicago by Bion J. Arnold for simplication of the plan and published in the report already referred to.[2] Arnold's proposal is shown in Figure 6·8, which indicates the economic advantages which would accrue to the city and the railroads. It would apply the through-routing principle by creating four through routes by means of connections between existing steam railroads serving the city and its suburbs. These connections would be made in the downtown area, involving two short subways and seven new stations. The reverse movements of one-half to five miles to and from coach yards for storage, required under the present system, would be eliminated.

It may be argued that Chicago's wonderful growth could not have been anticipated even by a city planner possessing exceptional imagination, and that anyone who, a generation or two ago, had attempted to make provision for the accommodation of the enormous railroad business which now exists would have been considered mad. This is doubtless true as to the magnitude of the business, but if all the railroads had been confined to certain well-defined and contiguous routes, and if places had been set aside for yards for classification and exchange of freight, it would simply have been necessary to enlarge these facilities, confining them to certain sections instead of allowing them to be scattered over the entire city, multiplying needlessly the number of unsightly spots.

It may be urged that a city of nearly three and a half million people needs a large number of distributing points, and that the more such points there are the shorter will be the haul through the city streets, but the tracks serving these distributing centers should be open to all lines. If a merchant or manufacturer receives goods from New York or New Orleans or Milwaukee, or if he wishes to make shipments to Pittsburgh or Indianapolis or Denver, he should not be compelled to go to a different

[2] *Ibid.* See pages 60–61.

part of the city to receive or deliver the goods arriving or leaving by a particular line. He should be able to use the nearest and most conveniently located freight station, whatever may have been the origin or whatever may be the destination of his goods or by whatever

use of carfloats; the largest of these are the Bush, Atlantic, and Baltic Terminals, all on the Brooklyn waterfront. On Manhattan, the railroads still operate their individual waterfront terminals, all but that of the New York Central Railroad being dependent on waterway

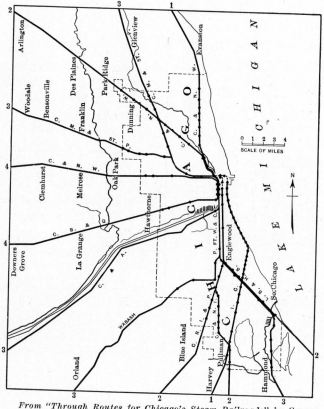

From "Through Routes for Chicago's Steam Railroads" by George Ellsworth Hooker, 1914. Courtesy, City Club of Chicago.

FIGURE 6·8. PLAN FOR THE SIMPLIFICATION OF THE TRUNK RAILWAY SYSTEM OF CHICAGO

A proposal by Bion J. Arnold, each line to use an existing right of way. Connections in the downtown area would permit through routing for all lines.

line they may be carried. This is a fundamental economic principle which holds good whether the town be large or small, whether the transportation lines serving it be few or many. The co-ordination of the railway lines and the distribution of the stations in Berlin provide an example of a good plan (see Figure 6·9).

In the Port of New York, through the flexibility provided by its many navigable waterways, there have long been union water-front terminals served by all railroads through the

connections. To remedy, in part, this situation the Port of New York Authority proposes a series of inland terminals for less-than-carload shipments to be served by motorized equipment operating to and from the railroads, with the overhead rights utilized for commercial purposes.

At the end of 1930 the executives of the eight trunk lines serving the port district entered into an agreement with the Port of New York Authority for the first unit of this type. It was opened October 3, 1932, in the block bounded by 15th and 16th streets and 8th and 9th avenues, one of the largest blocks in Manhattan. On these four acres of ground, a two-level station platform is operated by a joint railroad agency with part of the space leased to the Railway Express Agency. Over 300,000 tons of railroad less-than-carload and express matter are handled yearly through the terminal. Shippers and receivers of freight are able to handle mixed truckloads for any or all of the

lines. Each station is expected to eliminate nearly 2,000,000 truck-miles per annum in local delivery operations. It would be possible later to provide a rail connection to the Newark Terminal if that should prove desirable.

The Port Authority has also established a union grain elevator and a union shipping terminal in the borough of Brooklyn, New York City, and has made proposals to the municipalities of Newark and Hoboken to rehabilitate

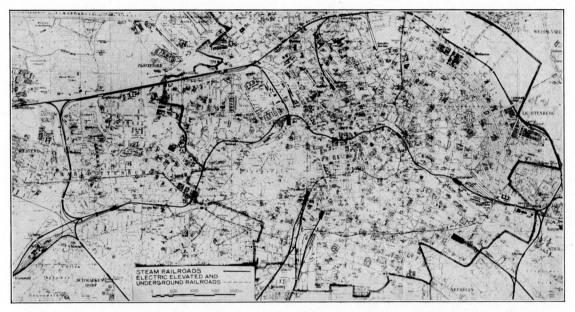

FIGURE 6·9. PLAN SHOWING THE EXCELLENT SYSTEM OF RAILWAY TERMINALS IN BERLIN

railroads at one platform, thereby decreasing their trucking expenses, saving time, and eliminating excess mileage on the city streets.

Construction began on similar union terminals for motor-truck freight in 1947. One of these is located in Manhattan between Washington and Greenwich streets and Spring and Houston streets, and the other in the Newark area south of the Ruppert Stadium, near U. S. Highway No. 1. These stations will have platforms over 1,000 feet in length, equipped with conveyors, and will be utilized as breakbulk points for over-the-road motor carriers operating to all parts of the United States east of the Mississippi River. Freight received at these stations will be made available to consignees' trucks and to joint pick-up and delivery contractors making store-door delivery on consolidated routes for the over-the-road

and develop union shipping terminals on their water fronts.

There are two great passenger railway terminals in New York City—the Grand Central Station of the New York Central, which also supplies trackage and terminal facilities to the New Haven system, and the Pennsylvania Station, the relative locations of which are shown in Figure 6·13.

While the Grand Central is strictly a terminal or dead-end station, its enormous size permits the serious limitations of such stations to be partly overcome by the use of loops on the two underground levels, the upper for express and the lower for local trains, enabling all trains, after entering the incoming part of the station, to pass around the stub-end tracks to the outgoing side without backswitching. (See Figures 6·10 and 6·11.) The elaborate yet convenient system of connections between this station and the various underground lines of the city's transit system which reach it is

South and West and for the Long Island lines from the East, has the advantages of a through station in its train movement, as all its trains

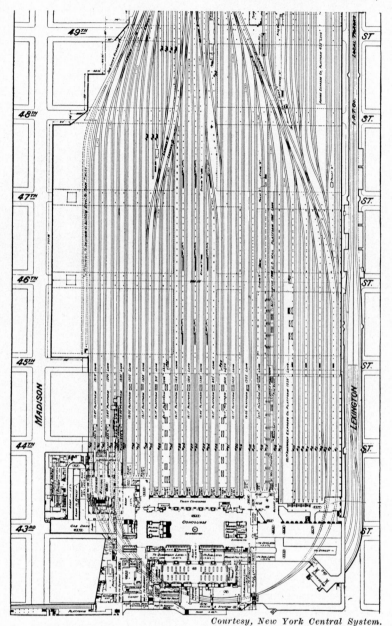

Courtesy, New York Central System.

FIGURE 6·10. PLAN OF THE UPPER, OR EXPRESS, TRACK LEVEL OF THE GRAND CENTRAL STATION, NEW YORK CITY

shown by Figure 6·12. The introduction of ramps instead of stairways is one of the features of this most modern of the world's great railway terminals.

The Pennsylvania Station, while really a terminal for the Pennsylvania lines from the

arriving from the South or West pass through the station and under the East River to a great terminal yard on Long Island (Figure 6·13). Through service from Washington to Boston is also provided via the Hell Gate Bridge over the East River (see Figure 6·5).

The character of these station buildings and their position with respect to the street system are referred to in Chapter 11, "The Location of

of such terminals include greater convenience to travelers transferring from one system to another; savings to the railroad companies

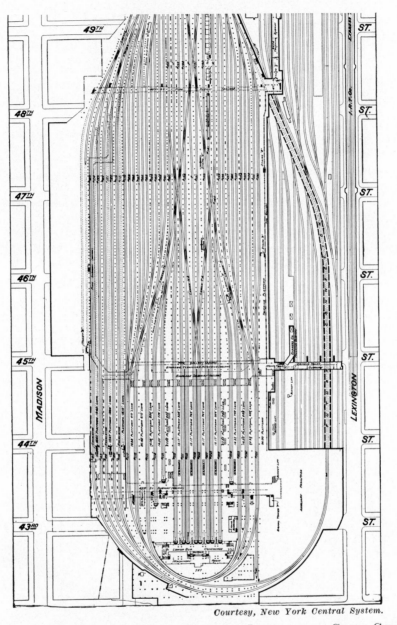

Courtesy, New York Central System.

FIGURE 6·11. PLAN OF THE LOWER, OR SUBURBAN, TRACK LEVEL OF THE GRAND CENTRAL STATION, NEW YORK CITY

Public and Semi-public Buildings" (see pages 220 and 242).

Union passenger terminals may be established with or without consolidation—the essential feature is unified control, through unified management and operation. The advantages

through elimination of some duplicate facilities; assignment of facilities, including trackage, yards, and accessory structures, for that use which best serves the public interest; greater economy and efficiency in operation; and non-discriminatory charges for services. Among the

Courtesy, New York State Public Service Commission.

FIGURE 6·12. GRAND CENTRAL STATION, NEW YORK CITY, AND ITS CONNECTIONS AS ORIGINALLY
PROPOSED

A—Surface of 42nd Street; B—Upper concourse connecting with subways; C—Original four-track sub-way, now operated as a shuttle line in 42nd Street; D—Lexington Avenue Subway; E—Proposed extension of Hudson and Manhattan Subway to New Jersey, not constructed; F—Elevators, later extended to "H"; G—Lower concourse connecting with subway, not constructed; H—Steinway Tunnel to Long Island, now a part of the city's subway system.

FIGURE 6·13. LOCATION OF PENNSYLVANIA STATION IN NEW YORK CITY, CONNECTING RIVER
TUNNELS, AND THE YARD ON LONG ISLAND

A indicates the Pennsylvania Station, and B the Grand Central Station.

disadvantages of union terminals which may be claimed are the greater concentration of traffic to and from the terminal, causing serious street congestion; the elimination of competition, resulting in a slackening in standards of service; and the necessity for some people to travel farther between their homes or places of business and a new union station.

Certainly the solution of the railroad-terminal problem in any community is vitally related to many other features of the city plan. For movement of bulk traffic the railroad is still the main carrier and will probably continue to be. Old downtown trackage, yards, and freight houses are, in some cases, using lands which could better be reclaimed for business uses with a great increase in realty values. Where tracks are at grade, they may be strangling the growth of the business center. Industrial sites benefit from good rail transportation and in many cases require their own rail sidings. The railroad plan and the land use plan must therefore be closely co-ordinated.

A good example of such co-ordination in planning is provided by the postwar plan for Manchester, England. In 1945 there were ten central freight terminals, each serving the whole area for freight destined to or from that part of the rail network each served. No adequate rail connections were available for interchange between the different railroad systems. The existing terminals were close-in because of their former dependence upon horse-drawn vehicles. They were described as large, unsightly, and generally dirty places, occupying sites which, in the redevelopment of the central area, might be more effectively occupied by other and more seemly buildings. It was suggested that all freight terminals should ultimately be transferred outside a proposed inner belt highway (ring road), and two new major terminals were proposed to replace and combine all but one of the present main terminals. Industrial and warehouse districts would be regrouped around and convenient to these new terminals, and in well-planned satellite communities.[3]

[3] See *City of Manchester Plan,* by R. Nicholas, Jarrold & Sons, Ltd., Norwich and London, 1945, pages 61–72.

Railroad Commuter Service

In large metropolitan areas there has been thrown upon the railroads the additional task of caring for the railroad commuter—he who lives in suburban, or in some cases quite distant, cities and travels daily by railroad to and from a place of employment in the main city. This situation is most pronounced in New York, Chicago, and Philadelphia, but is found to a lesser extent in such cities as St. Louis and Cleveland. Generally the commuters are brought into the same terminals as the long-haul passengers, resulting in crowding and inconvenience for both types of passengers.

In the New York region, various proposals have been made since 1920 for a unified suburban rapid-transit system which would include downtown distribution lines for commuter trains separate from the trunk lines. The New York Regional Plan, in discussing such a distribution system, recommended, "In planning added facilities into or through Manhattan these should be placed so as not to add to congestion but to make for a more homogeneous city by developing heretofore neglected and backward sections." [4]

In the last few decades the railroads supplying commuter service have seen considerable traffic diverted to motor buses and private automobiles, but the lack of adequate downtown terminals for such vehicles has in many cases resulted in greater discomfort for the rider. Railroad electrification has greatly increased the attractiveness of commuter rail service and is essential for any separate distribution system. If motor vehicles continue to increase the street congestion in downtown areas, increased mass transportation by rail may offer the best solution in metropolitan areas as part of a sound city and regional plan.

Railroad-highway Grade Separations

With the rapid development of the railroad systems which took place in the United States,

[4] *Transit and Transportation,* Vol. IV, Regional Survey of New York and Its Environs, by Harold M. Lewis, with supplementary reports by William J. Wilgus and Daniel L. Turner, 1928, page 63.

thousands of railroad-highway grade crossings arose in urban as well as suburban and rural areas. The elimination of these is a long-time program, but much progress has been made in the last few decades. Many states have now adopted laws to require that any new lines be carried over or under existing streets, but rarely is any effort made so to locate the tracks, either with respect to lines or grades, as to provide for carrying streets which may be mapped but not yet built over or under the tracks at a minimum of expense and disturbance of the street plan. Railroads built through thinly settled districts which produce little business for them are obliged to keep their original construction cost down to the lowest possible figure and to provide for betterments from their future earnings. This policy is often followed even with respect to the portions of their lines entering or passing through urban districts. While very reasonable from the railroad point of view, it may be disastrous in its effect upon the city plan.

In the densely populated countries of Europe, where the railway lines are relatively short and a larger capital expenditure for initial construction is justified, grade crossings are rarely permitted in either urban or rural districts, but the entire railroad right of way is enclosed, so that access to the tracks is difficult or must be so deliberate as to be in the nature of trespass. As the city grows and its street traffic increases, the dangers and delays incident to grade crossings of the railroads become intolerable, and their elimination becomes necessary. The cost of this work is so great that many large cities put up with the inconvenience until the annual loss of life is so great that action can no longer be deferred.

The safety feature of grade-crossing elimination was one of the main subjects discussed at the National Conference on Street and Highway Safety held in Washington in December, 1924, and the final report of that conference recommended that priority be given to such projects "in the allocation of capital funds by the railroads and of public moneys for highway building, over expenditures for other safety measures designed to protect the public." In the President's Highway Safety Conference,

held 22 years later in 1946, such projects were still stressed as follows:

The only positive method of preventing collisions at highway-railroad crossings, as at other traffic intersections at grade, is by separation of these grades. Principal railroad grade crossings of major traffic thoroughfare should be separated in the order of their relative hazards and economic benefits. Where it is not possible to separate major crossings, suitable standard-type barriers should be provided, and, at less important crossings, standard-type signals and signs should be installed. In all instances where separation is effected, complete closure of the old crossing should be accomplished.

In the interest of safety and the early activation of this program, it is important that there be a division of the costs involved on the basis of relative benefits to the railway and highway interests concerned. The present state and local laws are not entirely modern in this respect.[5]

Because of the great expense of such projects a complete program for any city can seldom be carried out in a wholesale fashion, but must be undertaken progressively. It is a mistake, however, to consider each crossing or even a group of crossings in close proximity to each other as a separate problem. As in all other city planning, a comprehensive scheme should be worked out in advance, even though it may be years before it is entirely completed. In studying one small section of a railroad line, it may be quite evident that the most economical treatment and that which will involve the least disturbance of existing conditions will be to elevate the railroad and depress the streets enough to carry them beneath it. On another part of the line, where the conditions have become so bad that the grade crossings must be abolished, the easiest and cheapest plan will be to lower the railroad grade and carry the streets over it. When the intervening section is to be treated, it may be found that to pass from a railroad on embankment to a railroad in cut will render it very difficult and expensive, or even impossible, to carry some important intervening streets across the tracks in any way. Had the entire length of the railroad in its relation to the street grades been studied in advance, the treatment of one of the limited

[5] *Action Program and Committee Reports Adopted by the President's Highway Safety Conference, Held in Washington, D. C., May 8, 9 and 10, 1946,* Report of Committee on Engineering, page 38.

sections might have been so modified as to give the best results along the entire line. Before the plans for any of the crossings are determined, a decision should be reached as to the manner of treating every other crossing of the entire line of every railroad entering the city. The work may be carried out step by step, but each step should be in accordance with a consistent and comprehensive plan.

The clearance which it is possible to secure will vary considerably. Railroad companies

tween abutments span the streets without intermediate supports; but where the length is greater, intermediate columns on the sidewalk just back of the curb are permitted, and, in exceptional cases, where the street is unusually wide or the skew is so great as to require a long span, columns are permitted in the middle of the roadway.

After the nature of the crossings and the clearance required in each case have been settled, the next thing to be determined is how

Courtesy, New York State Department of Public Works.

FIGURE 6·14. A GRADE CROSSING ELIMINATION BY DEPRESSING THE HIGHWAY

On Route 20 at Sangerfield in Oneida County, New York. Slopes were seeded to prevent erosion, and an accident hazard was eliminated.

desire and actually require a minimum of 16 feet, and for freight lines, more particularly at the entrance to yards, they prefer about 22 feet in order that trainmen may stand on the tops of freight cars without danger. Such a clearance can seldom be secured in populous districts, and in some places standing on the tops of cars is forbidden by law or by the regulations of Public Service Commissions. Where streets pass under the railroad, a clearance of 16 feet is desirable; this clearance is frequently reduced to 14 feet, and in some special cases to 12 feet; but this should be avoided wherever possible.

New York City requires a minimum clearance of 14 feet at the center line of a roadway, which may be reduced to 12 feet at the curb line where arched spans are used. Since 1939 it has effectively opposed any exceptions to this rule. It also has a general requirement that all railroad bridges 75 feet or less in length be-

much each grade line is to give way to the other. In the case of an undercrossing this involves determining whether the street shall be lowered to such an extent as to reduce to a minimum the height of the railroad embankment (Figure 6·14) or whether the railroad shall be so raised as to avoid the need of any great departure from street grades. In the case of an overcrossing it must be decided whether the street shall be carried over the railroad with little change in the latter, whether the railroad shall be depressed sufficiently to permit the street to pass over it with little disturbance of its natural grade, or whether the one shall be lowered and the other raised about equally (Figure 6·15). The solution of these questions will frequently be governed by the need of providing for the drainage and sewerage of the territory, a substantial depression of either street or railroad being likely to interfere seriously with adequate provision for drainage.

Owners of property in the vicinity naturally prefer to have the railroad placed out of sight, and its complete depression is generally urged. Such treatment is more expensive, especially if it involves the lowering of tracks which are in use, and it seriously interferes with the provision of industrial spurs and sidings. If the railroad is slightly lowered, the street grades must be substantially changed in order to carry them over, and this involves either steep grades or long ramps, resulting in damages to abutting property, which will be left below grade. The

Where the bridge carries the highway over the tracks, little besides its roadway, sidewalks and protecting railing will be seen, and the chief consideration will be its adequate capacity and its safety; but where the railroad passes over the street its appearance is of the greatest importance. The railroad is a utility upon which the growth and prosperity of the town depend, and its practical purpose can be frankly recognized and expressed in the structure which will carry it across the public highway. To try to make a railroad bridge look like a tri-

Courtesy, New York State Department of Public Works.

FIGURE 6·15. THE RAILROAD RAISED AND THE HIGHWAY DEPRESSED IN A GRADE CROSSING ELIMINATION AT FORT EDWARD, NEW YORK

The elevated sidewalks protect pedestrian traffic and reduce the rise and fall in sidewalk grade.

raising of a street above the natural surface always results in much greater damage than does its depression below the surface. If the railroad is to be raised, every additional foot of elevation is opposed on account of the barrier which a high embankment will place between the districts on the two sides of the tracks. There is, however, a great advantage in permitting the streets to remain as close as possible to their natural grade rather than allowing the introduction of depressions, which it will be difficult to drain and which will obstruct the view of vehicles approaching from the opposite direction. Considerations of cost will be likely to control the decision, the state, the city, and the railroad company all sharing the expense in most instances. The preservation of the traffic value of the street and the avoidance of interference with the drainage system should in all cases be given careful consideration.

These details being settled, the next question is the character of the structures to be erected.

umphal arch is absurd. On the other hand, the erection of a few steel columns and girders with wooden cross-ties separated by open spaces —in other words, a structure which will simply get the tracks across the street and permit traffic to pass under them—should not be tolerated. This is quite generally recognized now, and an effort is usually made to erect bridges which will be attractive in appearance, an object which can be attained more easily than was formerly possible and within reasonable limits of cost owing to the advances in reinforced concrete construction.

Often a realignment of the highway will permit a great improvement in both safety and appearance, particularly where the highway is being widened and modernized and the topography is rolling. (See Figures 6·16 and 6·17.)

A difficult and interesting problem was presented by the three bridges over Queens Boulevard in New York, all being within a distance of 2,700 feet. The relative position of these crossings and the angles at which the railroad lines cross the street are shown by Figure 6·18. It was necessary that the two outside bridges,

tect to collaborate with their engineers in working out the plans of these three bridges in such a manner that they would bear a proper rela-

Courtesy, New York State Department of Public Works.

FIGURE 6·16. AN ATTRACTIVE BUT SIMPLE PLATE-GIRDER RAILROAD BRIDGE REPLACES A LOW ARCH ON A DANGEROUS CURVE

A solution involving a realignment of a state highway east of Poughkeepsie, New York.

Courtesy, New York State Department of Public Works.

FIGURE 6·17. A MODERN HIGHWAY ELIMINATES AN UNDERPASS DESIGNED FOR "HORSE AND BUGGY" TRAFFIC

A relocation of Route 22 at Dover Plains, New York, substitutes a four-lane, steel-beam overpass for a one-lane masonry arch.

one carrying six tracks and the other two, should be placed at as low an elevation as possible and leave sufficient clearance for the street, while the intermediate bridge, carrying a railroad that crosses over the other two, had to be much higher. The railroad companies were advised to secure the services of an archi-

tion to each other, and Arnold W. Brunner of New York was retained for this purpose. The manner in which the problem was solved is indicated by Figure 6·19.

In the lower bridges substantial piers were provided—actually used for storage buildings for supplies and tools of street-repair forces—

thus reducing the bridge spans and avoiding too much emphasis upon the somewhat scant clearance over the roadways. In the higher bridge, arches were used. These designs recognized the practical purpose of the bridges and did not attempt to make them appear other than what they are—the means of carrying railroads across a highway; but this was done

and the railroad companies have appeared not to care how they look.

The difficulty of financing grade-crossing eliminations has been a retarding factor. Often the projects have been delayed until serious accident records, involving numerous fatalities, have aroused the state to exercise its police power to require the construction of an over-

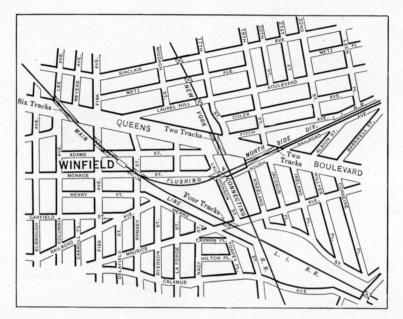

FIGURE 6·18. PLAN SHOWING THREE RAILROAD BRIDGES CROSSING A BOULEVARD IN CLOSE PROXIMITY

Within a distance of about one-half mile the three bridges shown cross a 200-foot boulevard, each at a different angle.

with as little disfigurement of the boulevard as possible.

Many other examples might be given of the way in which this problem of carrying highways over or under railroads has been solved, but the purpose of this discussion is simply to emphasize its importance as a part of the general city plan and to urge that it be approached as a thoroughly practical one. To disguise the railroad bridge in an effort to make it look like something other than the useful and necessary thing it really is will render it ridiculous, which is as undesirable as the unmitigated ugliness which has often characterized such structures where no intelligent control has been exercised by the public authorities

pass or underpass. The following recent accident records of three states are indicative of the losses of human life resulting from remaining grade crossings:

Connecticut, year ending Sept. 30, 1945: 41 accidents, involving 4 fatalities.

Massachusetts, year ending Nov. 30, 1940: 32 accidents, involving 4 fatalities.

New Jersey, year ending Dec. 31, 1944: 171 accidents, involving 32 fatalities.

The apportioning of the cost of eliminating grade crossings has been a controversial question from the beginning. For many years state legislatures required the railroads to bear the entire cost. They were considered to have introduced the danger of such intersections and were held responsible for their removal. The public believed that they could readily absorb the and the municipality; then the states assumed a portion of the expense; later federal funds were made available.[6]

Courtesy, President Borough of Queens, New York City.

FIGURE 6·19. VIEWS OF RAILROAD BRIDGES CROSSING QUEENS BOULEVARD IN THE BOROUGH OF QUEENS, NEW YORK CITY

These views show the bridges on the map in Figure 6·18; that in the upper view carries six tracks, and those in the lower view each carry two tracks.

cost involved. The departure from the principle that the railroads were solely responsible came earlier in some states than is commonly realized—in the 1880's in Connecticut and in 1890 in Massachusetts; still earlier, in 1872, New York City had been authorized to contribute one-half the cost of eliminating New York Central grade crossings on Manhattan Island. It first became the practice to finance such projects jointly by the railroad company

In general, the ordering of elimination projects is now the responsibility of a state regulatory agency, such as a Public Service Commission, Public Utilities Commission, or Railroad Commission, which also rules on the division of the costs, although in some states this division is established by state law. Construc-

[6] See *Public Aids to Transportation*, Vol. II, Federal Co-ordinator of Transportation, Government Printing Office, Washington, D. C., 1938, pages 268–290.

tion plans and contracts must generally be approved by the Commission.

The most comprehensive grade-crossing-elimination work in the pre-World War II period was undertaken by cities under special statutes. Buffalo did a great deal of work through a special commission and, while the distribution of cost varied somewhat, the general policy laid down by the commission was that all expenses for right of way be paid by the railroad company, that the cost of other land needed for the structures and the cost of the bridges be paid two-thirds by the railroad and one-third by the city, while the damages were shared equally. In Chicago many millions were expended by the railroad companies in the elevation of their tracks, the city's contribution being less than one per cent of the total cost, this representing consequential damages. In Detroit the railroad companies paid for all the physical work and the city the damages, which amounted to 25 per cent or more of the total expense. In Philadelphia the practice varied from time to time, the railway originally paying the cost of construction and the city assuming the damages, while under special agreements the expense in some cases was shared equally; in others the railroad company paid one-third, and in still others two-thirds of the cost, and the city the balance.

During the Public Works Administration in the 1930's, federal grants and loans became available for grade-crossing eliminations, and many projects were financed in this way. Under the Federal Highway Act of 1940 the following formula was established for the allocation of federal grants for such projects authorized by Congress: one-half on the basis of population, one-quarter on the basis of mileage of federal-aid highways, and one-quarter on the basis of railroad mileage. Although originally such funds had to be matched by state funds, this requirement was later eliminated, and the 1944 Federal Highway Act authorized that these funds need not be limited to construction costs, as formerly, but might also finance a share of the costs of any new or additional rights of way needed for a grade-crossing elimination.

New York State and New York City have attacked this problem boldly. In 1925 the state voted a bond issue of $300,000,000 for eliminating railroad-highway grade crossings throughout the state, on a basis of dividing the costs as follows: 50 per cent by the railroad company, 25 per cent by the state, and 25 per cent by the locality. In 1927 this was changed to require payment of 50 per cent by the railroad company, the balance to be apportioned by the legislature between the state and the locality. In 1938 the locality was relieved of financial responsibility, and it was decreed that the state would be reimbursed by the railroad company for any portion of the improvement not an essential part of elimination and for the net benefit to the company from the elimination, such benefit not to exceed 15 per cent of the cost, exclusive of incidental improvements.

In 1939 a committee of the Board of Estimate of New York City, headed by Robert Moses, submitted a program for the elimination of all remaining grade crossings within the city limits. This involved 113 crossings; projects for the elimination of 78 of these were already under way. Although wartime shortages interfered with the execution of this program, it is hoped that it can be completed in the postwar period of construction.

Port and Harbor Facilities

Although the design of port and harbor facilities is not a part of city planning in the ordinary acceptance of the term, the setting aside of suitable and adequate areas for that purpose and their correlation with other phases of the master plan, particularly with the transportation system, are of vital importance to the city planner. While the last half of the nineteenth century saw a great expansion of European ports, both on the Continent and in Great Britain, the last two decades have witnessed phenomenal growth in American ports. This emphasizes the need of taking into account the possibility of such development and the necessity of so planning our cities as to make the provision of these facilities possible without needlessly great expense and without serious disarrangement of the city plan.

The city planner should be familiar with the various types of docks and piers, as their space requirements and their adaptability for interchange from ship to other carriers and for industrial or other use of the water front vary greatly. There are six general types: [7]

1. The pier and slip, where the pier extends beyond a bulkhead line and the water moves

the center. Such facilities are found in Hamburg, Antwerp, Rotterdam, and Southampton.

3. The marginal quay constructed on the edge of, and parallel to, the waterway. This is well adapted to rail interchange and upland warehouses. Such quays are found in New Orleans, in Rio de Janeiro and on the edge of the River Scheldt in Antwerp.

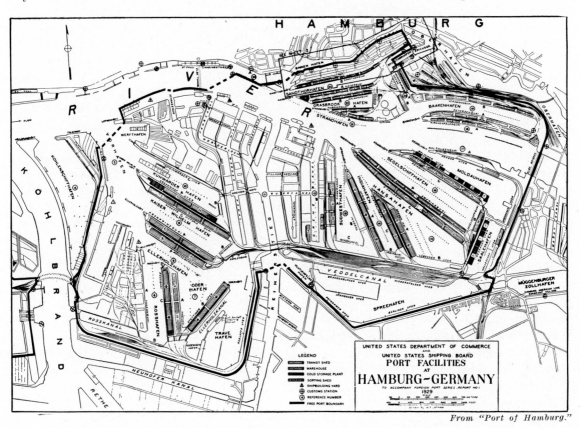

From "Port of Hamburg."

FIGURE 6·20. PLAN OF PRINCIPAL PORTION OF THE HARBOR OF HAMBURG, GERMANY

freely beneath it. The pier is generally at right angles to the shore line, as in New York, or at an acute angle, with its outer end pointing partly downstream. A modern pier for ocean-going vessels should be up to 1,200 feet long and preferably at least 125 feet wide.

2. The quay and basin, where the quay is on solid fill, generally long enough to accommodate two or more ships on each side, and wide enough (200 feet or more) to have railroad tracks along each edge and warehouses in

4. Double pier and slip, or quay pier, where the quay is about 400 feet wide, has rail facilities down its center with storage sheds on each side, and provides wharfage both along its sides and across the outer end.

5. Trunk and branch, where a main quay extends at right angles to the shore and has a series of slips and piers extending diagonally toward the main waterway on each side.

6. The oyster fork, where a wide quay has two piers at its outer end with a slip between. The quay could extend to a bulkhead line some distance offshore and the piers continue to an established pierhead line.

[7] For more detailed descripton see *Ports and Terminal Facilities,* by Roy S. MacElwee, McGraw-Hill Book Company, Second Edition, 1926, pages 23–61.

Some statistics are given below concerning the harbors of a few outstanding European and American ports.

The port of Hamburg, Germany, 65 miles from the mouth of the Elbe River, dates from 1847. At that time, according to Edwin J. Clapp in his book descriptive of the port,[8] the Hamburg-American line started with a sailing ship of 717 register tons called the *Deutschland*, which was the pride of the city, while in 1914 this company had the world's two largest ships, the *Imperator* and the *Vaterland*, each of about 50,000 tons. It required a vast expenditure to improve the harbor and the channel leading to it in order that these great ships and the large number of other vessels frequenting the port could be accommodated. Clapp said that from 1850 to 1906 Hamburg spent 62,000,000 marks in improving the channel of the Elbe between the city and the sea, and that the cost of constructing the harbor was 400,000,000 marks, this including 9,500,000 marks for the harbor works at Cuxhaven at the mouth of the river, but not including the Free Port warehouses.

The new piers of the Hamburg-American line were built by the city at a cost of 32,000,-000 marks and leased to the company at an annual rental of 1,350,000 marks, representing slightly less than 4¼ per cent on the investment. The total water area of the harbor in 1930 was 1,935 acres, of which deep-water basins comprised 1,250 acres. It had a water frontage of 30 miles, practically all developed (Figure 6·20).

After World War I, Antwerp, Belgium, ranked fourth among world ports in the amount of tonnage handled, being outranked only by London, New York, and Liverpool. It is an outstanding example of quay development and in 1924 had 12 miles of docks which could accommodate 2,000 ships. It is reached over 60 miles of the River Scheldt, from which two sharp turns have been eliminated in improving the channel. Most of the shipping is handled in tidal basins. A distinctive feature of the river-front development is the promenade built

[8] *The Port of Hamburg,* by Edwin J. Clapp, Yale University Press, New Haven, Conn., 1911.

over the outer edge of the dock sheds, affording visitors an extensive view of the busy harbor (Figure 6·21).

In both these cities the rivers that serve them must be constantly dredged at enormous cost to maintain a sufficient depth of water for the accommodation of shipping and have been deepened as the size of ocean-going vessels has increased. Frankfort, Germany, is still more remarkable in this respect, although its port can serve only small-draught river vessels.

FIGURE 6·21. GENERAL VIEW OF FREIGHT SHEDS, PROMENADE, AND FREIGHT-HANDLING EQUIPMENT ON THE RIVER FRONT OF ANTWERP, BELGIUM

Located on the River Main about 25 miles from its confluence with the Rhine, which is, in turn, more than 300 miles from the mouth of the latter at the Hook of Holland, Frankfort has always been a prosperous city with a large inland trade. Nevertheless, to make itself an important terminal where rail and water lines meet and so to co-ordinate these lines as to offer what were said to be among the best and cheapest pre-World War II manufacturing sites in all Europe, required vision and courage of a high order, which, however, were characteristic of Oberburgermeister Adickes and his associates in the city government. On what was known as the new East Harbor the city spent some $18,000,000, a third of which was for real estate, a half for construction, and the rest for warehouses, equipment, and interest on capital during construction. This development covers 1,180 acres, of which 350 acres were devoted to streets, railways, and embankments, 110 acres to water basins, and the remaining 720 acres to sites for storage and handling of freight, warehouses, and industrial plants. All industrial sites have adequate connections with the railway system. The property for this development was purchased before it took on a speculative value. The purpose of the city was to lease rather than sell the industrial sites, but finding it difficult to do so, it sold them on terms which, while liberal financially, contained rigid restrictions. As stated in the report of the New York State Barge Canal Terminal Commission:

In the case of sale the city protects itself against the possibility of speculation by providing in the contract a condition that the site may only be used

neys, elevators, heaps of mine refuse are everywhere to be seen. Thickly populated cities and centers of trade lie close together, humming with industrial activity. Furnaces, iron and steel works, foundries, factories, zinc and copper-smelting works, and many manufactories, some of them of the largest, unite in making a picture of industrial development unrivaled in all Europe.[10]

In each of these cities the shipping terminal was not considered one enterprise, and the railroad terminals another. They are intimately related and efficiently operated as a single unit, railroad tracks being brought to each dock, basin, and warehouse, so that it is a combined shipping and rail terminal.

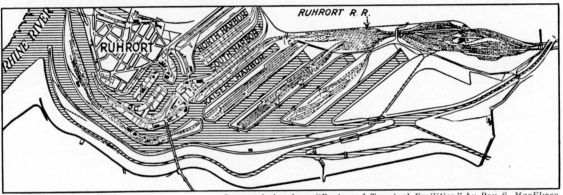

FIGURE 6·22. A PORTION OF THE RIVER PORT OF DUISBURG-RUHRORT, GERMANY

for a certain purpose, previously agreed upon. The industry must be established within a fixed period, previous to the expiration of which the plot is not allowed to be resold. Should an attempt be made to disregard these conditions, then the city has a right to demand the return of the site, without compensation for the loss of interest.[9]

A particularly good illustration of the complete co-ordination of rail and water transportation facilities is offered by the remarkable harbor of Duisburg-Ruhrort on the Rhine 135 miles above Rotterdam and 45 miles above the boundary between Holland and Germany (Figure 6·22). The greatest inland port of prewar Germany, it was the commercial center of the Rhur industrial district, an area which has been described as follows:

A closely woven network of railroads covers the entire region; coal mine succeeds coal mine; chim-

London, although 50 miles from the mouth of the Thames River, is one of the most highly developed ports in the world. It is under the control of the Port of London Authority. London does not have its water and rail facilities as closely co-ordinated as do the Continental ports described above, because, like the older American ports, it had its dock system well established before the development of the railroads. Before World War I the docks and wharves under control of the Port of London Authority had an appraised value of some $185,000,000. The port included a total land and water area of 2,467 acres, a river frontage of about three miles, 28 miles of quay walls, and about 120 miles of railway. As the tidal range in London is from 17 to 20 feet, the docks are provided with gates. The Tilbury docks, which are the most modern, are about 23 miles

9 "Report of the New York State Barge Canal Terminal Commission," *Senate Document* 30, 1911, Vol. I, page 370.

10 *Ibid.*, page 348.

below London Bridge, and included four wet docks having a length of 1,600 feet each and widths of from 250 to 600 feet and a tidal basin, all with a depth of 45 feet below high water, the combined water area being 73 acres. Between the tidal basin and the wet docks, there was a lock 700 feet long divided into two chambers having lengths of 145 and 555 feet respectively. Sheds and warehouses with railway

290 to 370 feet wide, and with 26-foot depth of water. The port is completely served by a belt railway over which its 6½ miles of quays are connected with every part of Great Britain. The expenditures of this municipality to convert itself into a seaport reached $85,000,000 before World War I. The co-ordination of rail and water facilities in Manchester is shown in Figure 6·23.

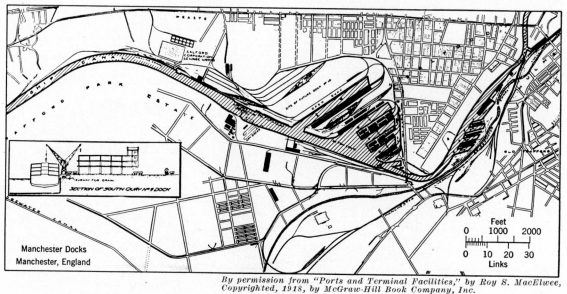

Manchester Docks
Manchester, England

By permission from "Ports and Terminal Facilities," by Roy S. MacElwee, Copyrighted, 1918, by McGraw-Hill Book Company, Inc.

FIGURE 6·23. THE INLAND PORT OF MANCHESTER, ENGLAND

tracks and hydraulic traveling cranes were located along all the quay walls.

The docks of Liverpool and Birkenhead, which form a single port, had, in 1929, a total water area of 654 acres and 38 miles of quay walls, all provided with warehouses, sheds, railway tracks, and freight-handling machinery. There were 32 graving docks. The tidal range at Liverpool is from 21 to 35 feet, necessitating the most costly and substantial construction, while constant dredging in the Mersey River and over the bar at its mouth four miles below the docks is a large item in the cost of the port improvement and maintenance, upon which a total of $200,000,000 was expended before World War I.

Manchester, England, is an example of an inland city which has become an important seaport. It has connected itself with the Mersey River by means of a canal 35½ miles long,

The two great capitals of South America have shown foresight and enterprise in improving their transportation facilities.

In 1889 Buenos Aires completed a system of great connecting docks, each over 2,000 feet long and more than 500 feet wide, with 23 feet of water at low tide, with tidal gates and a basin at each end, and approached by channels having depths of 19 feet and 21 feet at low water. The original works cost about $40,000,000 in gold, and extensive additions and improvements completed about 1920 cost $20,000,000, the new docks having 30 feet of water alongside and being approached by a channel of the same depth. The "Port Railway," owned and operated by the government of Argentina, connects these docks with all the railroads of the country.

After these improvements, and obviously as a result of them, there has been an enormous increase in the tonnage of the port. In 1880 this tonnage amounted to about 700,000 tons. When the first improvements were undertaken, a proposed capacity of 2,000,000 tons was considered extravagant, but when the new docks were first opened in 1889, the capacity had grown to 3,800,000 tons and reached about 12,000,000 tons in 1912. The total exports and imports of Argentina, a very large proportion of which passes through the port of Buenos Aires, reached a pre-World War II peak of 28,570,000 tons in 1937, representing a gain of 108 per cent in exports and 38 per cent in imports above 1913 figures. The population of Buenos Aires has increased from about 400,000 in 1887 to 2,620,827 on January 1, 1945.

Rio de Janeiro, founded, like Buenos Aires, in the middle of the sixteenth century, is the only world capital located in an equatorial region, but, owing to the lofty mountains encircling the Bay, not only does it possess a picturesque site, but also its immediate surroundings cover a remarkable range of climate, which changes with the altitude above sea level. This city also has developed its harbor to meet the needs of commerce, constructing about 1910 a quay wall 2½ miles long, backed by a great system of warehouses and sheds provided with electric cranes and railroad tracks, with a large anchorage approached by a channel dredged to a depth of 33 feet. On another part of the water front there has been constructed one of the world's most beautiful boulevards. The city's resulting growth in commerce has been attended by an increase in population from 975,000 in 1913 to about 1,942,000 in 1945.

In North America, in both the United States and the Dominion of Canada, vast sums have been expended for harbor improvements since 1925. National, state, and local funds have been contributed. The developments on the Pacific Coast were speeded up by the construction of the Panama Canal, but a similar activity of construction has been maintained by the Gulf and Atlantic ports.

The Vancouver Harbor and Dock Commission spent about $30,000,000 for docks, supplemented by an expenditure of $2,500,000 by the Dominion Government. The port of Seattle, Washington, had 166 piers in 1938, located along both salt-water and fresh-water harbors. The United States Government spent $16,000,000 on improvements at the mouth of the Columbia River and an additional $4,000,000 on the river channel. The Port of Portland Commission now has full control of the Columbia and Willamette rivers from Portland to the sea and also operates two airports. The Commission of Public Docks of the city of Portland, Oregon, owns and operates three municipal terminals, including two drydocks, one of 10,000-ton and one of 15,000-ton capacity. At the end of 1940 the commission had issued bonds totaling $10,560,000.

San Francisco's port has been under control of a Board of State Harbor Commissioners since 1863, and in 1923 the tangible assets of the Commission were worth about $50,000,000, including a belt railroad with 54 miles of trackage serving 37 out of 40 water-front piers. All the wharves and piers in the port were owned by the Commission.

Los Angeles, 20 miles inland with no natural harbor, has made itself a seaport by "shoestring" annexes (Figure 6·24). Its harbor is protected by two breakwaters with a 2,200-foot opening; the outer harbor has an area of 981 acres, and the inner harbor (Figure 6·25) of 804 acres. Through June, 1940, the Los Angeles Board of Harbor Commissioners had authorized bond issues totaling $29,900,000; the total expenditures of the federal government at the port had totaled about $18,447,000. Construction was started in 1912, and the first terminals were completed in 1914 in time to receive the first merchant ship to pass through the Panama Canal. Of the 25½ miles of water front in the port area, less than half was still undeveloped in 1940, at which time the total improved wharfage was as follows: [11]

	LINEAR FEET
Freight and passenger	27,361
Lumber industry	13,623
Petroleum industry	12,534
Shipyards	6,021
Fishing industry	5,150
Miscellaneous	8,575
Total	73,264

[11] 1940 Annual Report, Board of Harbor Commissioners, Los Angeles (year ending June 30, 1940).

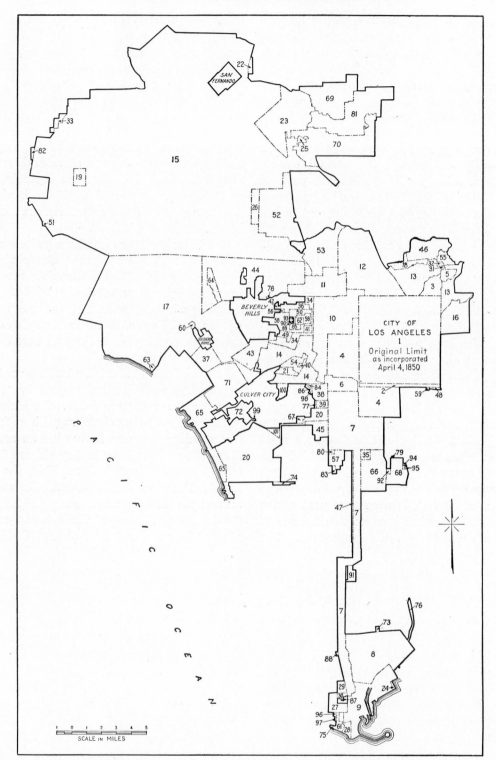

FIGURE 6·24. PLAN SHOWING SUCCESSIVE ADDITIONS TO THE CITY OF LOS ANGELES UP TO JANUARY
29, 1947

From map supplied by Lloyd Aldrich, City Engineer. The date and area of each addition are shown in
Table 30, Chapter 19, Volume II.

On the Gulf of Mexico, Houston, Texas, has been connected with Galveston Bay by a ship canal 50 miles long and 150 to 400 feet wide, originally financed by the federal government and the county of Harris. First dredged to a depth of 25 feet, it was later deepened to 30 feet and in 1935 had a project depth of 32 feet.

ment at Toronto, Montreal, Halifax, and other ports. Originally under divided ownership, the water front of Toronto was, in 1933, 99 per cent owned and controlled by the city of Toronto and its Harbor Commission, created in 1911. Montreal, although 1,000 miles from the ocean, has a channel 30 feet deep and is able to ac-

FIGURE 6·25. AIR VIEW OF SECTION OF INNER HARBOR, PORT OF LOS ANGELES

An example of the close co-ordination of water, rail, and highway facilities.

At that time the port of Houston had 48 wharves, bulkheads, and moorings, providing berths for 58 sea-going ships. New Orleans completed in the 1920's, at a cost of about $20,000,000, an Inner Harbor Navigation Canal, 30 feet deep, which cuts across the city to connect its main harbor along the Mississippi River, which has ample depth for the largest vessels, with Lake Ponchartrain, an arm of the Gulf of Mexico.

Harbor developments in the Atlantic ports during the last three decades have included large expenditures by the Canadian Govern-

commodate ships of 20,000 gross tons. At Halifax, a $30,000,000 program was started in 1912, interrupted by World War I, but later carried through to completion. It has a year-round port with a channel 50 feet deep at low tide. Seven main piers and wharves provide 16,000 linear feet of berthing. There are 13 transit sheds, a grain elevator, and a cold-storage terminal. The total cargo handled reached a wartime peak of 6,258,000 tons in 1944.

The port of Boston, with a total water frontage of over 140 miles, has been developed jointly by the federal government and the Commonwealth of Massachusetts. The federal government has provided a main entrance channel 600 feet wide and 40 feet deep, an anchorage area of equal depth, supplementary channels, sea walls, and riprap. The Commonwealth had, up to 1936, built or purchased 10 wharves, three of which are important terminals, and reclaimed large areas of flats, on a portion of which the city has developed an airport.

The port of Baltimore has been developed by the federal government and the city through its Port Development Commission. In 1920 the Maryland State Legislature authorized the city to borrow $50,000,000 for building piers for lessees. Its comprehensive plan includes an entrance channel 600 feet wide and 35 feet deep and three new groups of piers.

The plans of the Port of New York Authority, established by the states of New York and New Jersey in 1921, have already been referred to on pages 65 and 68 and illustrated in Figure 6·6. They are also described briefly in Chapter 22, Volume II.

Free Ports

The "free port" is an adjunct of a seaport which has been developed extensively abroad. It has been defined as "an area of a port separated from the customs area of a nation by a stockade. Ships may enter such a port, discharge, load, and depart without customs formalities. The goods may be stored, repacked, manufactured, and re-exported without customs formalities. Only when the goods pass the barrier to reach the consuming public of the country do they undergo customs revision and pay the necessary duty." [12] Such a free port should be located where it can readily be fenced off from the rest of the harbor, but should have convenient access to housing and business areas. Foreign free ports include those at Hamburg, Budapest, Genoa, Fiume, Newfoundland, and three locations in Mexico.

[12] *Ports and Terminal Facilities,* by Roy S. MacElwee, McGraw-Hill Book Company, 1918, page 276.

In the United States such ports were first authorized as "foreign-trade zones" under a federal law approved by the United States Secretary of Commerce January 29, 1936. The first such zone was opened in New York City in 1937, utilizing five piers on Staten Island; during World War II it was temporarily transferred to five Manhattan piers. A second foreign-trade zone was established at Mobile, Alabama, in 1938, but was discontinued the following year.

Federal Aid in Port Development

Many cities and towns of moderate size located on navigable waterways, or on waterways which could readily be made navigable or the channels of which could be deepened, are either unable to undertake expensive improvements or are disposed to rely upon the state or federal government to make such improvements at general public expense. The aggregate annual expenditures of the federal government on projects of this kind have been enormous. In 1940, just before the entrance of the United States into World War II, and in the postwar year 1947 (in each case for the fiscal year ending June 30th) the federal budget included the following:

	1940	1947
For improvement of existing rivers and harbors	$30,000,000	$52,690,000
For maintenance of existing rivers and harbors	41,000,000	67,871,500
Total	$71,000,000	$120,561,500

The United States Engineer Corps acts as the agent of the federal government in the investigation, design, and construction of any river and harbor projects, but the initiation of such a federal project must be local. The following seven steps are involved:

1. A bill is introduced in Congress by a local Congressman, at the request of local groups and citizens, to authorize a preliminary examination and survey of the proposed project.

2. The project is approved, either as a special bill or as a part of the annual Rivers and Harbors Bill.

3. An examination is made and a preliminary report is submitted by the District Engineer to the Chief of Engineers through the Division Engineer and Board of Engineers for Rivers and Harbors.

4. If the Board has made an adverse recommendation, the Chief of Engineers so reports to Congress through the Secretary of War. If the Board has tentatively approved the project, it is referred back to the District Engineer for a thorough survey, definite plans and specifications, and an economic analysis of benefits and savings which would accrue. This is again reviewed by the Division Engineer and the Board of Engineers for Rivers and Harbors.

5. If approved, a report is transmitted by the Chief of Engineers to Congress, where it is studied by the appropriate committees in both Houses.

6. If adopted by Congress and approved by the President, it is authorized by law and takes its place on a list of approved Army Engineer Corps projects.

7. As Congress appropriates funds for rivers and harbors, they may be expended by the United States Engineer Corps for the construction of any projects on this approved list. The Engineer Corps selects projects from the list in the order of their importance.

There is thus a pretty sound guarantee that federal funds will be available only for worthwhile projects. In many cases there have been worked out co-operative programs under which cities and communities have assumed a share of the financial burden, and the federal government has been inclined to extend assistance first to those cities and communities which have manifested a desire to help themselves.

An excellent illustration of such co-operation is afforded by the Jamaica Bay improvement in New York City. In 1906 a commission was created to study and report on the possibility of converting into a harbor this bay, which lies between the Rockaway peninsula and the Brooklyn shore. It then had a water area of 16,170 acres, while within its limits and about its shores were marsh lands, completely covered at extreme high tides, comprising an additional area of 12,700 acres and making a total of 45 square miles. The commission's report con-

templated using the whole bay for port and industrial purposes. The new harbor would have a natural entrance directly from the ocean, avoiding the long passage through the lower and upper bays and the Hudson or East River.

The federal government investigated the feasibility of the project, and an agreement was made with the city of New York to the effect that, when the city should have provided $1,000,000 towards the cost of the improvement, the government would undertake to dredge the main channels, or if the city did the work of dredging, the government would allow the city eight cents a cubic yard for all material removed. The first contract made was for a price slightly under eight cents a cubic yard, so that the physical work was begun without expense to the city. The dredged material was used to fill in the lowlands adjoining and make them suitable for industrial development, and the city's funds could thus be devoted in large part to the acquisition of the bordering land and the creation of the subsidiary channels.

The city did not push the improvement or provide the sum stipulated by the federal government for a number of years, and it was not until 1921 that a plan for partial improvement of the channels and the building of a group of piers was determined upon. Later the larger scheme was abandoned, Idlewild Airport was constructed on the northeastern shores of the bay, and the city decided to maintain the islands and much of the shores for recreational purposes, concentrating port and industrial developments at the west end. A high-level highway bridge was built across Rockaway Inlet in 1937, and the federal government has constructed a jetty on Rockaway Point to protect the harbor entrance from silting. A marginal railroad to serve the water-front sites is still needed. The general layout of the bay, as shown on the city map in 1947, is indicated in Figure 6·26.

Special Freight Terminals

In general, it may be said that the efficiency of a port will depend on the efficiency of its terminals; at least, that is where the bottle-necks most often occur and where the costs of handling pile up. Railroad freight terminals have already been discussed briefly (pages 66 to 73), but mention should be made of some of the special terminals that may be required in a

such as sand or gravel, require storage bins and machinery for unloading.

Foodstuffs are handled in their own terminals and generally require prompt handling, facilities for auctions, and refrigeration. Fruits and vegetables, meats, live poultry, fish,

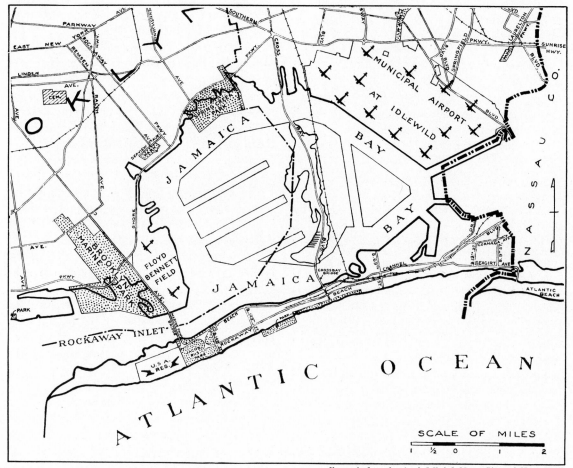

From index sheet of Official Map, City of New York.

FIGURE 6·26. PRESENT PLAN FOR JAMAICA BAY AREA IN NEW YORK CITY

large port, and the need of tying them in with other parts of the city plan.

Special terminals may be needed for the handling of coal and ore, which generally enter or leave a port by shiploads or complete train-loads. A section of the water front should be reserved for receipt or transshipment of one or more of these products and must be equipped with special machinery for prompt handling.

Oil also enters a port in bulk and needs special facilities for handling and storage. Grain requires grain elevators. Building materials,

oysters, livestock—each of these may require its own separate wholesale markets and its own special type of facilities. The design of these facilities is not city planning, but their location so as to function without congestion and without creating nuisances to residential areas is of definite concern to the planner.

Selected References

LEWIS, HAROLD M., with supplementary reports by WILLIAM J. WILGUS and DANIEL L. TURNER: Transit *and Transportation,* Vol. IV, Regional Survey of New York and Its Environs, 1928. Distributed by Regional Plan Association, Inc., New York. See, particularly, chapter on "The Transportation Problem" and section on "The Suburban Rapid-transit Situation" in Part I, Part II, and report by Col. Wilgus in Part III.

MacElwee, Roy S.: *Ports and Terminal Facilities,* McGraw-Hill Book Company, New York, Second Edition, 1926.

Mayer, Harold M.: "Railroads and City Planning," *Journal of the American Institute of Planners,* Vol. XII, No. 4 (Fall, 1946), pages 4–20, 77 Massachusetts Avenue, Cambridge, Mass.

New York [State], New Jersey Port and Harbor Development Commission, *Joint Report with Comprehensive Plan and Recommendations,* J. B. Lyon Company, Printers, Albany, N. Y., 1920.

Port Series (a series of reports dealing with the principal ports of the United States), U. S. War Department, Washington, D. C., various dates.

"Railroad Transportation and Railroad Terminals— A Symposium," *Transactions of the American Society of Civil Engineers,* Vol. LXXXVII (1924), pages 680–892.

"Report of the New York State Barge Canal Terminal Commission," *Senate Document* 30, Albany, N. Y., 1911. (Includes descriptions and maps of the principal ports of the world.)

Report with Plan for the Comprehensive Development of the Port of New York, Port of New York Authority, New York, December 21, 1921.

Transportation and National Policy, National Resources Planning Board, Washington, D. C., May, 1942.

Turner, Daniel L.: *Suburban Transit Problem* (report, as Consulting Engineer of the Transit Commission, recommending a Metropolitan Transit System to Serve New York City and Its Environs), Transit Commission, State of New York, April 23, 1924.

Questions

1. What are some of the planning problems that have resulted from uncontrolled competition between railroad companies in urban areas?
2. What are the main functions of an outer belt railroad? How can it best be operated?
3. What are the principal features in the Comprehensive Plan of the Port of New York Authority?
4. What are the relative advantages of separate passenger terminals and of a union passenger terminal serving all railroads?
5. Describe two types of union freight terminals.
6. What is a stub-end railroad terminal? A through terminal? Give examples of each.
7. What clearance is desirable where a highway passes beneath a railroad? Where a highway passes over a railroad?
8. How have railroad-highway grade separations been financed, and what is the trend in such financing?
9. Name and sketch the principal types of docks and piers.
10. What are some of the ways in which the rail and water facilities of a port may be co-ordinated?
11. How have port authorities aided in port development?
12. What is a free port? Give examples.
13. What are the various steps involved in the carrying out of a harbor improvement by the United States federal government?
14. What are some of the principal types of special freight terminals?

7

THE LOCAL TRANSIT SYSTEM

As factories and general business are attracted to a city or town, its population increases, and its problems of internal communication must be solved. A properly designed system of local facilities is therefore required. The design of such a system is complicated by shifting uses, resulting in shifts in population. As business increases, the central portions of the town will be given over to it, the land will become too valuable for residential use, and those who had their homes in these districts will move farther out. The workmen in the mills and shops will, unless proper houses are provided for them in the vicinity of their work, go as far as the time consumed and the rate of fare will permit in order to secure decent homes for their families on terms that they can afford, either as home owners or tenants. The results of such shifting of population, while presenting some serious problems, are beneficial. The report of the London Traffic Branch of the Board of Trade for 1913 stated that "no one can doubt the benefit conferred on the community by the migration of population which has taken place and is still in progress from the central area to the healthier and happier surroundings on the outskirts, and this beneficial process can best be stimulated by the provision of such additional traveling facilities as will enable new and more distant areas to be opened up for building."

Various Forms of Transit Facilities

As cities have grown beyond the walk-to-work scale, various forms of transit have been developed. The horse-drawn coach, the horse car, the trolley car (street railway), elevated railways, and the modern rapid-transit subway have each successfully increased the radius of the area that could be served. With the development of the gasoline engine came a return to private vehicles in the form of the automobile, then fleets of taxicabs and the motor bus. In recent years the trolley coach, a free-wheeled vehicle deriving its power from overhead wires, has been gaining in popularity. The motor bus and the trolley coach are rapidly forcing the trolley car out of the picture, at least in central areas. The last trolleys in the borough of Manhattan in New York City gave way to motor buses in 1947.

In the following discussion, local transit is subdivided into rapid transit, in which movement is either on private rights of way or directly above or below the street surface, thus insuring expeditious movement, and transit over the city streets, which is subject to frequent interference from other forms of surface traffic, requiring much lower rates of speed.

To plan the streets of a city so that any one or all of them may accommodate transit lines would be folly. Some of these lines will be much more intensively used than others; that is, some will be trunk lines, and others will be feeders. In a large city the trunk lines will carry such a heavy traffic that its accommodation on the street surface will be impossible unless it moves very slowly, and slow speed means restricted capacity. They must therefore be placed over or under the streets, on elevated structures or in tunnels. Some of the most important lines, also, will need three or four tracks to accommodate the traffic.

Elevated Railroads versus Subways

The construction of elevated railroads for urban rapid transit started with the operation in 1871 of a line in New York City from the Battery to 31st Street. They soon spread the length of Manhattan; after the opening of the Brooklyn Bridge in 1883, they spread rapidly through the then city of Brooklyn; later they

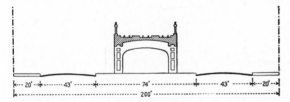

FIGURE 7·1. CROSS-SECTION OF QUEENS BOULEVARD, NEW YORK CITY

Showing a three-track elevated railway on a reinforced-concrete structure in the center of a 200-foot right of way.

reached out into the boroughs of The Bronx and Queens. Similar structures appeared in Boston, Chicago, and Philadelphia.

But elevated railroads offer such serious obstruction to light and air, are so noisy, and, as commonly constructed, disfigure the streets to such an extent that they will not often be tolerated. New York City started many years ago to tear them down in central areas as the subway system was expanded, with the result that in 1947 only one of the original four north-south lines in Manhattan remained, and the Fulton Street line in Brooklyn had been replaced by a subway.

In the elevated railroad in Philadelphia, which is built with a solid floor and is stone ballasted, the noise has been greatly reduced. If the steel structure is encased in concrete, the disfigurement of the street is much less, and the noise can be still further reduced. Of the latter class is the elevated railroad through the Fenways in Boston. The three-track elevated railway in Queens Boulevard, New York City, is composed of a series of arches between piers which are themselves pierced by arched

openings originally designed to accommodate a double-track surface railroad, but buses operating over the main roadways have replaced the trolleys. This street is 200 feet in width, the part in which the elevated railway is located having two roadways each 43 feet wide, the space between being 74 feet in width, so that there is room for planting on each side of the elevated structure, which is itself 77 feet from the side lines of the street. Consequently there is no obstruction of light and air, while, with a solid floor, stone ballast, and parapet walls outside the tracks, there is very little noise (Figure 7·1). This is probably the best type of elevated railway yet built within street lines. While streets can rarely have such unusual dimensions, if a few avenues leading directly out from the main centers of large cities were given a width of 150 feet, it would be possible to provide elevated lines of this kind, which would be far more agreeable to ride on and would cost less to build than subways.

FIGURE 7·2. MONORAIL ELEVATED RAILWAY BETWEEN ELBERFELD AND BARMEN, GERMANY

A structure built over a stream without damage to abutting property.

The advantages and disadvantages of an elevated railroad, when compared with an underground railway, or subway, were summarized as follows by George D. Snyder:

From the standpoint of the passenger, the elevated is much preferable, as artificial ventilation and artificial illumination during daylight hours are unnecessary, and the passenger has a view from the windows instead of the bare walls of the subway at which to look. From the standpoint of the user of the public thoroughfares and the owner or tenant of abutting property, the underground railway is much to be preferred; and moreover the trains are not subject to delay from bad conditions of weather. An elevated railway is an obstruction in the streets, an eyesore, and an interference with the light, air, and quietude of its surroundings and, when worked by a steam locomotive, it is a creator of smoke, cinders, and dust.

The first elevated lines were claimed by the owners to be a proper use of the public streets, just as the tramways were, but, after long litigation, the courts have decided that the elevated railways must pay damages on account of interference with light,

rights of way were available, and no space had been left for them in the layout of the many underground structures in the modern city. If such lines could be laid out as part of the original city plan, many of these difficulties could be avoided. When a subway will ultimately be required, but it is decided to build transit lines in advance of development and before surface traffic is great, and where

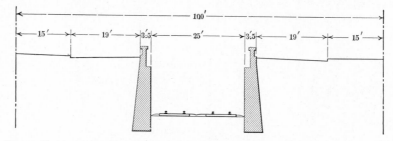

FIGURE 7·3. OPEN CUT FOR A DOUBLE-TRACK RAPID-TRANSIT RAILROAD IN A STREET 100 FEET WIDE

To be converted into a two-track subway when necessary.

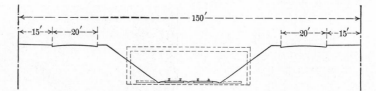

FIGURE 7·4. OPEN CUT FOR A DOUBLE-TRACK RAPID-TRANSIT RAILROAD WITH SIDE SLOPES IN A STREET 150 FEET WIDE

To be converted into a four-track subway when necessary.

air, and access. In narrow streets, where the property is fully developed with high-class buildings, such damages may equal the difference in cost between an elevated and an underground road; but in some cases the courts, in deciding the amount of damages, have considered the compensatory benefits accruing to the property from its increased accessibility to the business centers. In many quarters the rateable value of property abutting on a street with an elevated railway is greater than in similar adjacent streets without an elevated line.[1]

The big obstacle to the building of subways in cities has been their tremendous cost. But this cost has been in large part due to the fact that such routes were afterthoughts, insufficient

streets are sufficiently wide, the subway tracks can be placed in open cuts which need not be covered until the space above them is required for street purposes. Where the street width is sufficient, the sides can be sloped and retaining walls omitted until the tracks are covered; the space occupied by the slopes can eventually be used for additional tracks. (Figures 7·3 and 7·4.)

New York City Rapid-transit System

Mention has been made of the expansion of New York City's elevated railroad lines in the latter part of the nineteenth century, but the great growth in its rapid-transit facilities started with the construction of the first sub-

[1] "City Passenger Transportation in the United States," by George Duncan Snyder, *Minutes of Proceedings of the Institution of Civil Engineers*, Vol. CXCIII, page 181.

way system. There have been three periods of growth: from 1904 to 1909, when about 100 miles of track were put into operation; from 1914 to 1921, when over 260 additional miles were opened; and from 1930 to 1943, when contracts," whereby the city contributed about one-half of the construction cost and two private companies contributed the other half. The third period involved the creation of a third operating system owned and operated by the

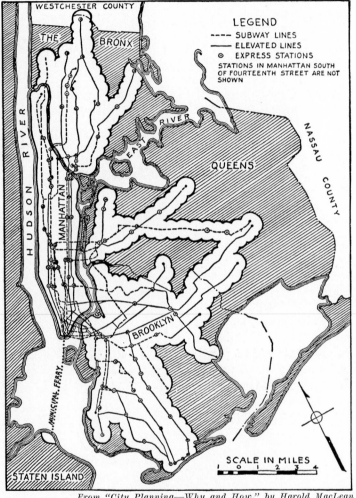

From "City Planning—Why and How," by Harold MacLean Lewis, 1939. Courtesy, Longmans, Green & Co.

FIGURE 7·5. AREAS IN NEW YORK CITY SERVED BY RAPID-TRANSIT LINES IN 1939

Areas left white are within one-half mile of a rapid-transit station.

about 185 additional miles were placed in service. As of June 30, 1946, about 100 track-miles of elevated railways had been demolished, and the track-miles, excluding yards, of all rapid-transit lines in operation totaled about 700 miles, comprising 238 route-miles. A fourth stage of development is contemplated under the city's postwar construction program.

The first two periods involved public construction and private operation under "dual

city; it led to the later purchase by the city of the rights of the two private operating companies and the consolidation of all rapid-transit lines into a city-wide system operated by the Board of Transportation. During the expansion of the subway system, several of the elevated lines were equipped with third tracks, permitting the operation of express service in the direction of the greatest passenger movement during the rush hours.

New York early established the policy of extending its rapid-transit lines outward into undeveloped areas in the expectation that, with a flat rate of fare, population would follow the transit lines. At the same time the city has continued to focus radial lines in southern Manhattan, piling up congestion there. It was not until the third period of subway development that a Brooklyn-Queens line was constructed, providing the first section of a circumferential route. The extent to which the four boroughs of Manhattan, Brooklyn, The Bronx, and Queens were served by rapid-transit lines in 1939 is shown by Figure 7·5. These lines are supplemented by a comprehensive system of trolley and bus feeder lines.

This policy has led to what has been called a vicious cycle. New radial lines have promoted intensive residential development along their outer borders and increased the concentration of business in the downtown areas—in other words, caused greater congestion. This has led to a demand for new lines paralleling the first ones, which again has led to congestion and demand for still more parallel lines focusing on the same central areas, and so on. As a result, calculations showed that in 1927 about 91 per cent of the total resident population of the city lived within that 40 per cent of the area then served by rapid-transit lines.

The construction of New York's subway system has been a major technical achievement. Difficulties were encountered which taxed the ingenuity of engineers and contractors; miles of subaqueous tunneling; the underpinning of hundreds of tall buildings; the care of the great number of subsurface structures in city streets; the maintenance, during construction, of traffic on the street surface. When the first subway was built, it was done by the cut-and-cover method, and business on the streets traversed was brought almost to a standstill. So vigorous were the objections to this method of carrying on the work that in all subsequent contracts plank decks were provided capable of carrying the surface traffic, and the excavation and placing of material were carried on beneath.

The most difficult project in the second period of construction was the line under Wil-liam Street in downtown Manhattan (Figure 7·6). The subway route follows this street for half a mile, and some of its features have been thus described by one of the engineers engaged in its construction:

The structure will be of standard two-track type, requiring an excavation about 29 feet in width,

Courtesy, Board of Transportation, New York City.

FIGURE 7·6. WILLIAM STREET, NEW YORK CITY

Beneath this narrow street a double-track rapid-transit subway was built which, at stations, occupies the entire width of the street.

which at stations will be increased to the full width of 40 feet between building lines to provide for island platforms, from which stairways will extend to a mezzanine passageway connecting with the entrance stairs to the surface. The depth to subgrade will vary from 25 to 31 feet below the surface, and in general the excavation will extend from three to five feet below high water, with a maximum of 14 feet at Maiden Lane and 20 feet at Pearl Street below that datum. As developed by the borings, the material will be coarse sand with some gravel, grading into fine sand which, below ground water, becomes quicksand.

Courtesy, Board of Transportation, New York City.

FIGURE 7·7. VIEWS SHOWING DIFFICULTIES ENCOUNTERED IN CONSTRUCTING NEW YORK CITY'S SUBWAY SYSTEM

Upper view shows a section built in tunnel, and lower view a section built by cut-and-cover method.

The cost of this section of double-track subway, 2,643 feet in length, including two stations, was $2,278,113 or about $862 a lineal foot, of which about 27 per cent represented

narrow, in lower Manhattan Island not yet put to such use.

Unfortunately it seems to have been taken for granted that every new transit line to be

FIGURE 7·8. BUILDING A SUBWAY BENEATH AN ELEVATED RAILROAD

Construction views along Sixth Avenue Subway, New York City, showing temporary wooden street surfacing (*above*) while elevated columns were shored up and subway was excavated (*left*).

the cost of underpinning and caring for buildings abutting on the street. This street was not selected as a route for a subway because it was thought to be well adapted to the purpose but because it was one of the few streets, all

built must pass through this part of the city, adding to the already excessive concentration in this limited area, rather than to try and develop new centers and diffuse traffic. Such policy is not only unwise but very costly. The large proportion of the cost represented by the underpinning and care of buildings will be understood when the narrowness of the street and the character of the soil are taken into account, and from the further fact that along the part of the street now occupied by the subway there were 45 buildings less than seven stories in height having an assessed valuation of $7,000,-000, 20 from seven to twelve stories high with a value of $18,000,000, and ten of from thirteen to twenty stories with a valuation of $15,000,-000. It would be difficult to find a more forcible illustration of the need of providing in the plan of a city sufficient streets whose position will make them available for rapid-transit routes and whose width will be sufficient to permit the construction of such lines without an expense prohibitive in most cities.

In the third period of construction the Sixth Avenue line offered many complications. This was built beneath an elevated railroad on which service was maintained (the structure was demolished shortly after the completion of the subway), and south of 34th Street the new subway had to go beneath and alongside the two tubes containing the tracks of the Hudson & Manhattan Company, operating between Manhattan and New Jersey. Some views illustrating typical construction problems are shown in Figures 7·7 and 7·8.

Other Rapid-transit Subways

The first subways in Boston were started in 1895, involving both four-track and two-track subways to take street railways beneath the surface in downtown areas. This initial program cost $5,000,000 and included about one mile of four-track subway and two-thirds of a mile of two-track subway. It has since been greatly expanded and includes regular subway trains in addition to tunnels for street railway cars.

Philadelphia adopted a program for rapid-transit railways by public referendum in 1923. The first contracts were let in 1924. The system includes a main four-track line about seven miles in length, which was estimated to cost about $100,000,000, and two-track lines intersecting it near City Hall.

The city of Newark, New Jersey, completed in 1937 a city subway located in the bed of the abandoned Morris Canal and running from the main station of the Pennsylvania Railroad to connect with trolley lines near the edge of the city. It is operated by the Public Service Co-ordinated Transport as part of its trolley and bus system.

In 1922 Chicago completed 7.7 miles of two-track rapid-transit subway in its downtown areas, made up of two separate routes, supplementing and connecting with its system of elevated railroads. These subways were built at a cost of about $57,400,000. Continuous stations were provided in the heart of the loop district, that on the State Street line having platforms 3,300 feet long, providing space for three double stops. Additional extensions to the west were contemplated.

Modern subway systems have been constructed abroad in the following cities: London and Liverpool in England; Glasgow in Scotland; Paris in France; Berlin and Hamburg in Germany; Madrid and Barcelona in Spain; Budapest in Hungary; Moscow in Russia; Tokyo and Osaka in Japan; Sidney in Australia; and Buenos Aires in Argentina.

The Streets as Transit Routes

In a city with a rapid-transit system, feeder lines and short-haul facilities must move over the city streets; but where transit is to be provided wholly by vehicles moving along the city's streets, the proper co-ordination of the street plan and the transit plan becomes even more important. In the small town the problem is a simple one, provided adequate facilities are made for offstreet parking [2] and private cars and mass-transit vehicles can use the same streets; and the increase of traffic which occurs on certain days adds a degree of life and interest which is an agreeable change from the monotony of existence in a provincial town. As the town becomes a city, and as the city continues to grow, the increase of traffic results in congestion with its attendant delays and dangers. The time comes when "Main Street"

[2] Discussed in Chapter 17, Volume II.

can no longer serve for shopping, general business, transit vehicles, and private automobiles. Greater diffusion of land use and a segregation of vehicular traffic are necessary. The city that has planned in advance can readily make the needed adjustments.

As the city grows, it becomes more and more necessary to think of its roadways as carriers of people rather than simply as carriers of vehicles. There must be a system of thoroughfares on which this movement of people will be concentrated and which will take them as directly as possible to where they want to go. Such a system is discussed in the following chapter, "The Street Pattern," and the design of its elements to accommodate the traffic demands is the subject of the succeeding chapter, entitled "Street Traffic and Design." General trends and principles are discussed herein.

Daniel L. Turner, former Consulting Engineer of the New York Transit Commission, gave much study to problems involved in the orderly development of urban transit systems, and reached the conclusion that, where a city is approximately semi-circular in shape or can be reduced to a semi-circular equivalent, about one mile of double-track transit line is required for every 200 acres, and that the number of different routes required for any city can be roughly determined by dividing the square root of the area of the city in acres by 6.3, a route being a continuous line from the business center to the outer limits of the city or a cross-town line from one side of the town to the other. He assumed that passengers should not be required to walk more than a quarter of a mile to reach a street railway which will carry them to the business center and that cross-town lines should not be more than a mile apart. Mr. Turner's discussion of this subject is well worth the careful study of those who are responsible for working out the plans for an urban district, in order that streets of adequate width may be provided to meet probable traffic requirements.

Often topography and other natural barriers limit the directions in which a city may grow, and in some cases transit lines must converge as they pass through restricted areas, such as Cahuenga Pass in Los Angeles County. Lake-front cities, such as Chicago and Detroit, have developed in a semi-circular form with the transit hub close to the water front. Movement through downtown areas will be facilitated if separate parallel thoroughfares are provided, one primarily for mass-transit vehicles and the other primarily for passenger automobiles.

There is a big variety in the capacity of individual transit vehicles. Street railway cars, or trolleys, generally have a seating ca-

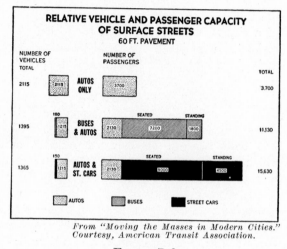

From "Moving the Masses in Modern Cities." Courtesy, American Transit Association.

FIGURE 7·9

pacity of about 50; motor buses vary greatly in size, but most of them have from 25 to 40 seats; both frequently carry heavy overloads of standees in urban areas, sometimes reaching 100 per cent of the seating capacity. In contrast with these figures, many independent checks of private automobiles have shown that their average load is about 1.75 persons per car, although during World War II pooling of transportation temporarily raised this figure.

An interesting analysis by the American Transit Association of the relative one-way vehicle and passenger capacity of a typical street with three lanes of traffic in each direction and no parking is shown in Figure 7·9. It is estimated that the three lanes available for one-way movement could carry a maximum of 2,115 passenger automobiles per hour, which, with 1.75 persons per car, would transport 3,700 persons per hour. Introducing a lane of buses or street cars would reduce the effective use by private automobiles to 1,215 per hour, but the buses, with a 25 per cent overload of standees, could carry 9,000 persons, or the street could move 11,130 persons, per hour. Street cars, with their greater capacity, including a 50 per

as the tram lines, although publicly owned and operated, do not enter the square mile of territory known as "the city" and are excluded from Westminster, except for a short distance under the Kingsway and along the Thames

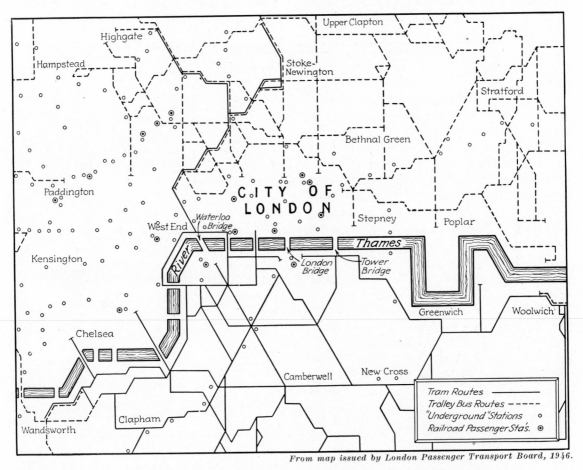

From map issued by London Passenger Transport Board, 1946.

FIGURE 7·10. TRAM AND TROLLEY-BUS ROUTES IN CENTRAL LONDON

cent overload, would bring the total up to 15,630 persons per hour.

Transit in London

In no community has the problem of moving people over the city streets been more serious or attracted more attention than in London, and some space can properly be devoted to a discussion of that city's problem and how it has been dealt with. The street railway, or "tram," system of London has been confined almost entirely to outlying districts,

Embankment, and from other large areas where the traffic is dense. This was necessary, as the streets in the old city are for the most part narrow and crooked and could not accommodate double-track lines, while even single-track railways would be practically impossible.

The use of buses was first introduced in London about the middle of the nineteenth century and soon became well established. By 1915 buses had practically all become motorized, greatly increasing the efficiency of the system. The service is popular and cheap for short distances, and the passenger-transportation service of London has developed chiefly as a free-wheel system (see Figures 7·10 and 7·11).

The subway system, or "underground," was in successful operation by 1903. Yet by 1913 the trams still carried 44.7 per cent of the total passengers, the buses 30.9 per cent, and the sub-

other cities, the number of passengers carried has increased much more rapidly than the population and has appeared to depend upon the type of facilities offered rather than on the number of people within reach of them.

An important phase in the history of the London traffic problem was the competition of

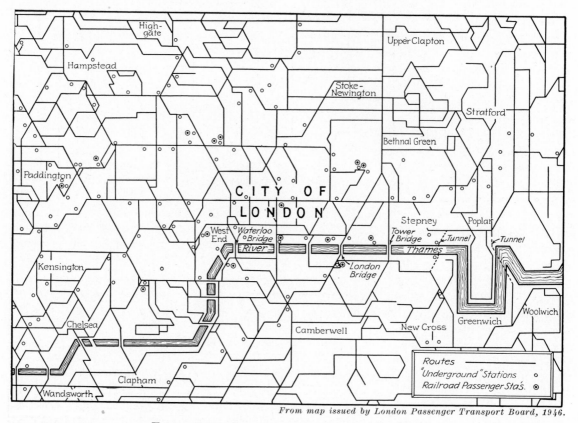

From map issued by London Passenger Transport Board, 1946.

FIGURE 7·11. BUS ROUTES IN CENTRAL LONDON

ways only 24.4 per cent, in spite of the fact that the trams were excluded from the portions of the city where the traffic is most dense. In 1912, however, the trams had showed a substantial decrease in traffic. In the year ending June 30, 1939, just before World War II, the subways carried only 12.5 per cent of the total traffic originating on the system controlled by the London Passenger Transport Board, the buses and coaches 58.7 per cent, and the trams and trolley buses only 28.8 per cent. In the year 1946, corresponding figures were 13.4 per cent by subways, 58.8 per cent by buses and coaches, and 27.8 per cent by trams and trolley buses. In London, as in

the privately owned bus lines with the publicly owned surface railway, or tram, lines and even with the trunk-line railroads carrying suburban traffic. This competition was not confined to the fully developed districts, but appeared constantly to extend farther from the central part of the city.

The tram lines were more seriously affected, although every effort was made to attract business to them. Large signs on the cars and elsewhere announced that "The quickest way is the tramway," or "The best way is the tramway." Yet not only the London lines but the tram routes operated by other Urban District Councils within the metropolitan area were run at a loss, as the bus lines had advantages over them that seemed very unfair. In spite of their public ownership, the tram lines were obliged to contribute to the upkeep and improvement of the streets traversed by them, besides being substantially taxed for their roadbeds. The bus companies, on the other hand, contributed nothing toward the expense of constructing or repaving the streets through which they ran and were unrestricted as to their routes or the fares charged. The tram cars, their motormen, and their conductors were licensed by the metropolitan police and subject to certain regulations, while the buses were registered as heavy motor cars and their drivers obliged to obtain licenses from the London County Council; the revenues derived from these sources were, however, very small.

The operation of the London surface-transit system was reorganized by the London Passenger Transport Act of 1933, designed to remedy the difficulties described above and to co-ordinate both surface and underground operations. This created the London Passenger Transport Board, which took over the following: four companies in the underground group and the Metropolitan Company; 61 bus concerns; 21 motor-coach concerns; 16 tram concerns (13 municipal and three private). Four amalgamated main line railway companies continued to supply transit services outside the Transport Board system.

The Board was charged with the general duty of securing the provision of an adequate and properly co-ordinated system of passenger transport throughout an area defined as the London Passenger Transport Area. It covers a total area of nearly 2,000 square miles with a population of over 9,000,000 people. There is defined in the act a "special area" within which, subject to certain exceptions, no person other than the Board is permitted after January 1, 1934, except with the written consent of the Board, to carry on any vehicle, while that vehicle is being used as a stage carriage or an express carriage, passengers other than those either picked up or set down outside the "special area." Under the act, provision was made for the purchase by, and transfer to, the Board of transport undertakings and for payment of

compensation to the person and companies previously operating them. The Board establishes fares for the lines under its control, but provision is made under the Act of 1933 whereby a Rates Tribunal may, on an application by a local authority or the Board, reduce or increase these fares. The motor-vehicle duty and other fees paid for motor vehicles and the gasoline tax now go into the National Exchequer Funds and are used for general purposes.[3]

Under the Transport Act of 1947, passed on August 6, 1947, the London Passenger Transport Board is, as from January 1, 1948, transferred to and vested in the British Transport Commission, a public authority set up under the act to provide, or secure or promote the provision of, an efficient, adequate, economical, and properly integrated system of public inland transport and port facilities within Great Britain for passengers and goods.

The buses of London demonstrated that the great advantage of this free-wheeled type of transit was its flexibility. It could concentrate its vehicles on certain routes where there was a temporary increase in traffic; it could lengthen some of its lines into the suburbs on Sundays and holidays and curtail the service in the business districts, restoring normal service the next morning; it could transfer a fleet of buses to some district entirely without the city to accommodate an influx of people attracted by races, regattas, or athletic contests; it could respond instantly to a rapid development in some section of the city or suburbs, while to supply a tram line would have involved great delay, first in securing franchises from the local authorities, and then in construction, which is necessarily slow in public streets; it could, if a change of route appeared desirable, from the viewpoint of either public service or more profitable operation, make such a change overnight; and finally, it was altogether free from the annoying interruptions to traffic caused by the disabling of vehicles, the obstruction of tracks, and the delays incident to periodical track repairs and reconstruction. The

[3] This and the following paragraph are from a letter from the Ministry of Transport, under date of September 2, 1947.

Courtesy, British Information Services.

Courtesy, London Passenger Transport Board.

FIGURE 7·12. CHANGES IN THE CHARACTER OF LONDON STREET TRAFFIC

Traffic in Long Acre in 1924 (*upper left*) and Cheapside under conditions just before World War II (*upper right*); postwar traffic at Hammersmith Broadway, showing both buses and trolley buses (*lower*).

same advantages have been responsible for the shift from "rails to rubber" which came somewhat later in American cities.

A summary of the trends in transit on the streets of London before the establishment of the London Transport Board is shown in Table 3. This shows figures for five-year periods,

TABLE 3

NUMBER OF LICENSES ISSUED BY THE LONDON METRO-POLITAN POLICE FOR CABS, BUSES, AND TRAM CARS, 1905 TO 1930

	Cabs		Buses		Tram Cars		
Year	Horse	Motor	Horse	Motor	Horse	Motor	Total
1905	10,931	19	3,484	241	786	1,124	16,585
1910	4,724	6,397	1,103	1,200	120	2,411	15,955
1915	962	5,832	36	2,761	2	2,725	12,318
1916	767	5,458	20	2,536	0	2,683	11,464
1917	630	4,717	11	2,414	0	2,624	10,396
1918	527	3,821	7	2,277	0	2,499	9,131
1919	587	5,391	15	3,299	0	2,619	11,911
1920	521	6,025	18	3,347	0	2,740	12,651
1925	223	8,258	5	6,028	0	2,738	17,252
1930	69	8,167	1	7,715	0	2,711	18,663

from 1905 to 1930, supplemented by annual figures from 1915 to 1920, indicating the effect upon all traffic of the conditions prevailing in London during World War I. The horse-drawn tram passed out of the picture in 1916, and the horse-drawn bus after 1930. It is surprising that, notwithstanding the increase in general street traffic, the total number of vehicles was higher in 1905 than in any subsequent year listed up to 1925.

Complete figures were not available for recent years, as the collection and publication of statistical matter were generally discontinued during World War II, but the following recent figures for cabs, still licensed by the Commissioner of Police, have been obtained:

NUMBER LICENSED

YEAR	Horse-drawn	Motor
1940	4	5,797
1941	2	5,478
1942	2	5,531
1943	2	5,604
1944	2	5,565
1945	2	5,543
1946	2	5,855

The buses and trams have, since 1933, been licensed by the Licensing Authority for Public Service Vehicles, scheduled to issue its first postwar report in 1948.

The trend from mass transportation to transportation by private cars is brought out by a comparison of 1924 and 1935 counts of vehicles at 28 comparable intersections in central London. It was found that the average number of buses and coaches observed had declined 12 per cent, whereas the number of private cars and commercial vehicles, other than buses and coaches, had increased 72 per cent. It was claimed, however, that the reduction in coaches and buses was due, in part at least, to their improved carrying capacity.[4]

Effect of Transit Vehicles on Other Traffic

Some figures on the growth of urban traffic and the capacities of streets are given in Chapter 9, "Street Traffic and Design" (see pages 160 to 164). A mere statement of the number of vehicles passing a given point, however, does not give an adequate idea of the resulting congestion. Some offer far more obstruction to traffic than others, depending upon their size, speed, and flexibility, and the roadway capacity may be such as to cause or prevent congestion. Enumeration is obviously the first step in a traffic census which will determine the amount of congestion, but the other factors just named must be given proper consideration before the degree of congestion can be determined. For purposes of comparison some common standard should be used, and this should be the same in different parts of the city, in different cities and in different countries.

An attempt at such standardization was made in London during the early days of the automobile, and, while some of the vehicles listed are now outdated or extinct, the figures are still of interest for comparison with present-day standards. They are given in Table 4. After enumerating the number of each class of vehicles passing a point, the factors were applied to these numbers, and the total number of units

[4] *Postwar Reconstruction in the City of London*, Report of Improvements and Town Planning Committee, 1944, page 25.

TABLE 4

THE RELATIVE OBSTRUCTION CAUSED BY DIFFERENT
VEHICLES, USING THE AUTOMOBILE AS THE BASE,
AS ESTIMATED IN LONDON

Trade Vehicles		Passenger Vehicles	
One-horse (fast)	3	Electric trams	10
One-horse (slow)	7	Buses (horse)	5
Two-horse (fast)	4	Buses (motor)	3
Two-horse (slow)	10	Cabs (horse)	2
Motor (fast)	2	Cabs (motor)	1
Motor (slow)	5	Carriages (horse)	2
Barrows	6	Carriages (motor)	1
Cycles	½		

was divided by the number of minutes in the period covered by the observations. The result was called the average traffic volume.

Courtesy, Philadelphia Transportation Company.

FIGURE 7·13. CONGESTED TRAFFIC ON A BUSINESS STREET WITH TROLLEYS AND MOTOR VEHICLES ON THE SAME ROADWAY

Illustrated by Chestnut Street, Philadelphia.

Under this London standard one motor bus would offer as much obstruction to traffic as three private automobiles or taxicabs. Approaching the problem from the point of view of the amount of lane distance occupied by buses of the Fifth Avenue Coach Company under observed conditions on a Manhattan street, the Committee on a Regional Plan of New York and Its Environs found that "on the average one bus space will accommodate 1.3 automobiles or taxicabs."[5]

When such figures are reduced to the basis of space occupied *per passenger* rather than *per vehicle*, the figures are much more striking. Daniel L. Turner, in a study of Fifth Avenue traffic made in 1921 for the New York Transit Commission, found that for every passenger carried in an automobile or taxicab, 21 passengers could be carried in motor buses in the same street space and that on typical days in June, 1926, buses on Fifth Avenue amounting to only 12 per cent of the vehicles carried 64 per cent of the persons (including drivers) transported along the avenue.[6]

An analysis by the Rapid Transit Commission of Detroit brought out the following figures:

In the downtown business district of Detroit at the rush hour, while automobiles and taxicabs make up 85 per cent of the moving vehicles, they carry but 28 per cent of the passengers (28.40), whereas the street cars and buses, comprising but 5.4 per cent of the total vehicles, carry 72 per cent of the passengers. If either type of vehicle is to be given preference over the other, it unquestionably must be the street car and bus that together represent only 5.4 per cent of the vehicles moving, and yet carry 72 per cent of the total passenger traffic.[7]

United States Trends in Local Transit

The trends in transit in the United States over the last two decades have been featured by two developments: (1) the increasing recognition by transit companies of the intimate relation between moving people over city streets and city planning, and efforts on the part of both transit officials and city planners to effect

[5] *Highway Traffic,* by Harold M. Lewis, in consultation with Ernest P. Goodrich, Vol. III, Regional Survey of New York and Its Environs, 1927, page 73.

[6] *Ibid.,* page 74.

[7] *The Relation of Individual to Collective Transportation,* Rapid Transit Commission, Detroit, Mich., 1928. See also reference to this report in Chapter 9, page 179.

Courtesy, Boston Elevated Railways.

FIGURE 7·14. EFFECTIVE USE OF A RAISED MALL FOR TROLLEYS ON A MAIN HIGHWAY
Illustrated by Commonwealth Avenue, Boston.

Photo by Press Association, Inc.

FIGURE 7·15. HEAVY BUS TRAFFIC ON A BUSINESS THOROUGHFARE
Illustrated by Fifth Avenue, New York City, in the Rockefeller Center district.

a true co-ordination; and (2) the development of improved and more efficient vehicles. The latter has been responsible for certain shifts in riding habits, which will be pointed out. The following discussion and accompanying illustrations have drawn freely on recent publications of the American Transit Association.[8]

Charles Gordon, who pointed out the great need for collaboration in the planning of urban highways and public transit improvements, said:

There is also a pressing need for a clearer understanding of the capacities and the civic forces generated by both types of improvement, and of their relation to and effect upon the pattern of city growth. Only then can we hope to achieve real coordination of city planning, highway development, and public transit. If we act wisely, the results will redound to the benefit of every urban interest, activity, and inhabitant. If we fail to do so, there is real danger that we shall merely expedite the process of urban disintegration that is already well under way. . . .

There is an urgent need to co-ordinate the viewpoints of those interested in city planning, highways, and public transit to obtain a better perspective of the overall problem confronting modern cities. Unless we do, there is danger of getting the cart before the horse; of providing the highways to give city dwellers access to the countryside—and more intercity and rural vehicles better access to already overloaded city street systems—before making provision for an internal transportation system adequate for the needs of those who must live and work in these cities. Unless we achieve such a perspective, there is real danger that we may merely expedite the process of destroying our cities as we know them today, and distribute their population helter-skelter over the surrounding countryside.[9]

The transit officials must know what the future city pattern will be, if they are to plan their routes and services efficiently. The city planner is concerned about the economic waste caused by the spread of blight through areas already served by fixed installations for transit (see Chapter 15, "Redevelopment of Blighted Areas," Volume II) and by the premature subdivision of outlying lands without transit or

other utilities (see Chapter 21, "Control of Land Subdivisions," Volume II). Both need to know the extent to which blighted areas may be revitalized by redevelopment with modern buildings.

The federal government has also been co-operating in studies of the transit problem through the Public Roads Administration. In co-operation with various state highway departments this agency has been conducting travel-habit surveys under a procedure of sample interviews, as outlined as follows by

Courtesy, Transit Research Corporation.

FIGURE 7·16. POSTWAR MODEL OF THE MODERN TROLLEY DEVELOPED BY THE PRESIDENTS' CONFERENCE COMMITTEE

Thomas H. MacDonald, Commissioner of Public Roads:

The size of the sample varies with the size of the city. In the smaller cities in which surveys have been conducted, those with populations up to about 150,000, a 10 per cent sample has been used. As the size of the city increases, and as the volumes of travel with which we must deal also increase, a smaller sample is adequate. In cities around 500,000 population a five per cent sample has been found to be sufficient, and for larger cities in which studies are now contemplated, it is probable that the sample will consist only of one address in forty.[10]

The two outstanding developments in improved vehicles for transit in city streets are the "P.C.C." streamlined trolley and the trolley coach. The former is the result of the appointment in 1929, by the presidents of the leading street railway companies, of a Presidents' Conference Committee to develop a modern car. Seven years later they produced the new car shown in Figure 7·16, and, while its manu-

[8] See *Moving the Masses in Modern Cities* and *Transit Fact Book, 1946,* both published by the American Transit Association, New York.

[9] From address by the late Charles Gordon, then Managing Director, American Transit Association, before Conference Committee on Urban Problems, U. S. Chamber of Commerce, January 11, 1945.

[10] "Analysis of Urban Travel by Survey Technique," by Thomas H. MacDonald, *American Transit Association Convention-in-Print*, Second Session, 1944, page 30.

facture was curtailed by World War II, it was serving successfully in 1947 in twenty-four of the largest cities in the United States. The trolley coach (Figure 7·17) has been referred to on page 92; it has been increasing in popularity, particularly in downtown areas where it

FIGURE 7·17. THE TROLLEY COACH IN ACTION

Illustrated by King Street in Downtown Honolulu.

has flexibility of movement within the roadway almost equal to that of the motor bus, but has further advantages in quietness, absence of gasoline-exhaust fumes, and smoothness in acceleration and deceleration. But some of the older types of vehicles still have their place, such as the cable car on the hills of San Francisco, illustrated in Figure 7·18.

Increasing emphasis is being placed upon the advantage of combining, in one right of way, express highways and mass-transit facilities in the form of either rail or bus operation. At a "transportation clinic" held in Los Angeles in

December, 1945, to hear and discuss reports of three consultants on general transportation, surface transportation, and city planning, respectively, all three consultants agreed that a substantial portion of the proposed 368-mile expressway system in Los Angeles County should be designed to include, as part of the cross-section of the route, separate rights of way for mass transit.[11] The new Hollywood Freeway, under construction in 1947, provides for bus movement over the main roadways with special turnouts for loading and unloading (upper view, Figure 7·19). A report by a

FIGURE 7·18. THE CABLE CAR CARRIES ON IN SAN FRANCISCO

Showing operation over a 25.5 per cent grade on Fillmore Street. Car going downhill counterweights that going uphill and cable power is augmented by an overhead trolley.

Committee on Urban Transportation of the American Institute of Planners[12] has suggested alternative methods of treating bus and rapid-transit stops on freeways, one of which is shown in the lower view in Figure 7·19.

Joint use of expressways by private cars and mass-transit vehicles was agreed on in 1946 in Toronto and is in operation on the Davidson Highway in Detroit (Figure 7·20).

[11] *City of Los Angeles—Recommended Program for Improvement of Transportation and Traffic Facilities in the Metropolitan Area,* by DeLeuw, Cather & Company, Harold M. Lewis, and Joe R. Ong, December, 1945.

[12] *Urban Freeways,* Committee on Urban Transportation, American Institute of Planners, published by American Transit Association, 1947.

Courtesy, Department of Public Works, Los Angeles.

From "Urban Freeways." Courtesy, American Institute of Planners.

FIGURE 7·19. SKETCHES SHOWING PROVISION FOR BUSES IN MODERN EXPRESSWAYS

Upper view shows design for bus turnouts on the Hollywood Freeway in Los Angeles. Lower view shows a suggested typical design for a freeway transfer station, with a bus stop within the freeway right of way.

Courtesy, Department of Street Railways, Detroit.

FIGURE 7·20. BUS TURNOUT ON THE DAVIDSON HIGHWAY, DETROIT

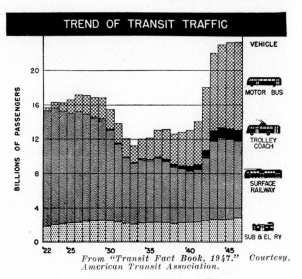

FIGURE 7·21. TOTAL PASSENGERS CARRIED BY TRANSIT COMPANIES IN THE UNITED STATES, 1922–1946

An over-all picture of trends in number of passengers carried by all types of transit vehicles is shown in Figure 7·21. The difference

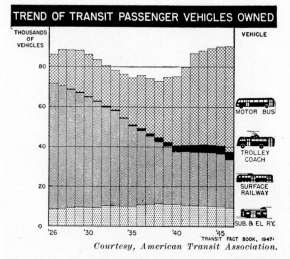

FIGURE 7·22. TRENDS IN NUMBERS OF TRANSIT VEHICLES OF VARIOUS TYPES IN THE UNITED STATES, 1922–1946

between this and Figure 7·22 reflects the unused facilities during the depression of the 1930's and the great lack of adequate facilities

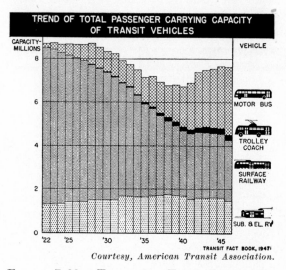

FIGURE 7·23. TRENDS IN TOTAL PASSENGER-CARRYING CAPACITY OF TRANSIT EQUIPMENT IN THE UNITED STATES, 1922–1946

during World War II and the period immediately thereafter.

The trends in types of street vehicles used, in comparison with facilities supplied by rapid-transit subways and elevated railroads, are shown in the diagrams reproduced as Figures 7·22 and 7·23. The former shows the numbers of vehicles of each type from 1926 to 1946. Applying to such figures the relative capacities of each type of vehicle gave Figure 7·23, which shows the total passenger-carrying capacity of each group from 1922 to 1946. The shift from surface railways to free-wheeled vehicles is pronounced. The reductions from 1928 to 1940 represented an attempt by the industry to adjust itself to traffic losses resulting from the business depression and a shift to private automobiles.

Prevailing Means of Transit in Cities

The extent to which the private automobile is serving as a transit facility and has, in some cases, taken business away from mass-transit facilities is shown by the figures on the following pages. But in established urban centers with limited street systems and still more limited offstreet parking facilities (see Chapter 17, Volume II), the trend is already in the opposite direction: toward the recognition of the greater efficiency, already pointed out, of the public transit vehicle in its use of street space.

The role of public transit in moving people varies greatly with the size of the city, as shown by the following figures, compiled by the American Transit Association, for the ratio of daily rides on public transit vehicles to urban population:

CITIES OF POPULATION GROUP	DAILY TRANSIT RIDES EXPRESSED AS PERCENTAGE OF POPULATION
25,000 to 50,000	20
50,000 to 100,000	28
100,000 to 250,000	38
250,000 to 500,000	48
500,000 to 1,000,000	72
Over 1,000,000	98

Hawley S. Simpson compiled some years ago figures showing the relative movement by mass-transportation vehicles and passenger automobiles to and from central business districts in certain cities. A summary of his findings is

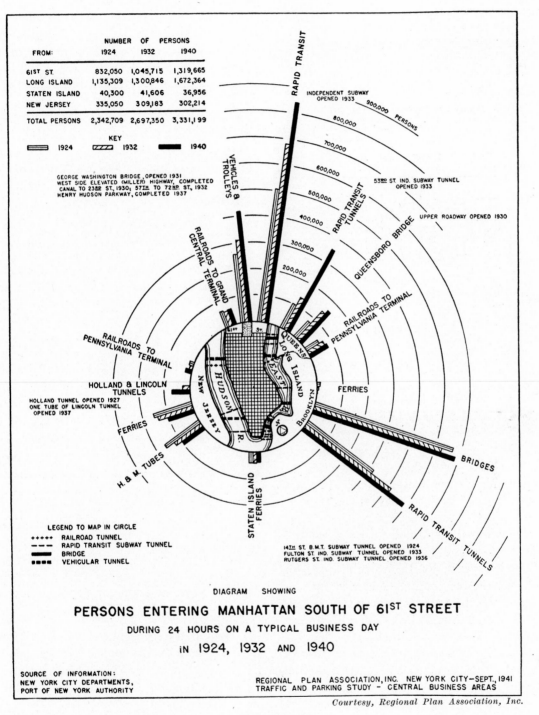

FROM:	NUMBER OF PERSONS		
	1924	1932	1940
61ST ST.	832,050	1,045,715	1,319,665
LONG ISLAND	1,135,309	1,300,846	1,672,364
STATEN ISLAND	40,300	41,606	36,956
NEW JERSEY	335,050	309,183	302,214
TOTAL PERSONS	2,342,709	2,697,350	3,331,199

KEY
▭ 1924   ▨ 1932   ▬ 1940

GEORGE WASHINGTON BRIDGE, OPENED 1931
WEST SIDE ELEVATED (MILLER) HIGHWAY, COMPLETED
CANAL TO 23RD ST., 1930; 57TH TO 72ND ST., 1932
HENRY HUDSON PARKWAY, COMPLETED 1937

INDEPENDENT SUBWAY OPENED 1933
53RD ST. IND. SUBWAY TUNNEL OPENED 1933
UPPER ROADWAY OPENED 1930
HOLLAND TUNNEL OPENED 1927
ONE TUBE OF LINCOLN TUNNEL OPENED 1937

LEGEND TO MAP IN CIRCLE
+++++ RAILROAD TUNNEL
--- RAILROAD TUNNEL ... RAPID TRANSIT SUBWAY TUNNEL
▬▬ BRIDGE
▪▪▪▪ VEHICULAR TUNNEL

14TH ST. B.M.T. SUBWAY TUNNEL OPENED 1924
FULTON ST. IND. SUBWAY TUNNEL OPENED 1933
RUTGERS ST. IND. SUBWAY TUNNEL OPENED 1936

DIAGRAM SHOWING

PERSONS ENTERING MANHATTAN SOUTH OF 61ST STREET

DURING 24 HOURS ON A TYPICAL BUSINESS DAY

IN 1924, 1932 AND 1940

SOURCE OF INFORMATION:
NEW YORK CITY DEPARTMENTS,
PORT OF NEW YORK AUTHORITY

REGIONAL PLAN ASSOCIATION, INC. NEW YORK CITY—SEPT., 1941
TRAFFIC AND PARKING STUDY - CENTRAL BUSINESS AREAS

Courtesy, Regional Plan Association, Inc.

FIGURE 7·24

given in Table 5. He concluded that approximately two-thirds of all the 29,000,000 people then in cities of more than 250,000 population were dependent on public transit for their daily travel to and from business areas.[13]

TABLE 5

MODES OF TRANSPORTATION TO AND FROM CENTRAL BUSINESS DISTRICTS OF LARGE CITIES

City, in Order of 1930 Population	Year of Survey	Percentage of Passengers Entering or Leaving by	
		Mass-transit Vehicles	Passenger Automobiles
Chicago, Ill.	1929	78.1	21.9
Philadelphia, Pa.	1928	79.2	20.8
Detroit, Mich.	1930	66.2	33.8
Los Angeles, Cal.	1924	65.3 [a]	34.7 [a]
St. Louis, Mo.	1930	65.4	34.6
Baltimore, Md.	1929	60.8	39.2
Boston, Mass.	1932	65.7	34.3
Pittsburgh, Pa.	1927	74.6	25.4
San Francisco, Cal.	1926	74.5	25.5
Milwaukee, Wis.	1926	50.4	49.6
Washington, D. C.	1930	36.7	63.3
Kansas City, Mo.	1930	48.9	51.1
Louisville, Ky.	1926	53.6	46.4

[a] A later survey, made in 1938, showed 44 per cent entering in 12 hours by "public transportation" as against 56 per cent by "private automobile." *Report of Traffic and Transportation Survey*, Citizens Transportation Survey Committee, City of Los Angeles, 1940, page 85.

More detailed cordon counts showing pre-World War II travel habits, compiled by the Eno Foundation for Highway Traffic Control, are given in Table 6. This separates motor vehicles into autos, buses, and trucks; the figures for "other means" would represent "mass transit," as listed in Table 5.

When the figures in the last column of Table 6 are compared with those for mass transit in Table 5 for the eight cities appearing in both tables, it appears that there was a substantial reduction in the proportion carried by mass transit, this being most pronounced in such cities as St. Louis, Detroit, and Pittsburgh.

New York City is a special case, but it is interesting to note that from 1924 to 1940 the Regional Plan Association found that the proportion of persons entering that part of Manhattan south of 61st Street by rapid transit remained almost constant—approximately two-

[13] "Use and Capacity of City Streets," by Hawley S. Simpson, *Transactions of the American Society of Civil Engineers*, Vol. 99 (1934), pages 1030–31.

TABLE 6

MEANS OF TRANSPORTATION USED BY PERSONS ENTERING CENTRAL BUSINESS DISTRICTS, EXPRESSED AS PERCENTAGE OF TOTAL ENTERING [a]

City	Percentage Entering by			
	Autos	Buses	Trucks	Other Means
Typical cities under 100,000 population:				
Glendale, Calif.	86.7	6.7	5.2	1.4
Hamilton, Ohio	75.5	15.4	7.9	1.2
Kenosha, Wis.	81.4	9.4	5.2	4.0
Lincoln, Neb.	81.2	5.0	10.5	3.3
Midland, Mich.	91.8	0.1	8.1	....
New Brunswick, N. J	73.2	11.9	13.0	1.9
Saginaw, Mich.	88.3	11.7	....	....
Schenectady, N. Y.	71.0	13.5	11.6	3.9
Averages	81.2	9.3	7.7	1.8
Typical cities of 100,000 to 500,000 population:				
Houston, Tex.	78.5	15.8	5.7	....
Louisville, Ky.	66.5	3.5	12.4	17.6
Oakland, Calif.	70.0	....	3.9	26.1
Portland, Ore.	74.2	....	....	25.8
St. Paul, Minn.	64.8	2.4	8.6	24.2
Youngstown, Ohio	60.3	....	7.2	32.5
Averages	69.1	3.6	6.3	21.0
Cities over 500,000 population:				
Boston, Mass.	35.6	3.5	6.4	54.5
Chicago, Ill.	30.3	6.9	3.1	59.7
Cleveland, Ohio	56.8	4.1	5.6	33.5
Detroit, Mich.	49.2	9.9	1.7	39.2
Los Angeles, Calif.	56.0	....	....	44.0
New York, N. Y.	14.2	12.0	4.6	69.2
Philadelphia, Pa.	35.5	4.4	7.2	52.9
Pittsburgh, Pa.	41.9	5.3	8.3	44.5
San Francisco, Calif.	41.3	....	6.1	52.6
St. Louis, Mo.	50.2	12.4	10.2	27.2
Averages	41.1	5.9	5.3	47.7

[a] From *Parking*, by Wilbur S. Smith and Charles S. LeCraw, Eno Foundation for Highway Traffic Control, December, 1946, page 26.

thirds of the total entering—while the total increased from 2,342,709 to 3,331,199. Figure 7·24, showing these trends, is included as an example of method of presentation.

Relative Costs of Different Types of Transit

There is a tremendous variation in the relative costs of different types of transit facilities. Absolute costs in the present postwar period have so mounted that there is little point in trying to estimate them in a book of this kind. As a picture of relative costs, estimates made in 1914 by J. Vipond Davies, Consulting Engineer, are still valuable and are given in Table 7. They include track and structural equipment, but do not include power, rights of way, easements, or franchise charge. All figures are reduced to cost per mile of single track.

TABLE 7

Estimated Costs, per Mile of Single Track, of Double-track Transit Facilities of Various Types and under Different Conditions (as Estimated by J. Vipond Davies[a] in 1914)[b]

Type of Structure	Cost
Overhead trolley railroad on public roads or private rights of way, where no pavement is required	$ 25,000
Overhead trolley railroad in city streets including asphalt or granite pavement between tracks and two feet outside	41,500
Underground trolley railroad in congested city streets, including pavements, conduits and care of subsurface structures under conditions such as those in Washington, D. C.	48,500
Same construction as above under conditions existing in New York City	126,500
Elevated railroad, steel structure, such as built by the Public Service Commission in New York City, including stations	113,000
Railroad in open cut, excavation by steam shovel, concrete walls, including bridges and stations	225,000
Railroad on masonry viaduct, stone ballasted, as on Queens Boulevard, New York City, including stations	330,000
Underground railroad near surface, excavation by steam shovel, little or no interference with subsurface structures, including stations	402,000
Underground railroad in streets like Broadway, New York, extreme interference with subsurface structures, support of surface tracks with underground trolley construction, including stations	1,190,000
Iron tube tunnels, concrete lined, under waterways or below water level, no stations	2,700,000

[a] "Provision for Future Rapid Transit," by J. Vipond Davies, *Proceedings of the Sixth National Conference on City Planning*, Toronto, 1914, pages 201–202.

[b] Owing to increases in cost of labor and materials prevailing in the pre-World War II period, costs were then about one and one-half times these figures, while in 1947 they were approximately three times these figures.

A modern four-track subway with two local and two express tracks has been estimated by the American Transit Association to cost from $6,000,000 to $18,000,000 per mile and to be capable of carrying 100,000 passengers per hour in one direction on two tracks. In announcing its plans in December, 1947, for a new Second Avenue subway in Manhattan, the New York City Board of Transportation stated that the cost of constructing and equipping such new lines would be approximately $5,000,000 per mile of track.

Selected References

American Transit Association, New York: "Transit's Part in Postwar Plans," *Convention-in-Print*, Nov. 3, 1944; *Moving the Masses in Modern Cities*, 1946; *Transit Fact Book* (annual).

City of Los Angeles—Recommended Program for Improvement of Transportation and Traffic Facilities in the Metropolitan Area (submitted to Mayor and City Council by consultants: DeLeuw, Cather and Co.; Harold M. Lewis; Joe R. Ong), December, 1945.

Lewis, Harold M., with supplementary reports by William J. Wilgus and Daniel L. Turner: *Transit and Transportation*, Vol. IV, Regional Survey of New York and Its Environs, 1928. Distributed by Regional Plan Association, Inc., New York. See, particularly, chapter on "The Transit Problem" in Part I, reports by Mr. Turner in Part III, and Appendix A.

Miller, John A., Jr.: "Increasing the Efficiency of Passenger Transportation in Streets" (with discussion), *Transactions of the American Society of Civil Engineers*, Vol. 90 (1927), pages 914–957.

The Relation of Individual to Collective Transportation (report by Daniel L. Turner and John P. Hallihan), Rapid Transit Commission, Detroit, 1928.

Urban Freeways (prepared by Committee on Urban Transportation, American Institute of Planners), published by American Transit Association, New York, 1947.

Questions

1. List in historical order the various types of vehicles used in local transit. What effect has each had on the growth and form of the city and its metropolitan area?
2. How can the street plan and the rapid transit plan be co-ordinated?
3. What is meant by the "vicious cycle" of rapid-transit development as it has occurred in New York City?
4. Under what conditions are rapid-transit subways justified?

5. What are the relative passenger-carrying capacities of a street if used by private cars? By trolleys? By buses?

6. What are the functions of the British Transport Commission as established under the Transport Act of 1947?

7. What are some of the advantages of buses over trolleys? Of trolley coaches over buses?

8. Describe two outstanding trends in local transit development in the United States since 1930.

9. How has the federal government co-operated in studying local transit problems?

10. Under what conditions is it desirable to provide for mass-transit vehicles within expressway rights of way? Give examples of such practice.

11. About what percentage of the people entering downtown areas are carried by mass-transportation vehicles in cities of different population ranges?

8

THE STREET PATTERN

WHILE A CITY CANNOT OFTEN BE PLANNED FROM the beginning, there are certain general principles which should be regarded in the laying out of the street system of a portion of a town, as well as that of a complete city. These considerations were outlined in a paper presented by Raymond Unwin at the London Town Planning Conference in 1910 in the following words:

Having settled the purpose of the different areas, determined the general character of growth and the approximate direction desirable for main and subsidiary highways, the town planner finds himself with the following component parts out of which to make his design, namely:

The main center-point, or climax, dominating the whole; the secondary centers in definite proportion and relation to it; and the main highways linking them up; the whole giving the bones or main framework of the design.

Within the space defined by this framework, having special relation to the secondary centers and proportion to the primary highways, we have the network of secondary highways; while within the areas which these leave, for the purpose almost solely of giving access to the buildings, we have the minor roadways or drives, which should be in relation to any subsidiary center-point, and both in relation and proportion to the framework of secondary highways. . . . No system cuts up the land into more awkward corners or more thoroughly destroys the street façades, than that which consists of a framework of diagonal highways laid upon a rigid gridiron system of minor roads, and from no system do such unsatisfactory road junctions result. In town planning it is essential to avoid being carried away by the mere pattern of lines on paper. Order, definiteness of design there must be, but there must first be grasped an understanding of the points where order is important and will tell, and of those where it matters little.

Most old cities have simply grown with very little planning. Comprehensive plans, where such have been prepared, are of comparatively recent date and have had to adapt themselves as well as might be to the older portions of the towns as they were, and to make designs for sections not yet developed conform with the haphazard growth which had already taken place. Plans of such cities, therefore, commonly consist of a number of separate designs, more or less unrelated to each other, abutting upon the confused and uneconomic system of streets in the old town, which in most cases persists as the actual center. In some instances expansion in all directions was possible, as in London, Paris, Berlin, and Brussels. In others the ancient town was so located that expansion was in a semi-circular form, as in Antwerp and Chicago, or the growth was confined to a single direction, as in New York.

The considerations which led to the adoption of the present plan of that part of New York City now known as the borough of Manhattan are outlined in the report which was filed with that plan in 1811, and are interesting reading at this time, when the needs of a great city are more clearly understood. The necessity of a more comprehensive plan was appreciated when, in 1807, a commission was created to prepare it. New York then had a population of about 85,600, while the built-up part of the city extended north to approximately Houston Street on the east side and Eighth Street and Greenwich Avenue on the west side, with scattered settlements along both sides of Manhattan Island up to the Harlem River.

The commission was authorized to prepare a plan for Manhattan Island, which had a length of some 13¾ miles and a maximum width of about 2¼ miles. The members had then a prophetic vision of a great city which would occupy this strip of land, and they felt that it was "no unreasonable conjecture that in half a century it would be closely built up to the northern boundary of the Parade and contain 400,000 souls," a prediction which was more than verified, as in 1860 the population was more than double this estimate, having reached 813,669. The "Parade" referred to extended approximately from 23rd to 34th streets and from Third to Seventh avenues, and was "set apart for military exercise, as also to assemble in case of need a force destined to defend the city." After another half century (in 1910) the population of Manhattan had reached 2,331,542. The developed area had extended to the northern tip of the island before 1900.

Cities may be classified by their principal function—as capital cities, port cities, manufacturing cities, or market cities. They can also be classified as planned or unplanned cities, or as old and new cities. The old cities are not necessarily unplanned, nor are the new cities always planned.

For the purposes of the following discussion, cities have been classified by their type of street system: (1) rectangular or gridiron; (2) radial, wheel, or spider web, focal points with radial and circumferential streets, or a combination of radials with a gridiron plan; and (3) the organic street pattern.

Rectangular or Gridiron Plan

While New York City is often considered an unplanned city, a study of the report of 1811, already referred to, indicates an earnest attempt at planning. It also shows a rather extreme adherence to the gridiron pattern.

One of the first questions considered by the commission was "whether they should confine themselves to rectilinear and rectangular streets, or whether they should adopt some of those supposed improvements by circles, ovals, and stars, which certainly embellish a plan, whatever may be their effect as to convenience

and utility." The conclusion reached by them was that "a city must be composed principally of the habitations of men, and that straight-sided and right-angled houses are the most cheap to build and the most convenient to live in. The effect of these plain and simple reflections was decisive."

Having decided upon a rectangular, or gridiron, plan as the most desirable, the members appeared to conclude that, as the traffic of the city would be principally across the island, or from river to river, the greatest number of streets or the greatest traffic capacity should be in this direction, and a series of streets 60 feet in width, with intervening blocks 200 feet wide, was laid out in this direction. As they realized that some of these cross streets would be called upon to accommodate a concentrated traffic, they laid out fifteen of them, or approximately every tenth street, at a width of 100 feet. At right angles to these streets and running in straight lines along the length of the island a series of avenues was laid out with a width of 100 feet each and separated by blocks ranging from 650 to 920 feet in length. The assumption that the principal traffic would be from river to river may have been a natural one when this plan was made, but it is found to have been a serious and costly blunder. Yet this plan has admirers who point to the dignity and character of the long straight avenues of Manhattan Island.

The recent growth of New York has far exceeded the wildest dreams of those who made its first plan, and instead of being chiefly confined to Manhattan Island, the city has extended over Long Island, the portion of which now within the limits of the Greater City had, according to the United States Census of 1940, a population of 3,995,919. The East River, which doubtless seemed to the early city planners an insuperable barrier to the further extension of the city in that direction, has been practically eliminated by the construction of five great city bridges accommodating vehicular, rapid-transit and pedestrian traffic; a vehicular tunnel (with a second such tunnel approaching completion in 1947); one railway bridge; and twenty-two tracks in tunnels beneath the river. Six tracks have been carried under the Hudson River to the adjoining state of New Jersey, which is also connected to Manhattan by two twin-tube vehicular tunnels and a great highway bridge.

While the expansion to the east and west may appear to have justified the early belief that the principal traffic would be across Manhattan addition, there is the 125th Street approach to the Triborough Bridge (Figure 8·1; see also Figure 6·5, page 65), by which traffic from Manhattan can go directly either to The Bronx or to Queens, and traffic from Queens can go either to Manhattan or to The Bronx without passing through Manhattan. The White-

Courtesy, Department of Parks, New York City.

FIGURE 8·1. THE TRIBOROUGH BRIDGE, NEW YORK CITY

View looking down the East River, with Randall's Island interchange in the foreground. The New York Connecting Railway parallels the bridge on the left.

Island, the growth northwardly has been equally great, and the few avenues are still overtaxed, notwithstanding the fact that subways have been built under four of them, an elevated railway was still operating over another in 1947, and the West Side Elevated Highway and the Franklin D. Roosevelt Drive (East River Drive) now provide traffic capacity in addition to that included in the original plan. There are twelve street bridges, two railroad bridges, and three subway tunnels across the Harlem River which take Manhattan traffic to The Bronx and the north. In stone Bridge takes traffic from the eastern portions of Brooklyn and Queens to The Bronx without passing through the crowded western portions of these two boroughs or Manhattan Island.

The plan of New York is an excellent illustration of the lack of appreciation—on the part even of men of high intelligence and ability, as were the members of the commission whose report has been quoted from—of the great value of a system of radial or diagonal streets affording easy and direct connections between different parts of the city.

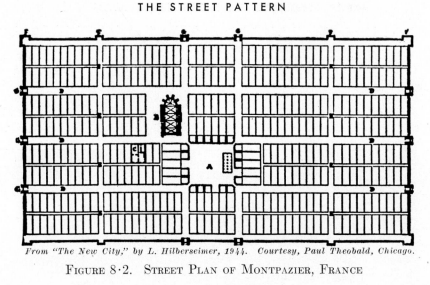

From *"The New City,"* by L. Hilberseimer, 1944. Courtesy, Paul Theobald, Chicago.

FIGURE 8·2. STREET PLAN OF MONTPAZIER, FRANCE

A thirteenth-century walled town with a rectangular layout.

Many people seem to think of the rectangular or gridiron street system as a modern improvement, but it is not new. It was common in ancient Egypt, Babylon, India, and China. The Greeks established many cities with rectangular street systems, which Aristotle found to be the most logical pattern. Selinus in Sicily and Alexandria in Egypt are notable examples. In the thirteenth century a number of towns were built in France on gridiron plans decreed by the King of England. (See Figure 8·2.)

In the American colonies many of the cities established by the English colonists had rectangular street systems. Philadelphia, established by William Penn, is noted for its gridiron street system and five small parks between the Delaware and Schuylkill rivers. The plan of Reading, Pennsylvania, was based on this model. One of the most interesting of these plans was made by General Oglethorpe for Savannah (Figure 8·3). The plan is said to have been derived from Bunyan's description of the Heavenly City in *The Pilgrim's Progress* and was intended to have a good influence on the debtors from the London prisons who were the original colonists.

The system of public land surveys, started at the suggestion of General Washington after the war of the Revolution, has made a profound impression on the plans of all cities which have grown up on the lands surveyed by

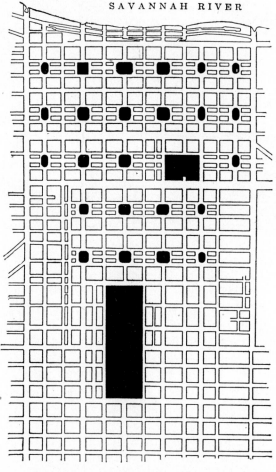

SAVANNAH RIVER

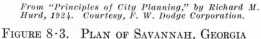

From *"Principles of City Planning,"* by Richard M. Hurd, 1924. Courtesy, F. W. Dodge Corporation.

FIGURE 8·3. PLAN OF SAVANNAH, GEORGIA

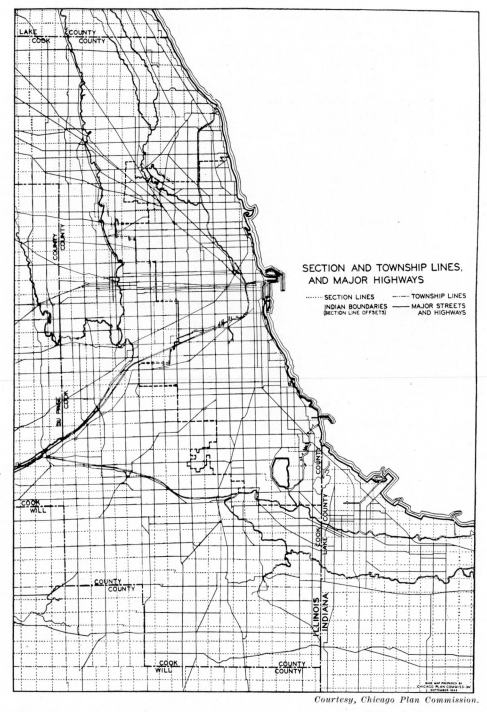

SECTION AND TOWNSHIP LINES,
AND MAJOR HIGHWAYS

.... SECTION LINES ——— TOWNSHIP LINES
INDIAN BOUNDARIES ——— MAJOR STREETS
(SECTION LINE OFFSETS) AND HIGHWAYS

Courtesy, Chicago Plan Commission.

FIGURE 8·4. EFFECT OF SECTION AND TOWNSHIP LINES ON PLAN OF MAJOR HIGHWAYS IN THE
CITY OF CHICAGO

these rules. Chicago, with its "section line" streets extending without interruption for over 26 miles, from the northern to the southern city limits and then extending into the country, is the most striking example of this effect. While the street systems between these "section line" streets are not all the same, and

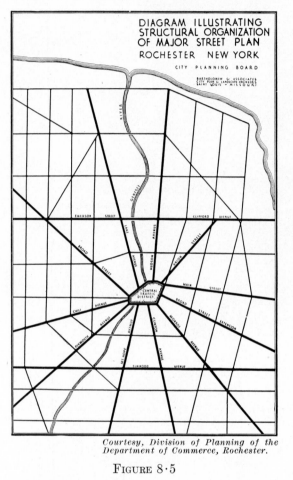

Courtesy, Division of Planning of the Department of Commerce, Rochester.

FIGURE 8·5

some are not rectangular, practically all the section lines are the center lines of long, straight streets. (See Figure 8·4.)

While the gridiron system has been tenaciously adhered to in the United States, efforts have been made to break away from it. Rochester, New York, for instance, provided in its Major Street Plan of 1929 for a system of direct thoroughfares connecting different parts of the city (Figure 8·5).

After a destructive fire in Detroit in 1805, a plan was prepared (Figure 8·6) which laid out a series of wide avenues radiating out from a

civic center, showing the influence of the Washington plan, but the present street system of the city, the general features of which are indicated by Figure 8·7, shows that it was only partly followed.

A variation of the rectangular street system is the proposed lineal city, in which all the governmental, business, commercial, and industrial establishments would be located on one main street. Minor residential streets would run at right angles thereto, extending about three-quarters of a mile on each side of the main street, with a continuous park on each side. Everyone could then live within walking distance of his work and have ample space for recreation.

Such a plan was suggested recently as a new and revolutionary idea for the rebuilding of Manhattan, New York City, with many arguments for its superiority. A similar scheme for an ideal city was proposed a few years ago by a group of professors in Washington, who would have had the main street go through the basements of the buildings, with elevators to take people to the stores on the ground level, these stores to be connected by sidewalks carried over the main and cross streets on footbridges. Above the stores would be offices, and over these, residences. Although this group thought they had found a new idea, a Spanish writer, Soria y Mata, had advocated *la ciudad lineal* in 1882, and a city on such a plan was built near Madrid about that time but has not been a success. As a matter of fact, the idea has been traced back to Egypt. When Amenhotep IV came to the throne in 1375 B.C., he left the old capital at Thebes, and founded a new city near the present Tell-el-Amarna on the Nile, half way between Thebes and Cairo. The whole city was never more than a quarter of a mile wide and was over five miles in length. This Pharaoh was succeeded by his son-in-law, Tutankhamen, who moved the capital back to Thebes. Apparently, the lineal city had not proved satisfactory.

Focal Point and Radial System

After the great fire of London in 1666, both Sir Christopher Wren and Sir John Evelyn

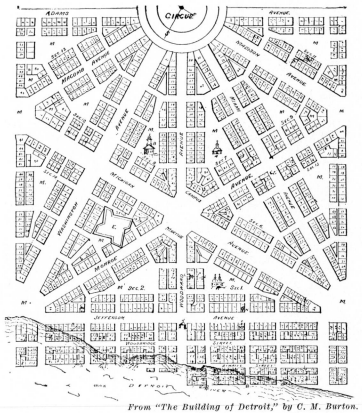

From "The Building of Detroit," by C. M. Burton.

FIGURE 8·6. THE GOVERNOR'S AND JUDGES' PLAN OF DETROIT, 1807

A destructive fire two years before had provided an incentive for replanning the city.

made what are said to have been simultaneous and entirely independent suggestions for the replanning of the streets of the burned district. These plans, the chief features of which are

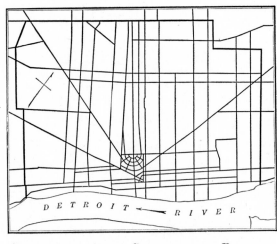

FIGURE 8·7. PLAN SHOWING THE PRINCIPAL THROUGH TRAFFIC STREETS OF DETROIT

shown in Figures 8·8 and 8·9, afford a striking example of the agreement of two careful students of the subject upon the fundamental principles which should govern the planning of intensively developed portions of a great city. They both employed an arrangement of focal points and radial connections.

In these two plans we are at once struck with the identical arrangement of the focal point where the Strand becomes Fleet Street,[1] from which eight main arteries radiate, one leading directly up to Wren's great cathedral, and from there directly to both the financial center at the Bank of England and to the north end of London Bridge. Evelyn's plan, by making his route to the financial center an extension beyond St. Paul's of this first artery, afforded an

[1] This is the site of the Strand-to-Holborn Improvement described in Chapter 3, pages 27 to 29. It is marked (1) on the Wren plan and (2) on the Evelyn plan.

admirable view of this great structure and its splendid dome from the east as well as from the west. Again, at the north end of London Bridge, we see in both plans almost exactly the same arrangement of radiating streets and closely similar systems having their center at

city in which the deformities and inconveniences of the old Town were remedied by enlarging the streets and lands, and carrying them as near parallel to one another as might be: avoiding if compatible with greater conveniences, all acute angles, by seating all the parochial churches conspicuous and insular, by forming the most public places into large piazzas the centers of eight ways; by uniting

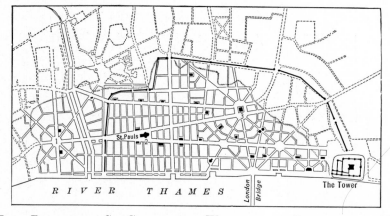

FIGURE 8·8. PLAN PROPOSED BY SIR CHRISTOPHER WREN FOR THE REBUILDING OF PART OF LONDON AFTER THE GREAT FIRE OF 1666

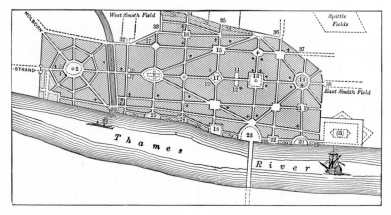

FIGURE 8·9. PLAN PROPOSED BY SIR JOHN EVELYN FOR THE REBUILDING OF PART OF LONDON

the bank. Unfortunately neither plan was carried out.

The manner in which Wren undertook his task and the controlling considerations which guided him in the preparation of his plan are given by James Elmes in his biography of Wren as follows:

In order, therefore, to a proper reformation Dr. Wren pursuant to the Royal Command immediately after the fire took an exact survey of the whole area and confines of the burning, having traced with great trouble and hazard the great plain of ashes and ruins, and designed a plan or model of a new

the Halls of twelve chief Companies into one regular space annexed to the Guildhall; by making a commodious Quay on the whole bank of the river from Blackfriars to the Tower. Moreover, in contriving the general plan the following particulars were chiefly considered and proposed:

The streets to be of three magnitudes; the three principal leading straight through the city, and one or two cross streets to be at least 90 feet wide; others 60 feet, and lanes about 30 feet, excluding all narrow, dark alleys without thoroughfares and courts. The Exchange to stand free in the middle of a piazza and be as it were the nave or center of the town, from whence the 60-foot streets as so many ways should proceed to all principal parts of the city; the building to be contrived after the form of the Roman Forum with double porticoes. Many streets also to radiate upon the bridge. The streets of the first and second magnitude to be carried on as straight as possible and to center in four or five piazzas.[2]

Special emphasis should be placed upon the fundamental importance of such an arrangement of focal points and direct connections between them, and the fact that its advantages were fully realized by at least two capable men nearly three centuries ago. The public authorities, however, failed to grasp their importance and take advantage of the suggestions, and, more strangely still, this lack of appreciation has continued to be quite general even to the present time.

Washington is probably the best-known instance of a city planned in advance and is an excellent example of the focal point and radial street system. A site was selected for the national capital of the United States in 1791, when the country consisted of a group of fourteen states strung out along the Atlantic Coast, one state having been added to the original thirteen during that year. The location chosen was at that time fairly central, being on both banks of the Potomac River, and partly in each of the states of Maryland and Virginia. While Washington is still about midway between the northerly and southerly boundaries of the country, it is only about 100 miles in a direct line from the Atlantic Coast and more than 2,000 miles from the Pacific. Were the capital city to be located today and given a fairly central position with regard to territory and population, it would probably be somewhere along the Mississippi River. The plan of the city, however, is so admirable, its natural surroundings are so attractive, and it has become so beautiful, that although it is at the easterly edge of a country of great territorial extent, no serious suggestion of a change in location has been made.

The focal point and radial street system usually breaks the city up into large blocks, which are subdivided by minor streets that usually meet the main streets at right angles. In the case of Washington, L'Enfant superim-

[2] *Sir Christopher Wren and His Times,* by James Elmes, London, 1852.

posed a rectangular plan made by Thomas Jefferson over his own radial plan. This produced the many awkward intersections, which are responsible for much of the traffic difficulties of the present day and produce many wedge-shaped lots that are difficult to build upon. Large areas are left at the street intersections. Irregular plots are formed which would be the despair of the real estate developer or of a town which is obliged to finance its street improvements in the ordinary way. (See Figure 8·10.)

Washington, however, is the national capital of a rich republic and has behind it what is even better than an imperial treasury, namely, the generous pride of a people and a legislature, the members of which, while representing different states and local constituencies, delight in seeing their capital city become one of the most beautiful in the world. Washington was planned on a large scale, the public buildings have great open spaces about them, the streets are very wide and are well planted with trees. The circles, squares, and other open spaces at the intersections of streets and avenues are used as sites for monuments, statues, and fountains, so that these generous open spaces are in scale with the rest of the city. But Washington is an exception which proves the soundness of the general rule enunciated by Unwin. Such a plan would be so extravagant as to be beyond the reach of the ordinary city, and is only possible for one like the American capital, where the entire urban life is closely related to the government and where manufacturing and commerce, other than that incidental to the accommodation of more than 660,000 people, are almost unknown.

In 1913 plans were prepared for Canberra, the proposed capital city for Australia, the competition for the design having been won by Walter B. Griffin of Chicago. In this case also there were no existing developments to influence the street pattern, and an exceedingly interesting plan was worked out to take advantage of the natural features of the site. Good locations were selected for the government center, municipal center, market center, manufacturing section, and four residential or suburban sections, one and one-half to two miles apart.

Radial highways extended outward from each of these, and the three main centers were interconnected by straight avenues forming an equilateral triangle. Views toward the highest surrounding mountains were made the main axes of the design, and an existing lake, its shores and tributary river banks, with the rugged admirable nucleus for the larger street plan. Although in planning for the future growth of an already existing city there is a natural and commendable desire to preserve everything that is old, picturesque, and of historic interest, to do so will frequently result in obstructing a free movement of the business and traffic of the city.

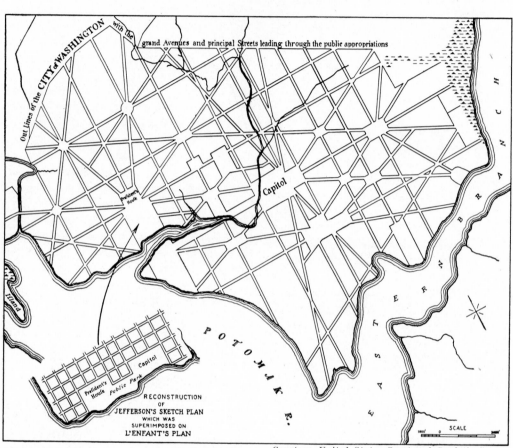

FIGURE 8·10. THE L'ENFANT PLAN FOR THE CITY OF WASHINGTON AND THE RECTANGULAR PLAN BY THOMAS JEFFERSON WHICH WAS SUPERIMPOSED ON IT

hillsides and hilltops, became the park system. (See Figures 8·11 and 8·12.)

Industrial cities have occasionally been built on entirely new sites, but, like Gary, Indiana, they often grow beyond the original expectations and take in parasitic suburbs, or even older villages, which were thought to be beyond the area that would ever be occupied by the city. The city planner usually finds that a beginning of his community has already been made, a beginning which may prove a serious handicap or may, though less frequently, be an

Few cities are fortunate enough to have had as their starting point a New England village green of generous proportions with a few wide highways radiating from it, or even to have had the beginning of a town plan like those of Buffalo and Detroit. Some of the cities of Continental Europe are built about an ancient château or schloss, the home of a prince who, after tiring of war, devoted his energies to the laying out of a city of which the royal residence should be the center; the result has been such a town as Karlsruhe or Mannheim.

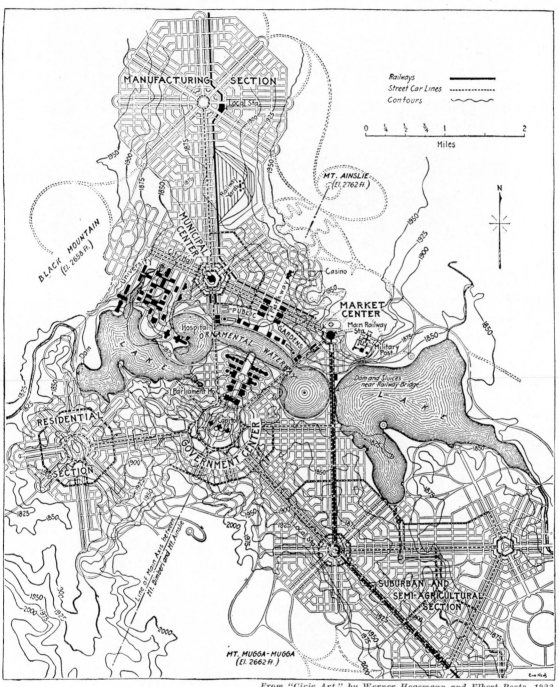

From "Civic Art," by Werner Hegemann and Elbert Peets, 1922.
Courtesy, Architectural Book Publishing Company, Inc.

FIGURE 8·11. PLAN FOR CANBERRA, THE CAPITAL CITY OF AUSTRALIA

This accepted design was made by Walter B. Griffin of Chicago.

Photo by E. P. Hamilton.

FIGURE 8·12. A VIEW OF CANBERRA AS DEVELOPED AND SHOWING ITS GENERAL SETTING

In Karlsruhe the fine radial streets were probably laid out for the purpose of providing dignified vistas of the castle or government buildings, or even for the purpose of defense against attack, rather than to facilitate free movement of traffic, but they have admirably performed both these functions. Again, the city may have been built about or under the shadow of the baronial castle, with little other purpose than to be near it and under its protection, as in the case of Edinburgh or Nuremberg.

In the replanning and reconstruction of Paris under Haussmann, an insistence upon some great focal points, with a system of thoroughfares radiating from them, the foci being connected by direct lines of special emphasis, and a system of circumferential streets, is seen to be the dominant feature (Figure 8·13). In many Continental cities a study of the ground plan will show this same arrangement, in some cases symmetrical and clearly defined, in others somewhat less obvious. It is especially apparent in Cologne (Figure 8·14), in Moscow, and in Vienna (Figure 8·15). The advantages are now quite generally appreciated, and the cities possessing these ring streets and radials have often been credited with more wise foresight than they have actually shown.

For generations, and even centuries, many European cities were hemmed in by fortifica-

tions which were deemed essential to their safety. Within the walls there was a maze of narrow and frequently squalid streets. Congestion was extreme, and the sanitary condi-

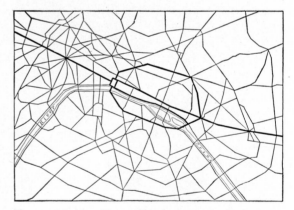

FIGURE 8·13. PLAN SHOWING THE PRINCIPAL TRAFFIC STREETS OF PARIS

What might be called the major axis of the city and the inner system of boulevards are indicated by the heavy lines. See also Figure 3·1, page 25.

tions were deplorable. A few highways led out of the cities through the walls and into the open country beyond, but these were not designed as arteries of traffic required by and contributing to peaceful commerce; they were rather routes of advance against or retreat before attacking forces, or were designed to facilitate predatory raids into the surrounding country. It was fortunate that when peace, rather than war, became a normal condition, and when the city walls could safely be demolished and the moats filled up, the possibility of converting the spaces occupied by them into great ring streets or boulevards and their peculiar availability for this purpose became apparent. (It is significant that the word "boulevard" originally meant the flat top of a rampart.) Here,

a maze of narrow, crooked streets, with churches and market places occupying the only open spaces. Not until the middle of the nineteenth century did Vienna feel that it could dispense with its encircling fortifications, and an ambitious plan was evolved for the use of the space occupied by them. There were delays owing to a dispute between the imperial government, the state, and the city as to the title to the land, but this was finally adjusted in

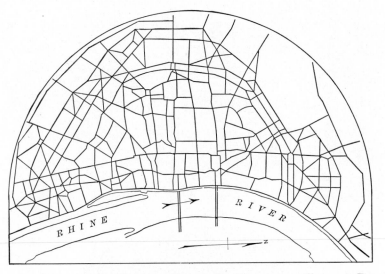

FIGURE 8·14. PLAN SHOWING THE GENERAL STREET SYSTEM OF THE CENTRAL PART OF COLOGNE

Both radial and circumferential streets are well defined.

then, was an area of publicly owned land, more than enough to provide a great encircling boulevard of generous width, with sites for important buildings which could advantageously be located along such a thoroughfare, with room even for open spaces and public gardens, and in addition, perhaps, land which could be sold at greatly enhanced value for sums which would go a long way toward meeting the cost of the physical improvement and of the public buildings. Such was the experience of Vienna, which glories in one of the finest, if not the very finest, ring street in the world, a street which Charles Mulford Robinson described as "an enormous circular stage devised for the spectacularly scenic entrance and exit of the Viennese throng."

In the eighteenth century Vienna was a typical fortified town with walls, bastions, sallyports, and moats. Behind these walls was

1857, and a competition was held to select a designer for the improvements. Eighty-five designs were submitted, and though none of the three prize-winning designs was literally carried out, they gave suggestions and set the standard for the final scheme. Vienna built its superb Ringstrasse as a result of these plans, setting aside sites for government and municipal buildings, museums of painting and sculpture, university, and cathedral, and even then had a considerable area left for private development. Albert Shaw says that about $80,000,000 was received through the sale of the surplus land.[3] There was also an outer line of fortifications which were razed in 1893 and their sites similarly used for another wide boulevard, the Gürtelstrasse, which extends from the Danube to the Danube. While this

[3] *Municipal Government in Continental Europe,* by Albert Shaw, page 422.

may not be considered far-sighted city planning, it affords an instance of intelligent appreciation of an unusual opportunity, which
was promptly and admirably availed of.

the plans have thus far failed of realization.
The old walls of Paris are still available as a
site for an encircling boulevard, and although
this city now has a very complete inner and

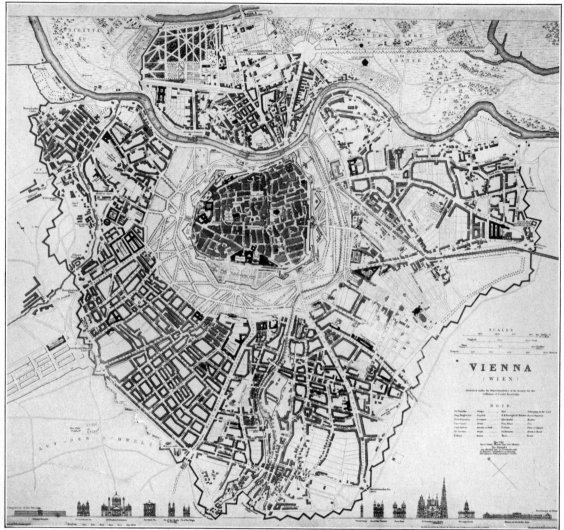

FIGURE 8·15. PLAN OF VIENNA, SHOWING RING AND RADIAL ROUTES

It is unfair to credit some of the ancient
European cities with a capacity for planning
these splendid streets, which are conspicuously
lacking in most towns. Moscow has them,
probably secured in somewhat the same manner
as Vienna secured hers; Cologne has replaced
her ancient walls by a ring street; but Berlin
has failed to take advantage of a similar opportunity. Such streets have from time to time
been planned for American cities, but most of

outer ring entirely surrounding the older parts
of the city, a third boulevard has been constructed along the old walls. Although few
towns have old walls which they can convert
into ring streets, the advantages of such streets
are so obvious that they are being planned by
many of the great cities, some of them at enormous cost for land and buildings, which must
be destroyed, with entire disarrangement of the
connecting streets.

Liverpool has in a less spectacular fashion, but in a far-sighted way, gone about the creation of such a street, which will permit traffic not destined for the central part of the town to pass entirely around it and avoid the most congested areas. The plans for this invaluable

the existing street systems or by coupling up fragments, widening here and extending there, to create the desired ring. The great semi-circular boulevard planned by the city of Chicago as part of the Burnham Plan of 1909 has been referred to in Chapter 3 (page 25). The

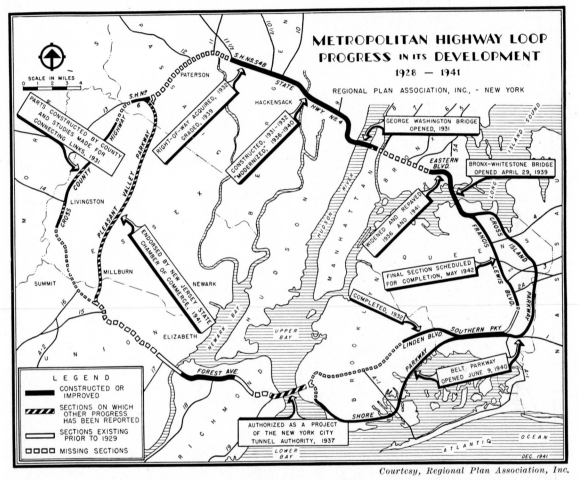

Courtesy, Regional Plan Association, Inc.

FIGURE 8·16. THE METROPOLITAN LOOP HIGHWAY IN THE REGIONAL PLAN OF NEW YORK AND ITS ENVIRONS AND PROGRESS TOWARD ITS REALIZATION

thoroughfare were made by City Engineer Brodie, and one section after another has been acquired and constructed until Liverpool found itself in possession of this improvement almost before the general public was aware that it was in progress. Brussels has laid out and is gradually improving a similar great boulevard, the easterly portion of which, traversing the most highly improved part of the city, is one of the finest streets in Europe.

American cities are making plans for such thoroughfares either by laying them out across

keystone of the highway system proposed in 1929 by the Regional Plan of New York and Its Environs was a metropolitan highway loop which encircled the main centers of business and commerce on both the New York and New Jersey sides of the Hudson River (Figure 8·16). In 1941 the Regional Plan Association reported that:

Excluding the parallel parkways, progress on the main Loop to date shows 48 miles, or 41 per cent, of its total length constructed and an additional 15 miles, or 13 per cent, having received official pre-

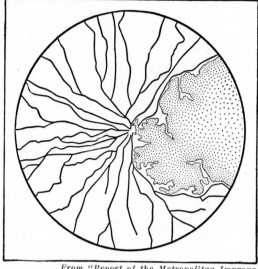

From "Report of the Metropolitan Improvement Commission, 1909."

FIGURE 8·17. RADIAL THOROUGHFARES OF
BOSTON

The largest gap in the radial system has been
filled in by the construction of the East Boston
Tunnel. These radials were partially tied together
at the center by one of the circumferential thoroughfares shown in Figure 8·18.

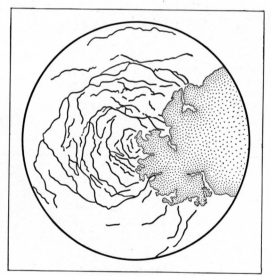

From "Report of the Metropolitan Improvement Commission, 1909."

FIGURE 8·18. CIRCUMFERENTIAL THOROUGH-
FARES OF BOSTON

Many of the gaps in the circumferential system
have not yet been filled in, possibly because the gaps
were large and the necessary construction expensive,
and also because the need was not so great as the
need for additional radial routes.

liminary action. Of this total, seven miles have
been advanced within the past four years.[4]

A careful examination of existing roads,
either in outlying districts or in the central
parts of a city, will frequently show how readily a system of radial and circumferential highways can be created by filling in a few gaps
and cutting through new streets for short distances. This is illustrated by the diagrams included in the report of the Metropolitan Improvement Commission of Boston on public
improvements for the metropolitan district
which was published in 1909, and, while these
diagrams have frequently been reproduced,
they so aptly illustrate the point that they
have been inserted as Figures 8·17 and 8·18.

The Organic Street Pattern

There is another type of street pattern exhibited in the mediaeval cities, which is sometimes thought to represent an extremely unplanned condition, but some people call it the
organic type of plan, or studied irregularity.
The streets are curving, discontinuous, and of
varying width, with irregular open spaces at
frequent intervals. The modern garden cities
usually have this kind of plans, as well as the
newer landscaped subdivisions. The name
"organic" applied to this street pattern is
derived from its resemblance to a microscopic
slide showing the cell structure of vegetable or
animal tissues.

While directness is desirable in the main and
even the secondary streets, it does not follow
that such streets should be perfectly straight;
in fact, straight streets are seldom interesting.
Neither need circumferential or curved streets
be laid out with perfect symmetry. The great
boulevards of Paris consist of a series of chords
of varying length, with deflections at different
angles, yet their pleasing effect is in no wise
diminished. Symmetry on a plan and symmetry on the ground are very different things.
In studying a plan the slightest departure from
such symmetry is noticeable, yet on the ground
it cannot be detected. One can ride or walk

[4] *From Plan to Reality—Three,* Regional Plan Association, New York, 1942, page III–3.

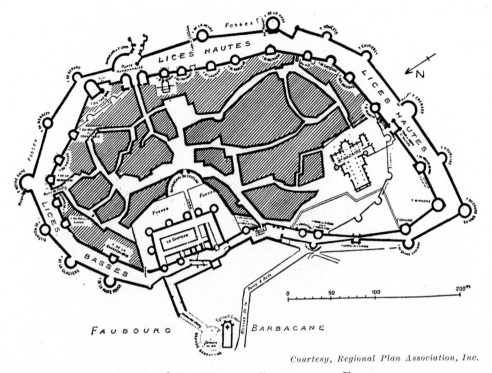

Courtesy, Regional Plan Association, Inc.

FIGURE 8·19. PLAN OF CARCASSONNE, FRANCE

An illustration of an organic plan.

From "Civic Art," by Werner Hegemann and Elbert Peets, 1922.
Courtesy, Architectural Book Publishing Company, Inc.

FIGURE 8·20. PLAN OF A SMALL SECTION OF PARIS

Showing the irregular yet pleasing arrangement of streets and boulevards affording admirable sites for monumental buildings.

along a boulevard following a sweeping curve and be unconscious of the fact that its radius is frequently changing, but if examined on a plan, these changes are at once apparent. Even if such a boulevard were broken into short tween the actual street and the plan has already been pointed out. Emphasis should be laid upon the fact, however, that it is the street itself and the buildings on either side of it that the people see, and irregularity or lack of

Photo by Hylite, Inc. Courtesy, J. C. Nichols Company.

FIGURE 8·21. A WELL-DESIGNED CURVED STREET

Illustrated by a view in the Country Club District of Kansas City.

straight sections, the utility of the street and even its beauty, so long as its general direction is preserved, are practically as great as though its lines were perfectly straight or symmetrical. It undoubtedly acquires added interest from the fact that important buildings located at the points where the direction is changed will show to excellent advantage, and attractive pictures may thus be formed. Such frequent changes in direction are conspicuous features of the plan of Paris (Figure 8·20). The difference be-

symmetry which may distress a draftsman will never be noticed on the ground.

In the minor streets within the smaller subdivisions, while there is no special reason for making them straight or even direct, the deliberate introduction of deflections, irregularities or "mere aimless wiggles," as Unwin calls them, may seem forced and irrational. A well-designed curved street is illustrated in Figure 8·21. In early twentieth-century planning in Germany there was a marked disposition to introduce deflections or even offsets in streets at frequent intervals, sometimes of one or two blocks, for the express purpose of creating in-

caused by these offsets would be very great and would be an excessive price to pay for the street pictures. Several methods of securing the de-

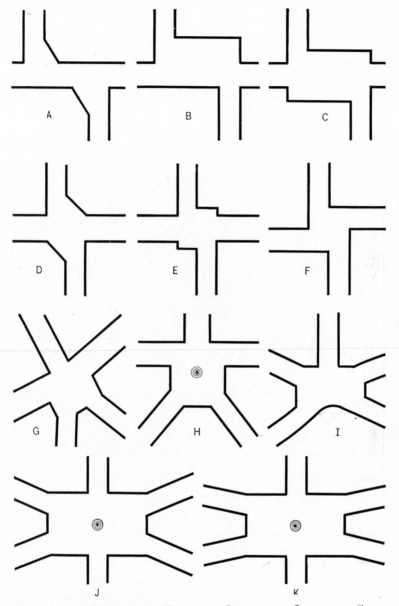

FIGURE 8·22.   DIFFERENT METHODS OF TREATING OFFSETS OR IRREGULAR STREET JUNCTIONS BY SLIGHT ENLARGEMENT OF THE OPEN SPACES

teresting street pictures. On strictly local and unimportant residential streets such obstacles to the free movement of vehicles may be of little moment, and the streets undoubtedly acquire additional interest by this treatment. If an unexpected amount of traffic should develop along these streets, however, the inconvenience

sired effects and at the same time avoiding embarrassment to street traffic are shown in Figure 8·22, such treatment being frequently adopted in German cities.

Perhaps no city to which modern planning has been consistently applied affords a better example of studied irregularity in its street system than Essen, located in the largest coal mining and industrial district of Germany (Figure 8·23). The old portion of the town lies north of the railroad, which traverses the city from east to west, and from the old center there is an excellent system of radiating traffic streets, while several ring streets encircle it. In the newer part of the city lying south of the

completeness with which this plan has been carried out is shown by the fact that the range of vision in the streets is as a rule limited to 650 to 1,000 feet.[5]

Further comments on the treatment of individual streets of Essen will be found in the discussion of street design in Chapter 9 (page 180).

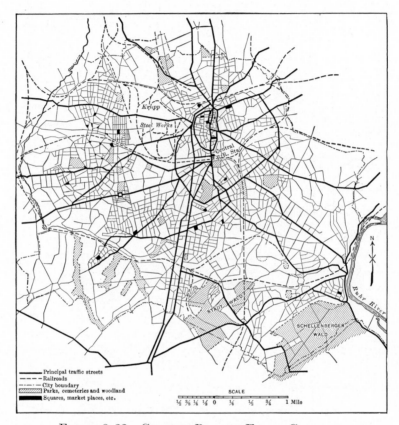

FIGURE 8·23. GENERAL PLAN OF ESSEN, GERMANY

Showing the studied irregularity of the street system.

railroad the irregularity of the minor street system is as conspicuous as in the older town, yet these streets were carefully planned by R. Schmidt, a former chief engineering official of the city. The Essen plan has been described as follows:

The streets at first seem to be hopelessly tangled and crooked, but as soon as this arrangement is studied it becomes apparent that this is a carefully planned disorder. . . . The aim of the planner was to furnish throughout the city constantly new and varied vistas not only in respect to the houses and their relation to the streets, but also to the width and arrangement of the individual streets. The

Many writers on city planning are enthusiastic over the picturesque attractiveness of the mediaeval Gothic towns of Germany, and they draw freely upon them for their illustrations. Perhaps there is a disposition to credit the planners of these towns, if they were planned in the modern sense, with a more serious intention to produce these effects than they are entitled to. The adaptation of the street plans to a rugged topography has resulted in some

[5] From article on the planning of Essen by Harold M. Lewis, *Engineering News*, August 20, 1914.

very charming street pictures, the origin of which is attributed to a finer sense of arrangement than is shown by modern town planners. Yet these results may be due in large measure, perhaps wholly, to a rational use of rugged sites for the buildings first required—castle, church, watchtower, etc.—and then, as the towns grew, to the fortunate location of the streets leading to and connecting them. Town halls and guild houses were not required in the early history of these towns. The people did not make their own laws and had little use for legislative halls or for the machinery of government. Their overlords attended to these details for them, as well as to such planning of their towns as was deemed necessary. No one will deny the charms of these old cities, but they grew out of social conditions which are fortunately unknown today. Their locations, the placing of their buildings, the arrangement and dimensions of their streets, reflected these conditions, which are exceedingly interesting to us. While none of their features should be reproduced in the more practical and livable cities which we are building today, it is worth while to study these mediaeval cities to find how the aesthetic effects were achieved and apply the principles so learned to our work today.

Some Engineering Problems

In every city there are large areas, not yet developed and not even planned, where opportunities are presented to design a street system, the different parts of which will be properly related to each other and to such modification of the system of the existing town as may ultimately be carried into effect. Too often these undeveloped sections are planned as if they were so many different urban areas unrelated to each other or to the original city, and too often the obvious blunders of the older sections are repeated in the new additions. Too often, also, small fragments of these areas are laid out by owners or by land speculators who have acquired adjacent holdings and whose only aim is to divide them into as many building lots as possible and dispose of them promptly, leaving the new owners to suffer the annoyance and loss incident to a later readjustment of street

lines. Municipal authorities, especially in America, have been strangely indifferent to this practice, and their excuse was often that they did not have the authority to control such operations. This was frequently the case, the laws being framed to protect the landowner in his so-called right to do what he pleases with his property, rather than to protect the public, which is the city, against the unwise exercise of such right.

In nearly all cases where a street plan is to be devised for such an area, two controlling conditions must first be taken into account— the topography and the existing roads. Although an accurate topographic survey of the entire territory will be of great value, the first step should be a determination of the lines of main drainage and the selection of routes for main arteries of travel which will give favorable grades; only the principal topographical features need be shown. This should not be understood as indicating a lack of appreciation of the value of a thoroughly good topographical map. The information obtained should be accurate so far as it goes, but it is unwise to go too far at this time. More complete topography will be needed when the minor details of the plan are worked out, but the time and expense of securing it can well be deferred for the present. Many street plans have been made which are very attractive on paper but which are found to be entirely impracticable when transferred to the ground. Had a sufficient topographic survey first been made, such impossible plans would not have been proposed.

The next essential is an accurate plan of the existing roads, showing their widths and the buildings fronting upon them. These roads will be of two kinds: (1) the old highways which serve to connect villages or centers of population, some within and others without the area to be platted, and (2) roads or streets which may have been laid out as parts of real estate developments and according to which property may have been sold, but along the lines of which there has been little or no building. Roads of the first class have an excuse for their existence, and they serve a useful purpose. They lead where people want to go and are likely to be fairly direct. Their alignment may be somewhat faulty, their grades may be excessive in some places, and their widths will be inadequate in view of the fact that they will naturally become the main lines of traffic for the urban district which will include them. With such straightening and widening as may be deemed necessary and such changes in line as will reduce excessive grades, those old roads will be the logical basis of the street plan which is to be prepared. When they have been platted, it will be obvious that additional roads will be needed, some to establish cross connections, others to give greater directness to the roads traversing the entire territory, others as by-passes around groups of buildings so located as to render the widening of some portions of the old roads unduly expensive, and still others to furnish lines of main drainage along the valleys through which the lateral sewers and subsidiary trunks must ultimately find their outlets. This system will be "the bones or main framework of the design" referred to by Unwin. There will probably be no main center or climax and no secondary centers to be connected at this time. If they already existed, there would also be a system of streets which would have to be reckoned with and which would make the problem one of replanning; such problems of replanning are those to which most writers on this subject are inclined to confine themselves.

We are considering now the planning of undeveloped territory in such a manner as to make replanning unnecessary. While no one can predict with any certainty the precise manner in which any city will grow, the purpose of the preliminary and initial design outlined is to establish lines of least resistance which future development will be quite likely to follow. Thus far we have considered only the roads which will probably become the main arteries of traffic and which will lead with reasonable directness where people will wish to go. These roads may divide the territory into a series of irregular figures having three, four, or more sides, which sides may be a quarter or a half a mile, or even more, in length. These areas must be subdivided by secondary roads, in the location of which regard should be paid wherever possible to property subdivisions, to the

possibility of some of them developing into main traffic roads and to the avoidance of awkward junctions with the main roads already laid down, which would result in confusion of traffic (Figure 8·24).

In laying out the secondary roads, as in the case of main highways, consideration should be paid to the topography although, perhaps, to a somewhat less degree, grades and directness being of less importance, although provision for surface drainage and sewers should always be borne in mind.

Lastly will come the minor streets, which will serve almost entirely for access to dwellings. As all these streets will connect directly with either the secondary or main highways, their alignment and grades are of little importance, as they will be used almost exclusively by private vehicles or those delivering supplies to the abutting houses. The chief concern is that they be laid out to furnish ample light and air and to discourage, if not prevent, a too intensive development. Wide blocks in downtown areas, resulting in excessively deep lots, may encourage rear buildings, if the city ordinances do not prohibit this menace to health and decent living, and thus increase the density. To plan far in advance the precise location of these minor streets is not necessary, if it be not unwise. Considerable latitude can well be allowed the individual developer in their arrangement, provided always that his plans are submitted to the proper municipal authorities for examination and approval before the development can proceed.

While the street system in the different small areas formed by the secondary streets may be similarly treated, the minor streets running directly across those of the secondary class, there is no special reason why this should be done. There is no reason why a street which is to be devoted to private residences should be long and straight. Among the most attractive features of a city are small residential areas treated in a distinctive way, each with a character of its own, which the visitor stumbles upon with agreeable surprise. If these minor subdivisions are planned at different times or by different persons, this variety in treatment is more likely to be realized. The important thing is that the diagonals or the main arteries be planned first, and that leading off from them will be highways of secondary importance, from which again will branch the smaller and less important streets. As pointed out by Unwin, the development of a street system is

embarrassed. Whenever a system of diagonal streets is superimposed upon a rectangular plan, the awkwardness of acute intersections with important diagonals is apparent. It would be better if connections with important thoroughfares were made as nearly at right angles to

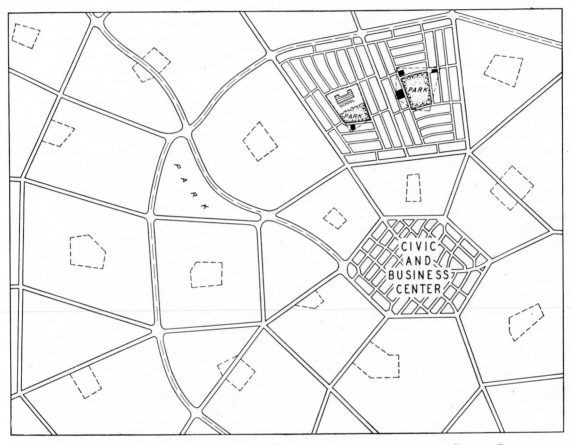

FIGURE 8·24. TYPICAL PLAN SHOWING DEVELOPMENT OF AN ARTERIAL STREET SYSTEM

Existing roads could be supplemented by additional connections, and acreage property could be acquired for small parks, sites for public buildings, and other public purposes.

somewhat analogous to the growth of a tree; first, the trunk, then the main branches, the minor branches, and the twigs, but the small branches and the twigs do not grow directly out of the main trunk. Connections between the secondary or minor streets and the main arteries of traffic should not be too frequent, or they will interfere with ease of movement. The idea that subsidiary streets should be connected with important thoroughfares at frequent intervals is a mistake. Not only is a large portion of valuable frontage taken by these openings, but also traffic movement is

them as possible, preserving thereby more desirable sites for important buildings on such streets.

Some special developments may already have been planned before the main and secondary street systems are established, and these, provided they have been laid out with reasonable skill and with due regard for sanitary conditions, usually can be incorporated into the final plan. This does not mean that such developments should be permitted without previous approval by the authorities having jurisdiction over the city plan. Although the need of absolute control of them cannot be too strongly insisted upon, in many American cities there is no provision for such control, and they may have been laid out before the area in which they are located became a part of the city.[6] Many or most of the lots may have been sold to innocent purchasers, and to ignore them or to lay out a new system of streets without regard for them would impose upon the new

FIGURE 8·25. PLAN SHOWING HOW A RECTANGULAR STREET PLAN HAS DISREGARDED EXISTING IMPROVEMENTS

Old streets have been ignored which could have been incorporated in the plan without serious objection.

owners a real hardship and an expense which might be serious; while the original developer is likely to have "unloaded" and to have put himself beyond the reach of punishment for his disregard of the public interest, if there has been such disregard.

It may be, however, that, although the plan which has been followed is not one that the engineer charged with planning the street system for the new area would himself have followed, it is not essentially bad and unsuited for incorporation into the new plan. It might well answer for one of the minor subdivisions.

Where the gridiron street pattern has been the standard, it sometimes has been extended

[6] See Chapter 21, "Control of Land Subdivisions," Volume II.

in a roughshod manner over old communities, ignoring existing improvements. An opportunity may thus be lost of retaining neighborhood atmosphere as well as maintaining property values. An example of this kind in that section of the borough of Brooklyn, New York City, mapped in 1874 as part of the then city of Brooklyn, is shown in Figure 8·25. It is of interest that forty years after this gridiron plan was adopted, some of the old streets in the original development were restored, as it was found that their elimination would involve such property damages that the cost would have been prohibitive.

The continuity of streets is important, but does not require their prolongation indefinitely in straight lines, but rather the provision of easy connections which will not be serious obstacles to traffic movement along the streets themselves or along those which they intersect or cross. In many private developments provision for such continuity is often overlooked and in some cases deliberately avoided. An instance is given by a British writer where two adjoining estates with areas of over 500 acres have been carefully laid out with the express purpose of preventing access from one to the other, and the by-laws were powerless to prevent this unwise action. At least one similar case has come to the notice of the author, where rival landscape architects engaged in planning the development of adjoining tracts deliberately located their roads in such a manner as to prevent direct communication.

Development of Parkway Systems

Up to this point the elements of the street thoroughfare system have been referred to on the basis of their classification in either a geometric pattern—such as radial or circumferential—or their importance as traffic carriers—such as major, secondary, or local. In addition, there have gradually been developed special-purpose highways forming separate networks over a large city or a region. The first of these appeared in the form of parkway systems.

These started out as a series of large and medium-sized parks connected by boulevards, so that people in carriages could take a drive through all the parks of a city and be in attractive surroundings on the entire trip. The boulevards were city streets with landscape and floral embellishments. The most expensive residences faced upon them, and all the streets

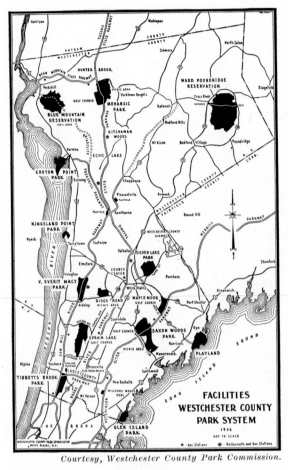

Courtesy, Westchester County Park Commission.

FIGURE 8·26

of the area crossed at grade. With the development of the low-priced automobile and the resulting rapid increase in traffic, a different type of park connection was called for. The result was the creation of the modern parkway.

A parkway has been defined as an elongated park through which passes a roadway to which the abutting owners have no right of light, air, and access. The roadway is usually restricted to private passenger vehicles. How parkway systems have been developed can best be shown by descriptions of three of the earliest and best-known examples.

The Boston Metropolitan Park System was started in 1893 under an independent Metropolitan Park Commission, but is now controlled by the Parks Division of the Boston Metropolitan District Commission. In 1930, 53 years after the acquisition of the first parkway, 2,353 acres of land had been acquired for 78 miles of parkways. A total of 73 miles of roadway had been constructed. The land had cost $12,197,746, and the improvements $26,854,546. The state of Massachusetts had paid one-half the cost, and the remainder was distributed to the city of Boston and the other communities in the district in an equitable manner.[7] In 1946, there were 104 miles of parkway drives under the jurisdiction of the Metropolitan District Commission, including about 60 miles lying within their park reservations; there were an additional 43 miles of driveways in the main inland and marine park systems under the jurisdiction of the Boston Park Department. (See Figure 8·27.)

In general, the parkways connect the larger parks, both metropolitan and municipal, and follow stream valleys or the seashore. As the original city and present business center was at the head of a deep bay, at a point where three rivers converged, the main parkways radiate from the center of Boston. Minor river valleys have been connected to give circumferential parkways.

The Kansas City Park System was initiated in 1892 as a method of controlling the growth of the city and preventing the spread of blighting influences which had started. The report of 1893 recommended the purchase of 324 acres of parks and the development of 9.85 miles of boulevards, 100, 110, and some over 250 feet in width, which generally followed the gridiron system of streets prevailing at that time. This program was completed, and additional plans have since been made and carried out. The latest plan, involving the development of the Blue River Valley, has not yet been carried to completion. The newer parkways follow the

[7] See *Parkways and Land Values,* by John Nolen and Henry V. Hubbard, Harvard University Press, Cambridge, Mass., 1937, pages 28–31.

streams, which are generally in deep ravines, and have added variety to the street system of the newer parts of the city. These parkways are 500 to 600 feet in width, according to the topography, and in some cases broaden out into medium-sized or large parks. There are three

sessments were the only available means for financing the improvements. These could not have been collected if it had not been possible to convince the property owners that the expenditure was justified by the certain increases in the value of their property.[8]   In 1946 the

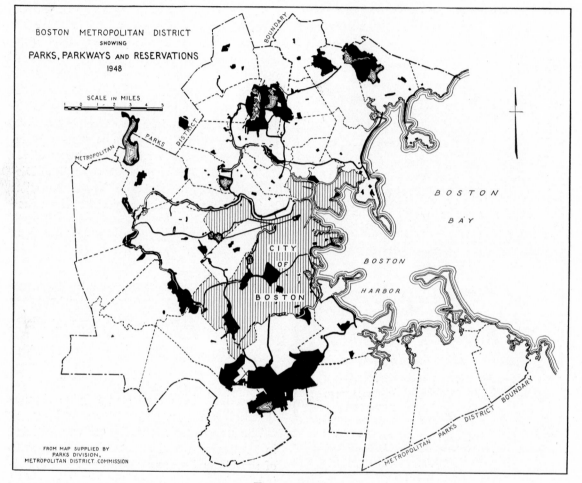

BOSTON METROPOLITAN DISTRICT
SHOWING
PARKS, PARKWAYS AND RESERVATIONS
1948

SCALE IN MILES

FROM MAP SUPPLIED BY
PARKS DIVISION,
METROPOLITAN DISTRICT COMMISSION

FIGURE 8·27

north and south routes and five east and west connections. (See Figure 8·28; for map, see Figure 10·2, page 198.)

By 1930 there had been 42 miles of boulevards constructed, and 800 acres of land acquired for 40 miles of parkway. For the parkways, the land had cost $4,000,000, construction $1,200,000, and maintenance $1,800,000, making a total of $7,000,000. This park work was started at a time when the borrowing capacity of Kansas City was exhausted, and special as-

Park Department controlled a connected system of 116 miles of improved boulevards and park and parkway drives.

The Westchester County Parkway System (Figure 8·26) started with the Bronx River Parkway, proposed in 1910 as a joint project of New York City and Westchester County. The Bronx River, which flows through Bronx Park in New York City, was so badly polluted that use of the park was threatened. Property

[8] *Ibid.*, pages 54–59.

FIGURE 8·28. VIEWS ON TYPICAL KANSAS CITY BOULEVARDS

Upper view, circle on Gregory Boulevard at Holmes Street; lower view, bridge by which 71st Street (Gregory Boulevard) passes over Paseo Boulevard.

along the stream in Westchester County was also badly blighted. The New York City Park Department suggested the improvement and agreed to assume part of the cost. The parkway is about 19 miles long in Westchester County and goes from the New York City line to the Kensico Reservoir.

Before this parkway was finished, the people of Westchester County were enthusiastic

That parkways can play an important part in the traffic picture is shown by the traffic counts made on the Westchester County parkways on a Saturday in August, 1940, and shown in Figure 8·30. On the Hutchinson River Parkway the 24-hour traffic reached 34,429 cars and on the lower Saw Mill River Parkway 42,217 cars (although there was some reconstruction under way at that point), compared with 20,803

Courtesy, Westchester County Park Commission.

FIGURE 8·29. BEFORE AND AFTER VIEWS OF THE BRONX RIVER PARKWAY NEAR WHITE PLAINS, NEW YORK

The view on the left shows the disorderly conditions preceding the parkway construction. The parkway roadway is in the upper lefthand section of the view on the right.

over the improvement, and a Westchester County Park Commission was provided for by law, which absorbed the personnel and staff of the Bronx River Park Commission as soon as its work was completed. In 1947 this commission owned about 17,000 acres of park land, about 9,000 acres of which were for parkway rights of way, and 9 miles of beaches. The parkway routes acquired, including one state parkway, totaled 160 miles. The county had constructed 57.1 miles of parkway and had an additional 10 miles under construction; the state had constructed 25.2 miles. Up to 1933 the county expended about $34,300,000 for land acquisition and $29,300,000 for improvements; the figures for parkways alone were $26,735,000 and $19,945,000, respectively. The state parkway cost $9,200,000 for both acquisition and improvement.

vehicles on the Boston Post Road (U. S. 1) near New Rochelle and 10,465 vehicles on the Albany Post Road (U. S. 9) north of Yonkers. As it became apparent that the parkways were important links in the major highway system and carried large amounts of through traffic, the state of New York took over part of the program and has constructed the Bronx Parkway Extension, the connection from that to U. S. 9 at Croton, and the upper end of the Briarcliff-Peekskill Parkway as state highways. It also proposes to complete the Briarcliff-Peekskill Parkway. To further assist the county the state legislature in 1947 authorized it to collect tolls on the Hutchinson and Saw Mill River Parkways.

Mention should also be made of the parkway systems acquired and constructed on Long Island by the Long Island State Park Commis-

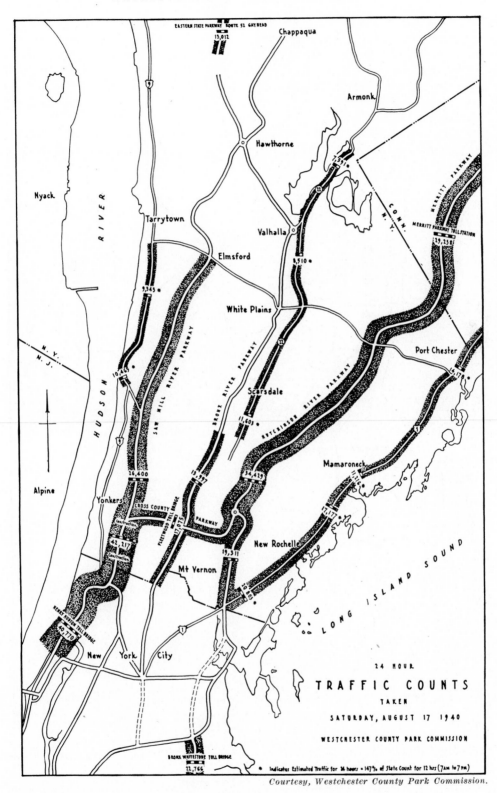

Courtesy, Westchester County Park Commission.

FIGURE 8·30. RELATIVE TRAFFIC CARRIED BY PARKWAYS AND OTHER MAIN HIGHWAYS IN WESTCHESTER COUNTY, NEW YORK

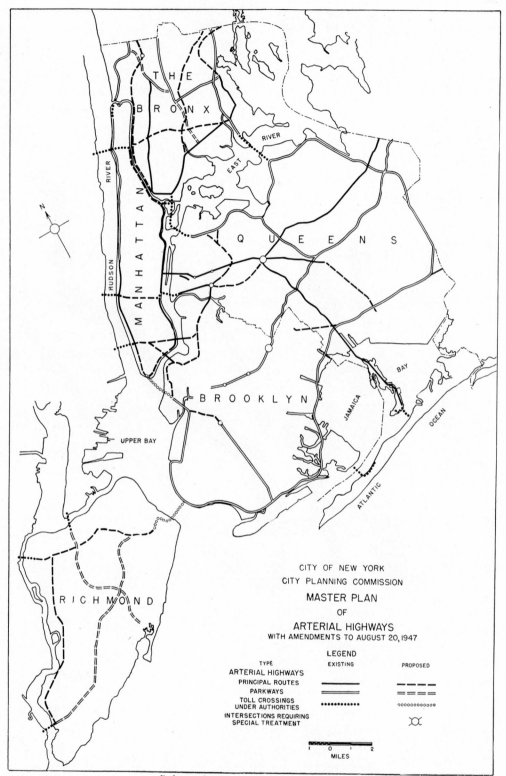

CITY OF NEW YORK
CITY PLANNING COMMISSION
MASTER PLAN
OF
ARTERIAL HIGHWAYS
WITH AMENDMENTS TO AUGUST 20, 1947

LEGEND

TYPE	EXISTING	PROPOSED
ARTERIAL HIGHWAYS		
PRINCIPAL ROUTES		
PARKWAYS		
TOLL CROSSINGS UNDER AUTHORITIES		
INTERSECTIONS REQUIRING SPECIAL TREATMENT		

MILES

Redrawn from map supplied by City Planning Commission, New York City.

FIGURE 8·31

sion and providing direct access to state parks on both shores of Long Island, the Merritt and Wilbur Cross parkways constructed by the Connecticut State Highway Department, and the extensive system of parkways developed in New York City by its Park Department, by the borough of Manhattan, and with the aid of various special authorities consolidated in 1946 into the Triborough Bridge and Tunnel Authority. (See Figure 8·31.)

The Modern Expressway

Because of interference of vehicles at intersections, the practical capacity of roadways is limited to less than half their capacity if there were no such interruptions. A number of ideas have been suggested and tried to increase the capacity of intersections to more nearly the capacities of the intervening roadways and are discussed in the following chapter, pages 171 to 175.

The studies of the staff of the Regional Plan of New York and Its Environs had shown by 1924 that a new kind of street or highway was needed for heavy truck traffic. Trucks cannot accelerate as easily as the lighter passenger cars, and are more affected by frequent stopping and starting and excessive grades. They also need thicker and more expensive pavements. The advantages of separate roadways for passenger cars had already been proved on the Bronx River Parkway, where grade crossings had been eliminated and such traffic was permitted uninterrupted flow at a speed of 35 miles per hour. Other cities had previously learned the advantage of separating trucks from passenger cars on the boulevards. While this practice left a little more room for trucks on the other streets, it was not enough. Elevated or depressed streets were suggested to provide streets at better grades without the interruptions of frequent cross streets.

As a cheaper alternative, the suggestion was advanced that main and secondary highways might be divided into parallel roadways by parking strips which would continue across minor intersecting streets, so that traffic from these streets would have to make a right turn into the main thoroughfare, proceed to an open-ing in the parking strip, wait for a chance to cross to the other side of the main street, go back and turn out on the cross street they were on. At intersections of the main thoroughfares traffic circles would provide for uninterrupted flow and a choice of any exit street. In 1929 such a system was worked out in detail by Fritz Malcher, and his proposed treatment of a dual roadway, whereby direct cross movement from intersecting streets is eliminated, was incorporated in the design of one of the main streets of Radburn, New Jersey, the "town for the motor age." [9]

In practice, it has been found that the steady-flow system, traffic circles, and such devices will work only for speeds of less than 18 to 21 miles per hour, and that some method of grade-crossing elimination is necessary to develop greater speeds with safety. About this time the clover-leaf intersection with one bridge was built in New Jersey. Sigvald Johannesson, in an economic analysis of such an intersection under 1930 conditions, concluded that it was economical for an intersection where each of the two crossing highways carried 12,000,000 vehicles per year.[10] Under similar conditions, if each of the highways carried less than 10,000,000 vehicles, the cost of constructing such an intersection would not have been justified.

At about this time the term "freeway" was coined by Edward M. Bassett as a name for "a strip of public land, dedicated to movement, over which the abutting owners have no right of light, air, or access." It was advanced as a type of general traffic highway, in distinction from the parkways for passenger vehicles only. Its application was developed in detail by the Regional Plan Association,[11] and it has been accepted as a logical solution of handling long-haul traffic. Many state legislatures have authorized the construction of state highways

[9] See *Steadyflow Traffic System,* by Fritz Malcher, Harvard University Press, Cambridge, Mass., 1935.

[10] *Highway Economics,* by Sigvald Johannesson, McGraw-Hill Book Company, 1931, page 112.

[11] "The Freeway, a Modern Highway for General Traffic in Metropolitan Areas," *Information Bulletin* 33, Regional Plan Association, Inc., December 14, 1936.

(and in some cases county and municipal highways) of this type under the name "freeways," "limited-access highways," or "controlled-access highways."

The Pennsylvania Turnpike, completed in 1940 between Harrisburg and the vicinity of Pittsburgh is a route of this type, utilizing an abandoned railroad right of way. Here the tap the urban areas and in metropolitan districts must cross through them. Although it has been suggested that a network of limited-access thoroughfares might provide the skeleton of the street pattern of an entire city,[12] it is doubtful whether such expensive construction would be justified on this scale. Few cities would ever need more than two or three

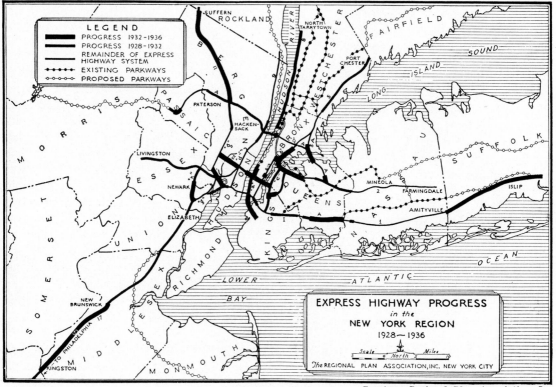

FIGURE 8·32

Courtesy, Regional Plan Association, Inc.

idea of acceleration and deceleration lanes has been applied effectively for speeds up to 70 miles per hour, so that vehicles entering or leaving the highway need not delay the other vehicles. In 1946 the state of New York broke ground on a route of this type to run the full length of the state and to form the backbone of a state-wide system. It was planned with maximum grades of 3 per cent and with curves having a minimum radius of 2,800 feet. Similar routes are found abroad in the German Reichautobahnen and the Italian Autostrade.

The greater proportion of such expressways will be constructed through rural areas, but if they are to function successfully, they must such routes and then only for streets carrying a large proportion of through traffic. These expressways are comparable to railways in cost and carrying capacity and should be treated very much the same in the city plan; in other words, they are not a part of the regular street pattern, although they should be tied in with it.

It is in metropolitan areas that expressways are most needed, and New York and Los

[12] See *New City Patterns,* by S. E. Sanders and A. J. Rabuck, Reinhold Publishing Corporation, 1946, page 153. The authors suggested that such highways divide the city into areas about ¾ of a mile wide by one mile long.

Angeles provide the best examples of their application in the form of both existing and proposed routes. The original proposals for general-traffic express highways in the Regional Plan of New York and Its Environs called for 253 route-miles, of which 3.5 miles were in existence in 1928. By 1936 there had been substantial progress on the rest of this system

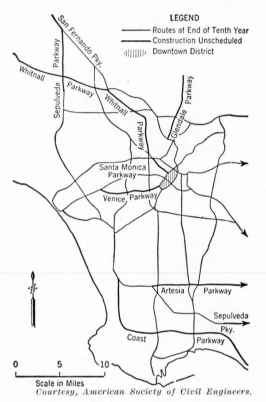

LEGEND
——— Routes at End of Tenth Year
———— Construction Unscheduled
⋅ı║║║⋅ Downtown District

Scale in Miles

Courtesy, American Society of Civil Engineers.

FIGURE 8·33. THE EXPRESSWAY PROGRAM OF THE CITY OF LOS ANGELES

(Figure 8·32). In its 1942 report of progress the Regional Plan Association reported, "The concept of the express routes needed for the Region has changed since the publication of the Plan by expansion to include the principal through routes in the Region." Its revised plan included 732 miles of expressways for mixed traffic, supplemented by 508 miles of parkways. The area served had an estimated 1945 population of about 13,000,000.[13]

The proposed expressway system for Los Angeles is shown in Figure 8·33. While the

[13] *From Plan to Reality—Three,* Regional Plan Association, Inc., 1942, page III–11.

routes are designated as "parkways," it is proposed to develop many of them for mixed traffic, particularly buses. In addition to about 10 miles of existing routes the system proposes 358 route-miles at an estimated cost of $582,-000,000. The entire county of Los Angeles, which includes the city of Los Angeles and had an estimated 1945 population of about 3,400,-000, would be served. About 220 miles of the new routes, costing $400,000,000, will be within the city. A 10-year schedule of construction, involving 287 miles, is shown separately in Figure 8·33.

While the New York region has about four times the population of Los Angeles County and about 38 per cent greater area, automobile use therein is not so intensive. In Los Angeles County there is one car for about every 2½ persons, as compared with one for every six persons in the New York region.

Spacing of Thoroughfares

As has been pointed out, a combination of radial and circumferential routes will lead to a splitting up of a city into districts bounded by main thoroughfares, the distance between these thoroughfares, and therefore the size of the districts, increasing the farther they are from main or secondary focal points. Where a gridiron system prevails, a more uniform spacing of main routes is often provided in the street pattern. Major streets 100 to 120 feet in width may be placed about one mile apart, with secondary streets about 80 feet in width half way between.

Ernest P. Goodrich has suggested a spacing varying with the type of neighborhood, as follows: "The main thoroughfares in single-family residence districts should be spaced not to exceed 3,000 feet apart, 2,000 feet in two-family house districts, and 1,250 feet in multi-family house districts. In industrial districts the main thoroughfares should not be spaced more than 750 feet apart."[14] In districts used for heavy industries the distance between main thorough-

[14] "The Design of the Street System in Relation to Vehicular Traffic," by Ernest P. Goodrich, *Proceedings of the 14th National Conference on City Planning,* Springfield, Mass., 1922, page 102.

fares should be great enough to accommodate
the industrial processes. For example, in a
steel-mill site it might be desirable to have no
thoroughfare within one-half mile of the industrial railroad, and in an oil-refinery site
even greater distances might be desirable.

Orientation for Sunlight

In recent decades architects and city planners
have given increasing attention to the orientation of streets so as to insure a certain amount
of direct sunlight for each building, particularly dwellings, on every day of the year.
A.-Augustin Rey, a French housing official,
pointed out in 1913 the former neglect of this
feature of town planning:

> The orientation of the public streets and the con-
> sequences that it entails dominate in reality the
> whole health of towns and dwellings.
> How could it have been forgotten that a public
> street on which buildings were to be placed, whose
> importance would increase, could be created in no
> matter what direction, having no matter what width,
> and bordered by buildings whose height would be
> fixed by rules without rational basis, without fore-
> seeing the disastrous consequences from a hygienic
> point of view arising from such negligences? The
> buildings covering, for example, the town of Paris,
> in the interior of the fortified enclosure, represent
> at the present time fifteen thousand millions of
> francs (three billion dollars). And no regulation
> whatever has concerned itself with the laws of
> light for an agglomeration of such colossal value.
> When we traverse the most beautiful towns of
> Europe and America it is really amazing to observe
> to what point this law of light has been outrageously
> violated in all the laying out of their plans.[15]

The amount of direct sunlight which will
reach any building is obviously dependent upon
the latitude of the locality, the direction and
width of the street, and the height of the
buildings. Rey found that, to insure two hours
of direct sunlight on the shortest day of the
year, a street in Moscow running east and west
and lined with buildings 21 meters high would
have to be 105 meters or 344 feet wide, while
in Washington a similar street with buildings
of equal height would have three hours of di-

rect sunlight if it were 42 meters or 138 feet
wide. On a north and south street in Moscow,
with buildings only eight meters high, there
would be one hour and five minutes of direct
sunlight if the street were 12 meters or 39 feet
wide, while in Washington there would be one
hour and forty-five minutes of such direct light
if the street were but eight meters or 26 feet
wide. Similar computations were made for
each of ten cities for each of the three heights
of buildings, and for streets running in four
different directions.

Some years later Rey's studies appeared in a
book prepared in collaboration with a Swiss
astronomer and a Swiss architect.[16] This contains a very complete set of diagrams for the
latitude of Paris (48° 8′). It was pointed out
that the most sunlight is obtained on a southern
exposure, but the greatest heat from the sun
is obtained on an approximately southwest
exposure. This leads to the establishment of
an *axe heliothermique*, which becomes the basis
for a city plan laid out on scientific sunlight
principles. For the latitude of Paris this axis
deviates 19° west of south. There is little
variation in this deviation for any communities
within the northern temperate regions. It is
stated that the façades of buildings should
front upon streets parallel with this axis. The
available sunlight on buildings depends not
only upon the width of the street, which should
be a function of the latitude of the community
and the height of buildings fronting on the
street, but also on the angle which the street
forms with the meridian. All of these should
be properly co-ordinated. Examples were given
for a replanning of different sections of Paris
to obtain the advantages of sunlight without
changing the main street system.

A study of sunlight and its relation to city
planning was included in the Regional Plan of
New York and Its Environs.[17] This laid par-

---

[15] "La ville salubre de l'avenir, principes scientifiques
d'orientation des voies publiques et des habitations,"
*Proceedings of the First International Congress of
Cities,* held at Ghent, 1913; also *Town Planning Review,* Vol. VI, page 2.

[16] *La science des plans de villes,* by A.-Augustin Rey,
Justin Pidoux and Charles Barde, Dunod, Paris, 1929.
See review by Harold M. Lewis in *Engineering News-
Record,* June 20, 1929.

[17] *Sunlight and Daylight for Urban Areas,* by Wayne
D. Heydecker and Ernest P. Goodrich, Vol. VII, Regional Survey of New York and Its Environs, 1929,
pages 142–209.

ticular emphasis on the beneficial effects of sun-light from the point of view of health and suggested as a reasonable minimum standard that every living or sleeping room should have such an amount of direct sunlight or its equivalent "as would be supplied by the sun shining for one-half hour at its maximum, or noon, intensity through windows of the prevailing

Local Street Plans

The pattern of local streets, with the subdivision of abutting lands into blocks and lots, has been too often left to an arbitrary extension of adjoining rectangular patterns, based on what has been the typical block and lot sizes in the city, or to the desires of a developer to

Fig. 8·34. Plan Showing the Overintrusive Use of Land by the Erection of Rear Buildings in Charlottenburg, Germany

dwelling-house size, facing south on the shortest day of the year." It was found that this standard could be met "in all rooms facing on streets which do not deviate more than 10° from north and south" in the latitude of New York (40° 45').

With the trend toward large-scale housing developments on large sites, including both public and private housing, it has often been possible to apply sunlight principles in the orientation of the *buildings* by placing them at angles to the existing street system without having to orient the *streets*. Where low coverage can be maintained and ample light and air provided around buildings, the exact orientation becomes of less importance.

obtain the largest possible number of lots. Planning boards are now, in many instances, obtaining better local street patterns through subdivision control, discussed in Chapter 21, Volume II, and the application of neighborhood unit principles, discussed in Chapter 13, Volume II.

In general, American cities have provided more liberal widths for local streets than have the communities in Europe. But have they not in many instances gone too far in providing wide streets? Or have they not, influenced, perhaps, by a passion for standardizing everything, lost sight of the great difference in the needs of traffic and business streets and those devoted entirely to residences, in many of which the chief consideration is the provision of decent and sanitary homes at a minimum of expense for land and improvements? The oldest cities in both Europe and America nearly always suffer from a lack of wide streets, and the cost of supplying them is so great as to be almost prohibitive. Yet too wide streets may prove to be a serious handicap in that they are likely to result in solidly built blocks of tall tenements, the rents in which are unduly high owing to the fact that extravagant street improvements must be paid for by the property. Thomas Adams expressed the opinion that the system of block dwellings found in Germany and Sweden is as much the result of too wide streets as the need of wide streets is the result of compactly built tenements. Werner Hegemann of Berlin also said, "Berlin, with her 200,000 families in one-room dwellings, is suffering from too wide, too well paved, and too highly organized roads, and from the extensive high tenement houses that seem necessarily to result from too expensive roads carried into purely dwelling-house districts." [18] Instances of overbuilding are frequently to be found in some of the much-admired German cities, an example taken from Charlottenburg being shown by Figure 8·34. While excessively wide streets may be provided in some cases, a lack of them is far more common. It is said that Paris has 102 miles of streets 98 feet or more in width, while London has but 8½ miles of streets of as great a width. Some desirable cross-sections of local streets are given in the following chapter (see page 170).

Block and Lot Layout

The customary size of the individual building lots and the manner in which they are combined into blocks determine the distance between local streets and to a certain degree their location. What, then, is the reasonable size of the building-lot units? It will of course vary with the type of use to which the lot is to be put, showing the importance of working out

[18] *Proceedings of London Town Planning Conference,* 1910, page 239.

concurrently patterns for streets and for land use.

The evil effects of arbitrary lot sizes may be illustrated by the former practices in the older sections of New York City, where the standard plot is 20 or 25 feet wide and 100 feet in depth. The width varies in the different parts of the city, but the depth of 100 feet is almost invariable. If an owner desires more than one lot, he buys several of these units. The buildings, with very few exceptions, have frontages which are multiples of this standard lot width, and only where they extend through the block from street to street is their depth more than 100 feet or such proportional part of that depth as the building laws permit to be occupied. The same sizes of lots will also be found in many other cities and even in suburban communities, where such a subdivision of land was inexcusable.

Where the same lot depth prevails in commercial, manufacturing, and residential districts, it is not surprising that certain uses will overcrowd the land, and others will be accompanied by disorderly back yards where land goes to waste and refuse and weeds collect.

Business and retail shopping districts need a larger percentage of street area, shorter blocks, more corner lots, and more space for parking than do residential districts. Apartment districts need wider streets and shorter blocks than high-class, single-family residence areas. Garden apartments need deep blocks to permit grouping of buildings around interior gardens and space for offstreet parking. Wholesale districts need deeper lots than retail districts, and industrial areas may require blocks several hundred feet wide and direct access to railroad rights of way. Variety and ingenuity are needed in planning the local street system.

There is considerable variety in the prevailing sizes of lots in different cities. A survey made in 1930 of subdivisions intended for low- or medium-cost houses showed that in cities of 500,000 or more population the average lot was 38 by 102 feet, while in cities of 50,000 to 100,000 it was 45 by 120 feet. The 50-by-100-foot lot was common, but in several cities

40 by 120 feet was a prevailing size. Only occasionally were lots 150 feet in depth found.[19]

In smaller communities there is no justification for residential lots narrower than 50 feet, and many have adopted minimum standards of 60 feet. Deeper lots are justified for individual home building than for large-scale developments which will include provision for community recreation and social activities. The man of wealth can afford to pay for a large plot to accommodate his home. When the street width, as well as the lot size, is rigidly standardized, the workman who desires a cheap home suffers a serious and unfair handicap. And it matters not whether he tries to own his own home or, as in most cases, rents one; the burden runs with the land, and if he does not pay in interest he pays in rent. The man in the low-income bracket should have the opportunity to pay for as little land as will provide the home he wishes with an insurance of sufficient light and air about it to make that home decent and healthful.

A cottage 25 or 30 feet in depth does not need a lot 100 feet deep to accommodate it. Why, then, should not the builder of such a cottage, whether it be for occupancy or rent, be able to secure a lot of suitable size and shape on which to place it? If the back yard abutting against a similar back yard on the next street were used as a garden, the case might be different. Even where there is room for them, however, gardens are seldom made, and in most cases the reduction in the cost of the site would more than offset the value of the rear garden, especially where there is space for some planting in the front or where public gardens or small parks are provided in the neighborhood. With lots of less depth the street widths could also be less, assuming always that the ordinances will prevent the intensive development of shallow lots with compactly built tenements three, four, or more stories in height.

Most of the lot subdivisions are determined by the real estate developer, who is naturally

[19] *Neighborhoods of Small Homes,* by Robert Whitten and Thomas Adams, Vol. III, Harvard City Planning Studies, Harvard University Press, Cambridge, Mass., 1931, pages 152–153.

disposed to divide each block into lots of the size that can most readily be disposed of at the time, although in many cases his purpose is to give a distinctive character to the neighborhood. Where the plots are of generous size, they can quite readily be adapted to changed conditions and other uses, but where the lot units are small, this is very difficult,

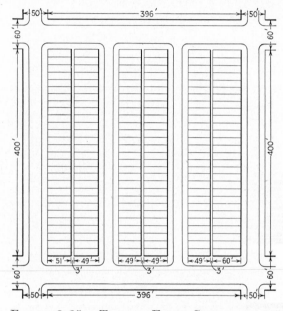

FIGURE 8·35. TYPICAL EARLY SUBDIVISION IN THE CITY OF PHILADELPHIA

A block 396 feet by 400 feet in size was subdivided to provide 168 building lots, or 46 dwellings to the acre.

owing to the fact that so many different owners must be dealt with in order to combine a number of small plots into sufficiently large units to meet the needs of the altered use of the property. The city authorities, recognizing the desire of the developer to provide lots and houses which are readily salable, are generally disposed to consent to the establishment of block dimensions which will make this possible. In Philadelphia a considerable portion of the city was originally laid out in blocks 396 by 400 feet in size, bounded by streets 50 and 60 feet wide, and, in order to provide for the single-family houses so characteristic of that city, these blocks have frequently been divided into smaller ones by introducing two additional streets 40 feet wide, resulting in the creation of

168 building plots varying from 14 to 16 feet in width and from 49 to 60 feet in depth, with passageways three feet wide separating the lots in the rear. The city ordinances prescribe a minimum width of 14 feet for any dwelling house and a minimum open space of 144 square feet for each lot, and these lots are used to the greatest allowable extent; some builders have attempted to count the rear passageway in the required open space. A typical plan of this

one of detached dwellings for one or two families.

Figure 8·37 shows how the same area might have been developed with narrower local

FIGURE 8·37. PLAN SHOWING AN ALTERNATIVE SUBDIVISION OF THE SAME TRIANGULAR AREA

Streets are 50 feet wide, with better junctions with the diagonal bounding street, lots are 50 to 60 feet wide and 80 feet deep, and a small neighborhood park is provided.

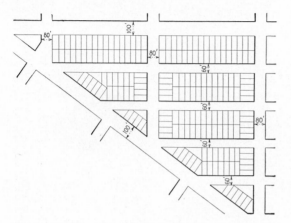

FIGURE 8·36. PLAN SHOWING A CONVENTIONAL METHOD OF SUBDIVIDING A TRIANGULAR AREA

Blocks are 200 by 700 feet and streets 60 and 80 feet wide, resulting in acute intersections with the diagonal bounding street, and providing building plots 40 feet wide and 100 feet deep.

subdivision is shown in Figure 8·35. This may be better than four- and five-story tenements on lots 25 by 100 feet housing four families on each floor, but it is a too intensive use of the land, which Philadelphia is trying to find means of correcting.

To illustrate some of the points discussed above there is shown in Figure 8·36 a street and lot plan taken from a section of one of the eastern cities of the United States, and in Figures 8·37 and 8·38 improved layouts for this same area are illustrated. As mapped, a building lot standard for the city, of 40-foot width and 100-foot depth, was used. The streets are simply a continuation of a rigid rectangular system covering the entire territory surrounding the area shown, which comprises about 25 acres, is triangular in shape, and has bounding streets 100 feet and 80 feet wide. The development contemplated was evidently

streets, elimination of acute intersections, wider lots better proportioned for detached dwellings, and an area set aside for a small park.

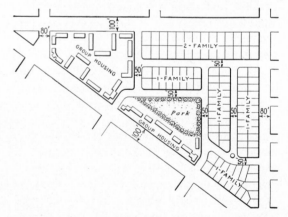

FIGURE 8·38. PLAN SHOWING A SECOND ALTERNATIVE SUBDIVISION OF THE SAME TRIANGULAR AREA

Streets are again 50 feet wide, but provision is made for variety in types of housing.

The monotony of the other plan is relieved, and a distinctive neighborhood character would be provided. A second alternative plan, based on a development that would include a combination of single-family, two-family, and group housing, is shown in Figure 8·38.

A statistical comparison of these three plans is given in Table 8. This indicates that the

TABLE 8

COMPARATIVE STATISTICS OF THE SAME AREA UNDER THREE DIFFERENT METHODS OF SUBDIVISION, AS INDICATED BY FIGURES 8·36, 8·37, AND 8·38

Item	Fig. 8·36	Fig. 8·37	Fig. 8·38
Street area, as percentage of total	24.0	23.6	16.4
Public park area, as percentage of total	0.0	5.7	7.7
Building block area, as percentage of total	76.0	70.7	75.9
Linear feet of streets	4,500	5,120	3,570
Total number of lots	202	196	216 [a]
Average area of lots, square feet	4,080	3,920	3,810 [b]

[a] Families.
[b] Per family.

advantages, described above, of the second plan could be obtained with approximately the same amount of street area and only a slight reduction in the number of lots. The same area, developed in part for rental housing in attractive groups of attached dwellings (Figure 8·38), would require much less street area and therefore lower cost for all required forms of public utilities and could accommodate an additional number of family units. Two-family dwellings would be provided with lots larger than those for the one-family dwellings.

As a community goes through a transition from acreage lots for large homes to smaller lots for more modest dwellings, special problems will arise in street layouts. In many cases dead-end, or cul-de-sac, streets have been used to develop irregular areas. Such streets are picturesque features of old cities but have been criticized as unsanitary, inconvenient, and hazardous in case of fire. Nevertheless, some writers on city planning have protested against their abolition, and it must be granted that a quiet street with but a single outlet, especially when provided with a court at its inner end about which buildings can be grouped, is a most attractive place for those who desire quiet homes. Many planning commissions require that such a street should not be over 400 feet long and should have a turnaround at its inner end with not less than a 35-foot outer radius.

Another type of solution for such an irregular area is shown in Figure 8·39.

In 1929 a new type of residential street pattern was originated for Radburn, New Jersey, already referred to as the "town for the motor age." The main highways that are regional in importance subdivide the town into "superblocks." Within these, access to the individual houses is by means of cul-de-sac streets. The

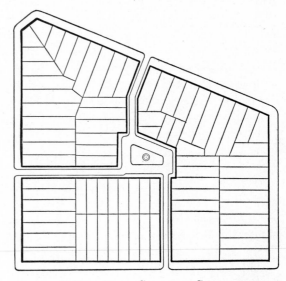

FIGURE 8·39. PLAN SHOWING SUBDIVISION OF AN IRREGULAR BLOCK BY THE CREATION OF AN INTERIOR COURT WITH A SMALL PARK AND THREE OUTLETS

houses face on park strips with footpaths which in one direction lead to the business center, and in the other direction to the school and a large park. These footpaths are carried under the thoroughfares so that children are never exposed to traffic hazards on their way to and from school. (See Figures 18·14 and 18·15, Volume II.)

Street Names and House Numbers

With the street pattern determined, it may be found that the system of street names and house numbers needs overhauling. City planners have taken an active interest in this problem in many communities. It is particularly serious where cities have grown rapidly and expanded to include former suburban communities. The engineering approach is a logical one to find a suitable solution.

The City Planning Division of the American Society of Civil Engineers formerly had a special committee on Street Names and Numbers. Although it was unable to agree on a standard system, its activities led to the presentation of a comprehensive paper on the subject by J. P. Schwada, City Engineer of Milwaukee, and a discussion by several authorities.[20] It was pointed out that the use of descriptive and characteristic street names soon becomes inadequate in large cities. Where a system of names and numbers refers to two base lines, it has been found helpful to have one approximately east and west and the other approximately north and south. Such a system works best with a rectangular street pattern but can be adapted to irregular patterns. Street names should be euphonious and easy to spell and should not duplicate names in adjoining communities. While there is often local pressure against changing long-established names, this can be overcome by public education.

Schwada referred to the systematic schemes in common use as of three general types. The first has numbered "avenues" and "streets" at right angles, a suitable layout where the city can expand in only two directions. The second, suitable where a city can be divided into quadrants, employs two central base lines and the designations N.E., N.W., S.E., and S.W., as in Washington, D. C., or prefixes the street and avenue number with the compass direction North, South, East, or West. The third substitutes word names instead of numbers for the avenues, but retains numbers for the streets, or vice versa. The names are in alphabetical sequence, using several names beginning with the same letter, if desired.

A system of street names suggested by Schwada as a suitable standard was outlined as follows:

[20] "Street Names and House Numbers," by J. P. Schwada, *Civil Engineering,* March, 1932, pages 186–189; also discussion, May, 1932, page 321, and June, 1932, pages 387–388.

Two base lines at right angles, called Main Street and Division Street.

N.E. quadrant:
Numbered avenues (N. and S.) with the prefix North; streets (E. and W.) named in alphabetical sequence with the prefix East.

S.E. quadrant:
Numbered avenues (N. and S.) with the prefix South; avenues E. and W.) named in alphabetical sequence with the prefix East.

S.W. quadrant:
Numbered streets (N. and S.) with the prefix South; avenues (E. and W.) named in alphabetical sequence with the prefix West.

N.W. quadrant:
Numbered streets (N. and S.) with the prefix North; streets (E. and W.) named in alphabetical sequence with the prefix West.

Thoroughfares extending diagonally across the city to be named Roads.

A successful solution of a difficult street-naming problem is found in the borough of Queens, New York City. When this was incorporated into the city, it contained a large number of villages, each with its own system of street names and house numbers. There were said to be about 40 Washington streets and almost as many Lincoln, Fairview, and other streets. The plan devised in 1911 provides numbered avenues generally east and west, with First Avenue on the north edge of the borough, and numbered streets generally north and south, with First Street on the west border of the borough. The change was made gradually by districts and has proved very satisfactory.

The accepted method of modern house numbering is the block system, whereby one hundred numbers are assigned to each block, odd numbers on one side and even numbers on the other. Adjustments are necessary where long and short blocks adjoin, where streets are not continuous, or where diagonal streets break up a rectangular pattern. The numbers can be assigned either by allotting one number for a definite amount of street frontage, or by use of a decimal system whereby each block front is divided into 50 equal spaces, to each of which a number is assigned.

Where streets are designated by numbers, it is customary to prefix the house number with the number of the street or avenue nearest the base line. A hyphenated number is helpful where streets or avenues may run into hundreds. Such a system has been carried out completely in the borough of Queens, already referred to, where 34-23 87th Street is located between 34th and 35th avenues, and 103-20 34th Avenue is between 103rd and 104th streets.

A very complete system of street names and house numbers by compass directions is used in Salt Lake City, where two central base streets are used. Starting at their intersection, the streets are named as follows: First North Street, Second North Street; First East Street, Second East Street; etc., around the compass. The house numbers, on a decimal block system, are followed by the compass direction from the base streets. For example, 728 East on Seventh South Street is seven blocks south of the center and 7.28 blocks east of the north-south base street.[21]

Selected References

Adams, Thomas: *The Design of Residential Areas,* Vol. VI, Harvard City Planning Studies, Harvard University Press, Cambridge, Mass., 1934.

Barnett, Joseph: "Express Highway Planning in Metropolitan Areas" (with discussion), *Transactions of the American Society of Civil Engineers,* Vol. 112 (1947), pages 636–700.

Goodrich, Ernest P.: "The Design of the Street System in Relation to Vehicular Traffic," *Proceedings of the Fourteenth National Conference on City Planning,* Springfield, Mass., 1922, pages 84–103.

Heydecker, Wayne D., and Ernest P. Goodrich: *Sunlight and Daylight for Urban Areas,* Monograph Two in Vol. VII, Regional Survey of New York and Its Environs, 1929. Distributed by Regional Plan Association, Inc., New York.

Hilberseimer, L.: *The New City,* Paul Theobald, Chicago, 1944.

Malcher, Fritz: *The Steadyflow Traffic System,* Vol. IX, Harvard City Planning Studies, Harvard University Press, Cambridge, Mass., 1935.

[21] See statement by Richard R. Lyman, *Transactions of the American Society of Civil Engineers,* Vol. 94 (1930), page 1325.

Nolen, John, and Henry V. Hubbard: *Parkways and Land Values,* Vol. XI, Harvard City Planning Studies, Harvard University Press, Cambridge, Mass., 1937.

"Planning for City Traffic" (a series of papers by different authors), *The Annals,* Vol. CXXXIII, September, 1927, The American Academy of Political and Social Science, Philadelphia.

Rey, A.-Augustin, Justin Pidoux, and Charles Barde: *La science des plans de villes,* Dunod, Paris, 1929. (Includes a study of orientation based on sunlight.)

Questions

1. What are the general principles to be followed in laying out a street plan of a city?
2. Give a brief description of the New York City plan of 1811. What factors influenced its design?
3. What was the principal contribution of each of the following to the development of street patterns: Georges Eugene Haussmann, Christopher Wren, Charles L'Enfant, Daniel H. Burnham?
4. What are the advantages and disadvantages of a rectangular or gridiron street system?
5. Give examples of circumferential highways, existing and proposed. What, in each case, is their main function.
6. What is meant by an "organic" street plan? Give examples.
7. What types of irregularity in pattern have been purposely introduced in street plans, and what is the justification of each?
8. What are some of the ways in which topography affects street planning?
9. Sketch the history of parkways and describe their place in a city-wide street pattern.
10. What is meant by the modern expressway? How should such routes be located in urban areas?
11. How have sunlight studies been used in determining street patterns?
12. What are the differences in local street plans suitable for a business, an apartment, and a one-family dwelling district?
13. What are some of the faults of typical subdivision plans in which city planning principles have been ignored?
14. How could the system of street names and house numbers in use in your town be improved?

9

STREET TRAFFIC AND DESIGN

THE PURPOSE OF AN ORDINARY CITY STREET IS twofold: to provide light and air and afford access to the abutting property, and to provide accommodation for such traffic as may pass through it. As was pointed out in the preceding chapter, some modern expressways are exempt from the first purpose. The design of a street will depend upon its relation to the adopted street pattern and its special requirements for either abutting property or traffic. The amount of traffic which may be classified as through traffic, that is, having both origin and destination elsewhere, will vary with the importance of the street in the main pattern for the community. Business traffic is likely to take the most direct route, while passenger-car traffic is inclined to take that which is most agreeable. Many streets are used also for the mass transportation of persons in public vehicles, and the problems which they create have been discussed in Chapter 7, "The Local Transit System" (see pages 99 to 106).

The relative amount of local and through traffic will vary greatly in different streets, and even in the same street, from day to day, according to weather and other conditions. This mixed traffic is a fruitful source of controversy, especially where the cost of the first pavement or renewals, or any part thereof, is assessed against the abutting property, the owners of which protest against paying for road improvements for the accommodation of what they call "alien traffic."

Automobile Registration and Relation to Traffic

In 1895 there were only four automobiles in the United States, or one for every 17,395,000

persons. By 1900 there were 8,000 motor vehicles, or one for every 9,512 persons. In 1905 the ratio was one motor vehicle to 1,062 persons, and five years later it was one to 197 persons. The curve in Figure 9·1 shows the trend

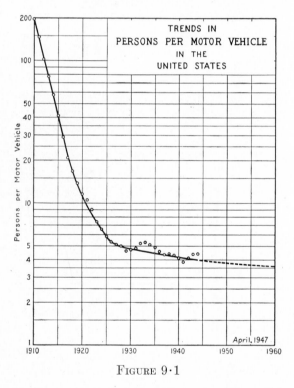

FIGURE 9·1

of this development, which was quite regular from 1910 to 1928; since then, the depression and World War II somewhat obscured the regular progression of this trend, but it appears that in the next 10 or 15 years there will be a motor vehicle for each 3½ to four persons in the United States. This means about one for each family.

The ratio will vary in different cities, and each should make its own study. If a relationship can then be established between registration and traffic, it becomes possible to make a reasonable prediction of future traffic based upon population estimates. The New York Regional Plan found this the best of three

they did not require any change in the lines based on the original data.

The same report established that maximum hourly traffic over arterial highways at approximately the center of each county in the region

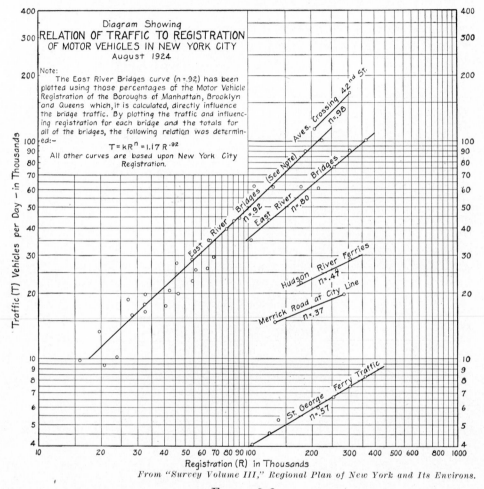

FIGURE 9·2

methods developed for predicting the future traffic on the main highways of the region. Their report plotted daily traffic as a function of registration for different types of highways and found that the daily traffic varied between the 0.37th power and the 0.98th power of the registration.[1] (See Figure 9·2.) The Regional Plan Association has since plotted later traffic figures on this same diagram, but found that

varied with the motor-vehicle registration in each county in accordance with the formula:

$$\text{Traffic} = (\text{Registration})^{3/4} \qquad (1)$$

This relationship was used in the following proportion, from which estimates were made of the total arterial traffic which might cross each county in 1965:

$$\frac{\text{Traffic in 1965}}{\text{Traffic in 1922}} = \frac{(\text{Registration in 1965})^{3/4}}{(\text{Registration in 1922})^{3/4}} \qquad (2)$$

The same procedure can be followed in a study of future traffic in any community.

[1] *Highway Traffic*, by Harold M. Lewis, in consultation with Ernest P. Goodrich, Vol. III, Regional Survey of New York and Its Environs, 1927, pages 104-113.

Growth in Vehicular Traffic

The growth in urban vehicular traffic has resulted not only from the greater movement

roads, trolleys, and pedestrians using the Hudson River ferries from New Jersey.

The growth in vehicular movement into southern Manhattan over this period is shown

TABLE 9

MEANS OF TRANSPORTATION USED BY PERSONS ENTERING MANHATTAN SOUTH OF 61ST STREET DURING 24 HOURS ON A TYPICAL BUSINESS DAY, 1924, 1932, AND 1940 [a]

Facility Used	1924		1932		1940	
	Number	Percentage	Number	Percentage	Number	Percentage
Rapid transit	1,530,716	65.4	1,751,705	64.9	2,195,483	65.8
Railroads	135,550	5.7	139,061	5.2	162,537	4.9
Motor vehicles	341,651	14.6	556,524	20.6	790,708	23.8
Trolleys and pedestrians	334,792	14.3	250,060	9.3	182,471	5.5
Total	2,342,709	100.0	2,697,350	100.0	3,331,199	100.0

[a] From *Traffic and Parking Study*, Regional Plan Association, Inc., December, 1942, page 9.

TABLE 10

SOUTHBOUND TRAFFIC ON AVENUES CROSSING 59TH STREET, MANHATTAN, ON A TYPICAL BUSINESS DAY IN JUNE, 1939 (BASED ON 16-HOUR COUNTS) [a]

	Estimated 24-hour Traffic, One-Way				Maximum Hour, All Types
	Passenger Cars	Trucks	Buses	Total	
First Avenue	12,830	4,510	12	17,352	1,309: 4– 5 P.M.
Second Avenue	9,520	1,025	5	10,550	734: 3– 4 P.M.
Park Avenue	28,300	310	224	28,834	2,488: 9–10 A.M.
Fifth Avenue	8,910	110	998	10,018	663: 8– 9 A.M.
Seventh Avenue	11,280	613	16	11,909	964: 9–10 A.M.
Broadway and Eighth Avenue [b]	18,358	2,050	752	21,160	2,139: 8– 9 A.M.
Eleventh Avenue	8,180	2,330	22	10,532	1,326: 8– 9 A.M.
Total, all avenues [c]	154,308	22,259	2,183	178,750	13,315: 9–10 A.M.

[a] From "Significant Trends in Highway Traffic in the New York Region," *Information Bulletin* 10, Regional Plan Association, Inc., December 12, 1932, page 11.

[b] All southbound traffic to Broadway routed through Eighth Avenue to West 58th Street, except cars from Central Park between 8 and 9:30 A.M. and certain buses between noon and 1 P.M.

[c] Total for 17 avenues, figures for only seven of which are given in this table; does not include through traffic on West Side Elevated Highway.

of persons and goods in our cities, but also from a diversion from other means of transportation. The extent of this diversion in the daily passenger movement into southern Manhattan, New York City, is shown in Table 9. It is indicated that in a 16-year period the proportion of persons entering by motor vehicles increased from 14.6 per cent to 23.8 per cent, this gain coming from diversions from rail-

by Figure 9·3. While the total movement from all directions increased about 80 per cent, that from New Jersey, encouraged by the construction of the Holland and Lincoln tunnels, increased 191 per cent. The composition of this traffic in 1932, as it crossed 59th Street on typical avenues, is shown by Table 10.

Cordon counts made in Los Angeles by the Automobile Club of Southern California in

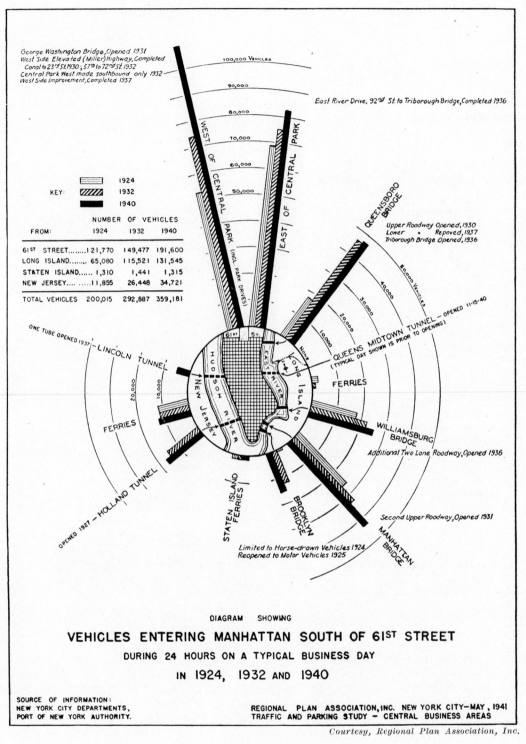

George Washington Bridge, Opened 1931
West Side Elevated (Miller) Highway, Completed
Canal to 23rd St. 1930; 57th to 72nd St. 1932
Central Park West made southbound only 1932
West Side Improvement, Completed 1937

East River Drive, 92nd St. to Triborough Bridge, Completed 1936

KEY:
▦ 1924
▨ 1932
■ 1940

QUEENSBORO BRIDGE
Upper Roadway Opened, 1930
Lower   "   Repaved, 1937
Triborough Bridge Opened, 1936

NUMBER OF VEHICLES

FROM:	1924	1932	1940
61ST STREET........	121,770	149,477	191,600
LONG ISLAND........	65,080	115,521	131,545
STATEN ISLAND......	1,310	1,441	1,315
NEW JERSEY....	11,855	26,448	34,721
TOTAL VEHICLES	200,015	292,887	359,181

ONE TUBE OPENED 1937 - LINCOLN TUNNEL

QUEENS MIDTOWN TUNNEL - OPENED 11-15-40
(TYPICAL DAY SHOWN IS PRIOR TO OPENING)

FERRIES

FERRIES

OPENED 1927 - HOLLAND TUNNEL

WILLIAMSBURG BRIDGE
Additional Two Lane Roadway, Opened 1936

STATEN ISLAND FERRIES

BROOKLYN BRIDGE
Limited to Horse-drawn Vehicles 1924
Reopened to Motor Vehicles 1925

MANHATTAN BRIDGE
Second Upper Roadway, Opened 1931

DIAGRAM SHOWING

VEHICLES ENTERING MANHATTAN SOUTH OF 61ST STREET

DURING 24 HOURS ON A TYPICAL BUSINESS DAY

IN 1924, 1932 AND 1940

SOURCE OF INFORMATION:
NEW YORK CITY DEPARTMENTS,
PORT OF NEW YORK AUTHORITY.

REGIONAL PLAN ASSOCIATION, INC. NEW YORK CITY—MAY, 1941
TRAFFIC AND PARKING STUDY - CENTRAL BUSINESS AREAS

Courtesy, Regional Plan Association, Inc.

FIGURE 9·3

1929 and 1936 showed the following significant trends for a 16-hour weekday, 6 A.M. to 10 P.M.[2]

	PERCENTAGE GAIN
Entering central business district	9.1
Entering at boundaries of outer congested district	17.1
Entering at boundaries of residential district	29.0
Entering at boundaries of suburban district	54.9

By comparing counts made by other agencies in 1923, 1939, and 1941, it is possible to obtain a picture of trends at certain identical points in downtown Los Angeles over about the same period of time as that covered by the New York figures given above. Table 11 shows these figures reduced to a basis of 12 hours, 7 A.M. to 7 P.M., on a weekday.

sections which handled the greatest number of vehicles in Detroit in 1936 are of interest: [3]

INTERSECTION	NUMBER OF VEHICLES
Dexter, Grand Boulevard and Grand River	87,734
Grand Boulevard and Second Boulevard	75,619
Grand Boulevard and Woodward Avenue	75,043
Grand River and Warren Avenue	72,037
Grand River and Livernois	68,241
Forest and Woodward Avenue	65,642
Grand Boulevard and Hamilton	63,969
Grand River and Vernor	61,503
Grand River, Forest and Fourteenth	60,654
Second and Warren	59,081

Street Capacities

The vehicular capacity of a street is its capacity for handling moving vehicles, but this is

TABLE 11

TRAFFIC TRENDS ON CERTAIN LOS ANGELES STREETS, 1923 TO 1941

Location	Vehicles Entering Business District 7 A.M. to 7 P.M. on a Weekday			Percentage Gain, 1923 to 1941
	1923 [a]	1939 [b]	1941 [c]	
From northeast				
Broadway at Sunset Boulevard	7,337	5,370 [d]	7,530	2.6
Figueroa Street at Sunset Boulevard	5,946	8,280	11,700	97.0
From northwest				
Sunset Boulevard at Figueroa Street	7,018	9,620	12,490	78.0
Temple Street at Figueroa Street	4,879	6,840	8,660	77.5
Pico Street at Figueroa Street	6,544	8,570	7,450	13.9
From southeast				
Eighth Street at Los Angeles Street	6,052	7,510	6,890	13.8
Sixth Street at Los Angeles Street	3,795	5,950	6,450	70.0
Third Street at Los Angeles Street	4,638	6,840	6,790	46.4
First Street at Los Angeles Street	5,779	6,420	6,280	8.7

[a] Based on 11-hour counts by Board of Public Utilities, Nov., 1923. *A Major Street Plan for Los Angeles*, May, 1924, page 35.

[b] From *Report of Traffic and Transportation Survey*, Transportation Engineering Board, City of Los Angeles, 1938–1939, page 71.

[c] Based on 20-hour counts in survey by Regional Planning Commission, County of Los Angeles. *Downtown Los Angeles Parking Study*, Downtown Business Men's Association, 1945, Plate IV. Of total, 85.2 per cent entered between 7 A.M. and 7 P.M.

[d] Part of traffic diverted to new parallel street.

As indicative of the magnitude of the traffic problem in large American cities just before World War II, the following figures for the 24-hour traffic flows through the ten street inter-

not capable of precise measurement. It is the custom to state capacity in the number of vehicles which can pass a given point in a fixed period of time, generally in one hour. But streets can carry overloads which increase driv-

[2] *Traffic Survey, Los Angeles Metropolitan Area*, Automobile Club of Southern California, 1937, pages 38–41.

[3] From *Street Traffic, City of Detroit, 1936–1937*, Michigan State Highway Department, page 33.

ing hazards and may so slow down the speed of vehicles that, even though a large number are handled, the efficiency of the street is greatly curtailed. A capacity which approaches, but does not exceed, the critical point at which loss in efficiency occurs is the one that should be used in highway design.

The basic formulas for the capacity of a single lane of roadway are:

$$C = \frac{5,280V}{p} = \frac{3,600v}{p} \qquad (3)$$

where C is the number of vehicles per lane per hour; V, the running velocity of vehicles, in miles per hour; v, the running velocity of ve-

Several different attempts have been made to develop theoretical curves or formulas, taking into account such other factors as braking distance, reaction time, and coefficient of friction. The Regional Plan of New York and Its Environs was a pioneer in these studies, and most of the later studies followed similar lines.[4] The Regional Plan also reported observations of the number of vehicles per lane per hour under different conditions and found that observed capacities occasionally exceed the theoretical limits, but that intolerable congestion is often experienced before those limits are reached. In general, the curves developed show capacity increasing quite rapidly as running

TABLE 12

VARIOUS DETERMINATIONS OF THE HOURLY CAPACITY OF A SINGLE LANE OF VEHICLES WITH UNINTERRUPTED MOVEMENT [a]

Maximum Capacity, in Vehicles per Hour	Speed, in Miles per Hour	Assumed Conditions	Source
3,320	20.8	Minimum spacing of individual cars	R. F. Kelker, Jr.
2,800	34.5	. . . .	A. N. Johnson
2,640	15.	. . . .	A. N. Johnson
2,600	23.5	. . . .	Regional Planning Commission, Los Angeles, Calif.
2,430	20.7	Average group spacings	R. F. Kelker, Jr.
2,264	15	"Emergency stop" spacing; half four-wheel brakes and half two-wheel brakes	Highway Research Board
2,045	16.5	Four-wheel brakes on all cars	Highway Research Board
1,969	22	"Ideal" conditions	Highway Research Board
1,880	15	Average group spacings	Regional Plan of New York and Its Environs
1,852	24.9	Average spacing of all vehicles	R. F. Kelker, Jr.

[a] From "Use and Capacity of City Streets," by Hawley S. Simpson, *Transactions of the American Society of Civil Engineers*, Vol. 99 (1934), page 1016.

hicles, in feet per second; and p, the average distance, in feet, center to center of moving vehicles. Where a vehicle is subject to frequent stops due to traffic crossing at grade, capacity is greatly reduced over that of a street permitting uninterrupted movement. For such interrupted movement the capacity of a lane of traffic will be:

$$C = \frac{3,600d}{(t_r + t_h)p} \qquad (4)$$

where d is the distance traveled between stops, in feet; t_r, the time of motion, in seconds; and t_h, the time of halt, in seconds.

velocity increases until a peak, or maximum, is reached; as velocity increases beyond that point, capacity will fall off. The variations in this maximum capacity and the point at which it would occur, as worked out by various authorities for various assumed conditions, and assembled by Hawley S. Simpson, are shown in Table 12.

It is interesting to compare these theoretical maxima with some of the observed maximum hourly rates compiled by Simpson for certain

[4] See *Highway Traffic*, Vol. III, Regional Survey of New York and Its Environs, 1927, pages 82–88.

points where traffic was moving without interruption.[5] These are given in Table 13.

Later observations have yielded still higher figures. For example, on U. S. Route 1, opposite the Newark Airport in New Jersey, traffic has flowed in a single lane at the rate of 2,700 vehicles per hour over a 20-minute period.[6] O. K. Normann stated in 1946 that lane ca-

type of traffic, roadway width, type of pavement, and interference from trolleys, columns, or other obstructions. Where traffic lights favor movement in one direction, one unobstructed lane may accommodate 750 vehicles per hour, but in the cross streets the lane capacity may be only 300 vehicles per hour. A committee of the Institute of Traffic Engineers found that

TABLE 13

OBSERVED RATES OF TRAFFIC FLOW PER AVERAGE LANE, ONE DIRECTION

Location	Number of Lanes	Maximum Hourly Rates for Period of					
		20 sec.	1 min.	5 min.	10 min.	30 min.	1 hr.
Baltimore-Washington Highway	1			1,968			
Lake Shore Drive, Chicago	2	2,070	1,830		1,392	1,365	1,349
Superior-Detroit Bridge, Cleveland	2½			1,958	1,874	1,699	1,557
East Grand Boulevard, Detroit	1		1,800		1,404	1,200	
New York City							
Holland Tunnel	2					1,253	
Queensboro Bridge	3					1,482	
Manhattan Bridge	2					1,300	

pacities over a full hourly period had, as far as was then known, exceeded 2,000 vehicles per hour at only two locations and that all reports of movement in excess of 2,200 vehicles per hour had proved to be incorrect. He referred to "a round figure of 2,000 passenger cars per lane per hour as the maximum under ideal conditions." [7]

From all this, it appears that the comfortable capacity of an uninterrupted lane of traffic may be somewhere between 1,200 and 1,500 vehicles per hour. On a parkway for "pleasure" traffic, a maximum of 800 under normal conditions is desirable, although under peak loads considerably more can be carried.

With grade crossings, the practical capacity for design purposes will be determined by the efficiency of the intersections or the timing of the traffic lights. It will vary also with the

the practical lane capacity for the center lanes of a major business street is 700 vehicles per hour.[8]

Typical Cross-sections of Streets

The predominant factor in determining the cross-section of an ordinary city street should be the traffic demands which its roadway will have to meet, as the greater proportion of its width is devoted to its roadway. Vehicles move in lanes, and where parking is permitted this also occurs in lanes. The sum of the widths of the lanes required for moving and parked vehicles is the width for which the roadway should be designed. To this would be added adequate sidewalks, and grass plots where suitable, to get the total cross-section. Heavy trucks require wider lanes than passenger cars; fast-moving traffic needs more "elbow room" than slow traffic; a parked vehicle can occupy a narrower lane than a moving vehicle. Widening a roadway is of little use unless a full additional lane will be proveded. Yet these rather obvious points have often been neglected in street design.

[5] From "Use and Capacity of City Streets," by Hawley S. Simpson, Transactions of the American Society of Civil Engineers, Vol. 99 (1934), page 1017.

[6] Traffic Engineering Handbook, Institute of Traffic Engineers and National Conservation Bureau, 1941, page 180.

[7] "The Capacity of a Traffic Lane," by O. K. Normann, Chief, Section of Traffic Operations, U. S. Public Roads Administration, 1946 Proceedings, Institute of Traffic Engineers, page 136.

[8] Ibid.

It is the usual practice of cities to fix by ordinance the roadway and sidewalk widths of all streets, and the roadway has commonly been given a width of approximately half the total street width, the remaining half being divided between the two sidewalks. In New York City the Board of Estimate and Apportionment, by a resolution of April 8, 1926, fixed the following widths:

STREET WIDTH, FEET	ROADWAY WIDTH, AS PERCENTAGE OF STREET WIDTH
Less than 20	100, less curbs
20 to 50, inclusive	60
55 to 75, inclusive	40, + 10 feet
80 to 140, inclusive	80, − 20 feet

In each case the balance of the street width, after deducting the roadway, is divided with two equal sidewalks. For a normal 60-foot street this rule gives a 34-foot roadway and two 13-foot sidewalks; for a 100-foot street, a 60-foot roadway and two 20-foot sidewalks. There was obviously no attempt to correlate roadway widths with the required widths of traffic lanes.

Many smaller cities have followed a simpler rule, designating three-fifths of the total width for pavement and one-fifth on each side for sidewalk and planting strips. These cities usually have streets 60 feet wide, so that the standard pavement is 36 feet wide, with six-foot planting strips, five-foot sidewalks, and one foot between each sidewalk and the property line in residence districts. In business districts the entire space between curb and property line is generally used for the sidewalk. This rule has the advantage of simplicity but often gives more total pavement than is necessary in residential districts, while not providing sufficient pavement width for heavily traveled streets.

In Milwaukee, which may be taken as a typical midwestern city, no fixed rules were in effect in 1947, but residential streets are normally 60 feet wide and a 30-foot roadway has usually been provided therein. In the remaining 15-foot sidewalk areas a six-foot sidewalk pavement is usually placed two feet from the property line, leaving a tree border of seven feet. In outlying business districts 66-foot rights of way have been subdivided into a 50-foot roadway and two eight-foot sidewalks, but such sidewalks have proved very narrow. In new subdivisions the city is trying to provide 36-foot roadways in residential areas and 60-foot roadways in business districts.[9]

Establishing standards for the subdivision of street widths is undoubtedly desirable, rather than leaving these details to be fixed according to the whim of the developer or the notions of

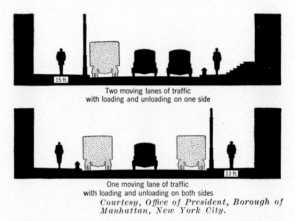

Two moving lanes of traffic
with loading and unloading on one side

One moving lane of traffic
with loading and unloading on both sides

Courtesy, Office of President, Borough of Manhattan, New York City.

FIGURE 9·4. CROSS-SECTIONS SHOWING TRAFFIC CONDITIONS ON TYPICAL 60-FOOT CROSSTOWN STREETS OF MANHATTAN, NEW YORK CITY

Upper drawing shows a 30-foot roadway, and lower drawing a 34-foot roadway.

the engineer in each particular case; but the standards adopted have not often been the result of a careful study of the needs of traffic of various classes. Before the days of intensive automobile traffic, eight feet was considered sufficient roadway width for the free movement of one line of vehicles, and many streets were constructed with pavements 32 feet wide to provide for two lines of traffic in each direction. Sometimes seven feet was assumed to be sufficient for a parked or slowly moving vehicle next to the curb, and the pavement was made only 30 feet wide. These pavements are generally inadequate today, as is shown by Figure 9·4, which indicates that either 30-foot or 34-foot roadways provide only one moving lane where large trucks are permitted to load and unload at each curb.

[9] Letter from J. P. Schwada, City Engineer, Milwaukee, December 22, 1947.

John H. Bateman has listed the following ranges of practicable roadway widths for city streets without street railway tracks, based on 10-foot moving lanes and eight-foot lanes for parking parallel to the curb: [10]

	FEET
Residential streets, land service only	26 to 40
Residential streets, through traffic	36 to 60
Retail business streets, primarily local	40 to 60
Retail business streets, through traffic	56 to 80
Industrial streets, minimum	60
Arterial streets	56 to 112

Provision for an odd number of lanes of moving traffic is not justified on urban highways, as the middle lane would be obliged to accommodate vehicles moving in both directions, and the interference would be so great that it would be of little use. However, pavement widths of 38 feet, which were thought to have an "extra lane" 20 years ago, are now considered a good width to provide two parking lanes and two moving lanes for higher-speed traffic. A street railway track will require a minimum width of nine or 10 feet. The New York City rules, quoted above, require not less than 30 feet where there is a single-track railway, thus allowing for exceptionally wide vehicles such as moving vans, ice wagons, or coal trucks standing at the curb without interfering with the free movement of cars. The space required for double-track railways is about 19 feet, and a single line of vehicles on each side would require a total roadway width of at least 35 feet, and two lines of vehicles 55 feet. The New York ordinance requires not less than 40 feet where there are double-track railways. This might be considered a minimum but is likely to slow up traffic almost to the point of congestion.

Although in nearly all cities there are some streets with roadways inadequate for the traffic which they attract, there are a far greater number with roadways that are much wider than required. This means a needless expense to the owners of the abutting property for the original improvement and a serious burden for the city in maintenance, repairs, and renewals.

[10] *Introduction to Highway Engineering,* by John H. Bateman, John Wiley & Sons, New York, Fourth Edition, 1942, page 68.

Street traffic gradually increases as the abutting property is improved, and the general business of the locality increases. While it is wise to lay out streets of sufficient width to permit as intensive development of the adjoining property as the ordinances will allow, there is no good reason for the laying and maintenance of an area of pavement which is obviously greater than will be required for some years to come.

In a single-family residential district, a street 60 feet in width will not need a roadway 30 feet wide unless it is called upon to accommodate a considerable amount of through traffic. Twenty feet or even less will in most cases be sufficient for the initial pavement, provided curbs, if used, are set back to conform to such ultimate width as may be required. (See cross-sections in Figure 9·10.) This saving of 10 feet in the width of the pavement will mean a substantial decrease in the burden of assessment for the first improvement, probably as much as $100 for each 25 feet of frontage. It may be that additional roadway width will not be required during the lifetime of the first pavement or even of two pavements, sometimes not at all. When more space is needed, the curb can be set back, and the sewer inlets can be readjusted. When there is such a reduction in width, the street appurtenances back of the curb, such as lamp posts, fire hydrants, and trees, can be so located as to conform with the ultimate position of the curb, so that it may be set back when necessary with a minimum of expense and disturbance of existing conditions. Such a policy, in case of a reduction of 10 feet in width and a pavement cost of $4 per square yard, would save the property owners on a block 700 feet long about $3,100 in the first cost of their pavement, and the city would save a substantial sum annually for maintenance. When a widening of the roadway is required, the cost of the additional pavement can properly be assessed upon the abutting property.

It is impossible to estimate with any degree of accuracy the width of sidewalks which will be needed. In ordinary streets pedestrian traffic varies greatly with the seasons and at different times of day, and in most cases there is an excess of sidewalk space which can advantageously be used for grass, trees, and other planting, a stone, concrete, or brick walk four or five feet wide being all that is required. In retail shopping streets, however, more generous sidewalks are needed, varying from a minimum of 10 feet to 25 feet in large cities. (See cross-sections in Figures 9·6 to 9·10.)

In such narrow thoroughfares as Hohe Strasse in Cologne and Kalver Straat in Amsterdam, the busiest shopping streets of these cities, the pedestrians use the roadways as well as the sidewalks, especially in the evenings. In the financial and office districts of London, New York, and other large cities the same use of the entire street by pedestrians is often seen during the busy hours of the day, when vehicular traffic is practically excluded. Where there is special need of sidewalk capacity on narrow streets, the roadway is sometimes reduced to a width which will accommodate but a single vehicle, and the traffic is confined to a single direction. It is apparent, therefore, that no general principles can be laid down as to the relative amount of roadway and sidewalk space which will be required. The best that can be done is to proportion the space according to anticipated needs, with some latitude, where possible, for future adjustment of the curb line to suit changing conditions; but it would be unreasonable to provide for the throngs that are likely to flock to a certain street on one or two days in the year, as, for example, for the crowds on Fifth Avenue, New York, on a pleasant Easter Sunday (Figure 9·5).

Exceptionally wide streets, of which there are some in every large city, present special problems. It is impossible to formulate any but the most general principles governing the subdivision of such streets. Not only do the conditions vary in each particular case, but also there is a great opportunity for the exercise of personal judgment and taste. A few examples of the treatment adopted for a number of such streets in some of the great cities of the world are shown in Figures 9·6 and 9·7. The simple dignity of the Avenue des Champs Elysees, 261 feet wide with its single roadway 114 feet in width, renders it one of the most notable streets in the world, if it is not indeed the most notable. It was a daring treatment,

however, which could only be successful in such a street, with the spacious Place de la Concorde at one end and the great Arc de Triomphe at the other. Streets of this expectional width are usually divided into two or three roadways, one of which is commonly restricted to passenger cars. The Detroit superhighways were proposed as a joint solution of the traffic and transit problems in the Detroit metropolitan

New York Herald Tribune Photo.

FIGURE 9·5. FIFTH AVENUE, NEW YORK CITY, ON AN EASTER SUNDAY

Street is 100 feet wide, with a 55-foot roadway and 22½-foot sidewalks. The Easter parade is permitted to use the full right of way.

area; many miles of 204-foot right of way have been acquired, but the transit proposals had been only partly carried out in 1947.

The Grand Boulevard and Concourse in the borough of The Bronx, New York City, in spite of its pretentious name, offers an example of a great excess of roadway capacity with an almost complete absence of the decorative features which its width would suggest and permit. A plan for its rearrangement has been carried out, but there is still a conspicuous lack of "boulevard" features. Figure 9·8 shows how slight was the change.

Street railway tracks were originally located in many of these boulevards but are fast being replaced by either motor buses or trolley coaches, free-wheeled vehicles obtaining power from an overhead trolley but able to maneuver within the roadway. They eliminate many of the objectionable features of the old street cars in heavy-traffic thoroughfares. An instance of an elevated railway in the central portion of a very wide street, with space for planting on each side of the structure, has been noted in Chapter 7 (see page 93 and Figure 7·1).

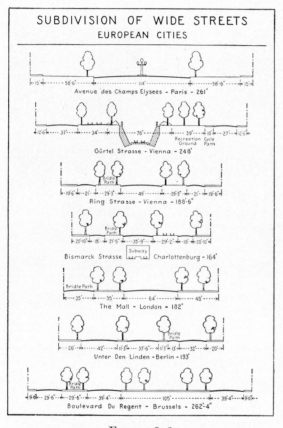

FIGURE 9·6

Most of the arterial highway system will consist of streets of more modest dimensions than the wide streets shown in Figures 9·6 and 9·7, where the objective of creating an impressive street which would be lined with monumental buildings frequently took precedence over the desire to meet an expected traffic load. The standards of width for ordinary primary and secondary thoroughfares have been increasing. As early as 1875 a Prussian law relating to the streets of Berlin provided that the main streets should be 95 feet or more in width, secondary thoroughfares from 65 to 95

feet, and local streets from 40 to 65 feet. Another standard was set for secondary German cities, which prescribed 85 to 120 feet as the width of main thoroughfares, 50 to 80 feet for secondary thoroughfares, and 35 to 48 feet for local streets.[11]

Early in the twentieth century the Royal Commission on London Traffic recommended the following width standards: main avenues 140 feet, first-class arterial streets 100 feet, second-class arterial streets 80 feet, third-class streets 60 feet, fourth-class streets 40 to 60 feet. These widths then seemed quite generous,

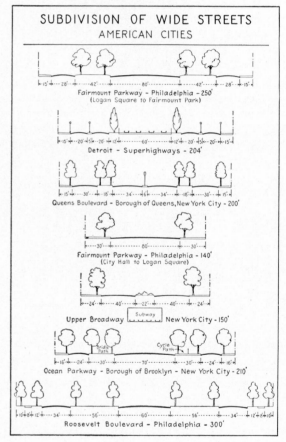

FIGURE 9·7

but justified by the handicap to London of its inadequate highways. In the 1943 County of London Plan of the London County Council, it was proposed that a "ring road" for fast

[11] *Modern City Planning and Maintenance*, by Frank Koester, McBride, Nast and Company, New York, 1914, page 58.

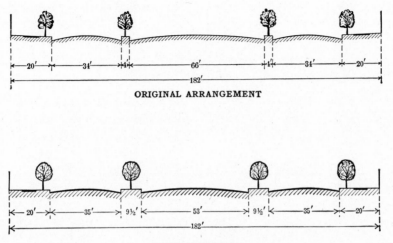

ORIGINAL ARRANGEMENT

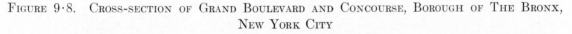

REARRANGEMENT

FIGURE 9·8. CROSS-SECTION OF GRAND BOULEVARD AND CONCOURSE, BOROUGH OF THE BRONX, NEW YORK CITY

An example of excessive provision for roadways on a very wide street to the exclusion of landscape features. The rearrangement corrected this in part, but might well have gone farther.

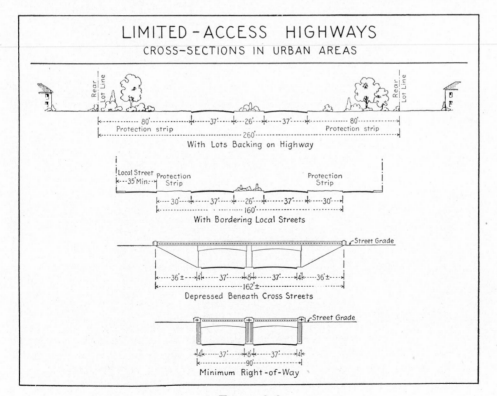

FIGURE 9·9

traffic should have a right of way varying from 130 to 200 feet in width.

In the 1930's and 1940's state highway departments in the United States were definitely

A parkway, which is really an arterial highway for passenger vehicles located in a strip of park land, will naturally have a varying right of way, depending on the topography and

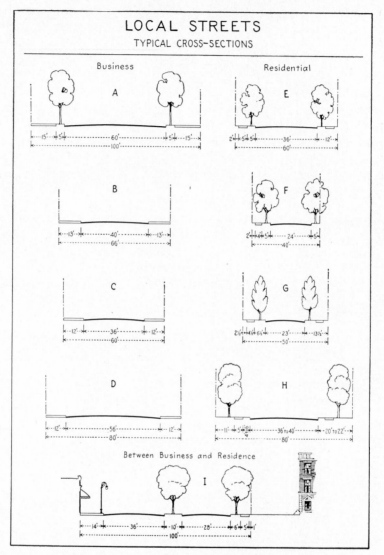

FIGURE 9·10. CROSS-SECTIONS OF LOCAL STREETS

Business streets:
A—Primary: Montclair, N. J., Master Plan
B—66-foot: New London, Conn., Plan
C—60-foot: New Rochelle, N. Y., Comprehensive Plan
D—80-foot: Montclair, N. J., Master Plan
    I—Boundary street between residence and

Residential streets:
E—60-foot: New Rochelle, N. Y., Comprehensive Plan
F—40-foot: suitable for low density development
G—50-foot: Roland Park, Baltimore, Md.
H—80-foot: Montclair, N. J., Master Plan
business: Montclair, N. J., Master Plan

"raising their sights" for widths of main routes in open country and were planning rights of way 150, 200, and up to 300 feet wide where 66, 80, or 100 feet had formerly been the practice.

the suitability of the adjoining lands for park treatment or uses. In general, such a thoroughfare should have a *minimum* right of way 400 feet in width. Where the topography is irregular, separate roadways at different levels for each direction of traffic are desirable, the distance between the roadways varying with the conditions. Even on level stretches, a division strip between opposing traffic lanes is recommended to insure safety of driving.

The modern limited-access highway is a special type described in some detail in the preceding chapter (pages 147 to 149). While it may, in developed areas, be bordered by local streets, such streets are not parts of the arterial route, as they would have no connection to it except through main intersecting highways. In rural areas rights of way of 200-foot to 300-foot widths are suitable for limited-access highways, but in urban or suburban areas this may be reduced to save land costs, as illustrated in Figure 9·9. Traffic lanes, because of the high speeds to be accommodated, should be not less than 12 feet, with a total of 37 feet for a three-lane, one-way roadway.[12]

The design of local streets is influenced by subdivision control,[13] supplemented by such standards as may be established by the engineering department of the municipality. In addition, master plans prepared by planning commissions frequently include suggested cross-sections of local streets as a guide to a developer. Some of these, for both business and residential streets, are shown in Figure 9·10.

Treatment of Intersections

From the discussion of roadway capacities above it is evident that the intersections are the critical points, and where they are at grade they reduce the street capacities to less than half what they otherwise would be. They are also the most dangerous portion of the highway system. Methods of increasing the capacities of intersections and making them safer are therefore of great importance.

Where several streets intersect and sufficient area is available to lay out a large traffic circle, a gyratory system of traffic movement has sometimes been employed. Under this scheme all entering traffic moves counterclockwise,

[12] See "The Freeway, a Modern Highway for General Traffic in Metropolitan Areas," *Information Bulletin* 33, Regional Plan Association, Inc., December 14, 1936, pages 3-7.

[13] See Volume II: Chapter 21 and Appendix C.

without stopping, along the circle to the desired exit, weaving through other traffic which entered first and turns off at a nearer exit. Such a treatment of urban intersections has been fully described by Raymond Unwin and Inigo Triggs in their books on city planning, and they have given diagrams showing its adaptation to specific cases and the great reduction in the number of possible collision points which would result.

It is said that the gyratory system was first tried out in 1905 at Columbus Circle, New York City, at the suggestion of William P. Eno of Washington, whose efforts to have it adopted in Paris and other large cities were quite successful. While it seemed to work well at first, it has been demonstrated that such a system breaks down at urban intersections handling heavy volumes of both vehicular and pedestrian traffic, as the latter has no opportunity to cross the intersecting streets in safety. It has become necessary to substitute some type of stop-and-go control or grade separation at such locations. This has been the case at the downtown traffic circles in Washington, D. C., and at Columbus Circle in New York. The rearrangement proposed at Columbus Circle, made possible by the substitution of buses for trolleys, is shown in Figure 9·11.

A gyratory system of traffic movement can be used successfully at the intersection of two main thoroughfares where ample space is available and no pedestrian movement is involved. Two solutions of this type are shown in diagrams A and B of Figure 9·12.

In such an intersection there must be sufficient distance for traffic to weave from one lane to another. This distance depends upon the speed and amount of traffic, and for high-speed traffic a large area is needed. Diagram A shows a design for gyratory movement at an intersection where one thoroughfare (an expressway) carries almost twice as much traffic as the intersecting thoroughfare and there is very little turning traffic. Traffic could flow continuously around the island in the center. The expressway has a divided roadway, and traffic could move on it faster than on the other thoroughfare, which is not divided. Around the island the express traffic would have to slow down to the speed of the cross traffic, but this is preferable to making a complete stop. Diagram *B* shows a circular design for an intersection of two thoroughfares carrying about equal traffic and with a small amount of turning traffic.

ment between the left-hand and upper routes. The intersection is designed for practically uniform speeds for through traffic and the heaviest turning movements. Only the lightest turning movements would require a severe checking of speeds after leaving the main

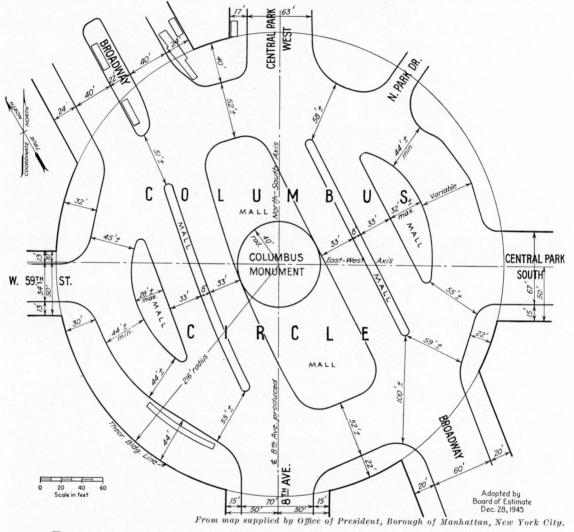

From map supplied by Office of President, Borough of Manhattan, New York City.

FIGURE 9·11. PROPOSED REARRANGEMENT OF COLUMBUS CIRCLE, NEW YORK CITY

Although gyratory or rotary traffic through such intersections permits continuous movement on all streets, it does not permit continuous traffic at full speed and so reduces the capacity of the highways. By separating the grades at intersections the capacity can be increased. Diagram *C* in Figure 9·12 shows a design for an intersection of two busy expressways with a particularly heavy turning move-

traffic stream. Two bridges are required to provide this unusual degree of freedom. The offsets in the direction of each of the thoroughfares permits a substantial saving in the area required for the intersection.

Diagram *D* illustrates the "clover-leaf" type of intersection, developed and used successfully by the New Jersey State Highway Department. This is best suited to intersections

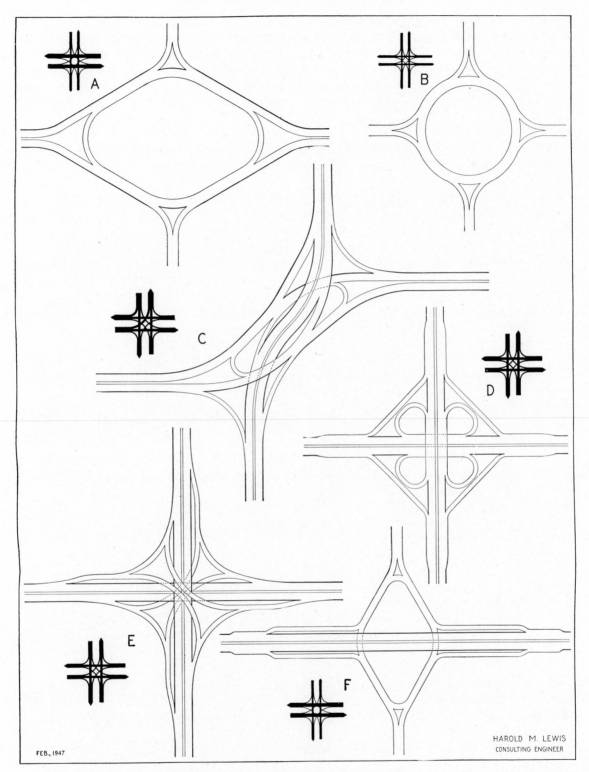

FEB., 1947

HAROLD M. LEWIS
CONSULTING ENGINEER

FIGURE 9·12. SUGGESTED METHODS OF TREATMENT FOR THOROUGHFARE INTERSECTIONS

The small diagrams show, by widths of lines, the relative amounts of traffic carried by intersecting highways and making the various turns for which connections are provided.

carrying about equal traffic in all four directions with little turning traffic, particularly left turns. The two streams of through traffic are separated by a bridge. Right-hand turns are made on the surface. To make a left-hand turn it is necessary to go past the intersection and turn to the right on the sharp curve which leads up or down to the other roadway.

Diagram *E* is for an intersection with a distribution of traffic similar to that in diagram *D*, but with a greater intensity of traffic at higher speeds. By the use of four levels, it permits direct left turns without the rather long and awkward routing required in the clover-leaf. This type of plan has been used in Los Angeles and is practical only where there is considerable variation in the topography. As in diagram *D*, the two main streams of traffic are separated by a bridge, and right-hand turns are made on the surface, but the curves have longer radii, and greater speed is possible. Left-hand turns from the expressway plotted horizontally to that at right angles thereto cross underneath the main grade separation, while left-hand turns from the highway plotted vertically to that plotted horizontally pass over the main grade separation. All turning roadways have long radius curves on which high speed can be maintained. Another advantage is that less ground is required for the entire intersection than is needed for a cloverleaf. The four levels require three bridges.

Diagram *F* is for an intersection with traffic distribution similar to that in diagram *A*, but where the expressway is more important and carries greater traffic. Express traffic crosses the intersecting highway on two bridges without any deviation from a straight line. Right-hand turns are direct and on the surface. To make a left-hand turn, it is necessary to go around three sides of the diagonal island which splits the intersecting highway into two one-way roadways. This design is a combination of a traffic circle and a grade separation. Vehicles making a right-hand turn into the expressway traverse only one side of the island and a slightly shorter distance than would be required at an ordinary right-angle intersection. This design would provide high speed and direct, uninterrupted movement in the di-

rection of the heaviest traffic, and uninterrupted movement at reduced speed, with a slight increase of distance, for the cross traffic. The left-hand turns, in all cases, would require reduced speed and increased distances.

The alignment and grades of the streets are determined by the original street plan, but certain details at street junctions may often be subsequently adjusted and improved in the interest of safety, convenience, and appearance. The most awkward intersections are those where there is an offset in the crossing street involving two right-angled turns; while an enlargement of the street area is desirable at all intersections where any considerable traffic may be expected, it is especially necessary where there are offsets. Such breaks in the continuity of a street have the advantage of affording opportunities for interesting street pictures and advantageous sites for buildings which require ample light and air and which are worthy of sites enabling them to be seen to advantage. Several methods of treating offset intersections are shown in Figure 8·22, page 135, from which it will be seen that by the acquisition of a slight additional area very pleasing results can be secured. At acute-angled intersections the street lines may be deliberately shifted in order to break the alignment without the slightest embarrassment to traffic, while the streets will acquire added interest and some admirable sites will be provided for important buildings, as shown by details J and K of Figure 8·22.

Where two important streets intersect each other either at right angles or obliquely, an enlargement of the area is always desirable, the open spaces being either rectangular or circular in form and occasionally irregular in shape. The circle is best adapted to cases where five, six, or more streets come together, when it can be made a conspicuous feature of the general plan. Among the symmetrical places of this kind are the Place de l'Etoile, with its twelve converging avenues and the Arc de Triomphe in its center, and the Place de la Nation, where ten streets center at the bronze group representing the Triumph of the Republic, both of these places being on what might be called the main axis of the city of Paris. Other examples are the circular place at Indianapolis with a diameter of 493 feet and the tall shaft of the Soldiers' Monument in the center, whence the four principal streets of the city radiate, and Columbus Circle in New York, 432 feet in diameter, where six important streets join at the Columbus Monument (Figure 9·11). Washington has many open spaces at the junctions of its great diagonal avenues with each other and with the streets of the rectangular

Highway Safety

While increased speed and flexibility may tend to relieve congestion, they are also likely to add to the dangers to pedestrians and increase the damage from collision. That this is the case appears obvious from the increase in motor-vehicle fatality rates from 1915 to 1930 or 1935, but since that time there has

TABLE 14

FATALITIES CAUSED BY MOTOR-VEHICLE ACCIDENTS, 1915–1944, IN THE TWELVE LARGEST CITIES OF THE UNITED STATES[a]

(MAXIMUM FIGURES FOR EACH CITY SHOWN IN ITALICS)

City	Population, 1940	Fatalities, 1940	Fatalities per 100,000 Population						
			1915	1920	Average Year 1926–30	Average Year 1931–35	Average Year 1936–40	1940	1944
New York	7,454,995	902	6.3	13.6	*18.2*	16.6	12.5	12.1	8.6
Chicago	3,396,808	683	8.6	17.3	25.6	*27.6*	22.3	20.1	15.2
Philadelphia	1,931,334	311	5.4	12.3	*18.5*	18.3	17.0	16.1	11.6
Detroit	1,623,452	292	12.2	17.2	*27.2*	22.0	19.6	18.0	13.2
Los Angeles	1,504,277	614	15.9	24.1	35.2	*41.3*	40.5	40.8	26.8
Cleveland	878,336	149	10.6	19.2	*33.6*	30.4	24.2	17.0	14.1
Baltimore	859,100	208	6.0	13.1	24.8	*26.8*	23.6	24.2	17.0
St. Louis	816,048	140	7.9	13.4	*23.3*	21.8	18.2	17.2	16.0
Boston	770,816	105	7.9	11.8	18.1	*20.1*	16.4	13.6	13.5
Pittsburgh	671,659	128	9.1	16.6	*31.2*	26.6	22.8	19.1	12.1
San Francisco	634,536	141	14.6	17.2	23.7	21.1	21.1	22.2	*25.4*
Buffalo	575,901	108	9.0	20.4	*29.8*	26.7	24.1	18.8	14.9

[a] From 1926–1944 *Annual Reports, Vital Statistics of the United States;* see *Statistical Abstract of the United States, 1943*, page 448.)

system. These, however, are not treated as traffic centers but as parks, and are planted and adorned with fountains, monuments, or statues in a manner suited to a great national capital.

Where large open spaces have been left within the roadways at intersections, the movements of vehicles cannot be predicted, and many accidents occur. Channelization by curbs and traffic islands confines the movements of vehicles to definite lanes and avoids or reduces the conflicting movements which otherwise occur. Channelization makes good driving easy and bad driving difficult.[14]

[14] See "Channelization of Motor Traffic," by Guy Kelcey, *Transactions of the American Society of Civil Engineers*, Vol. 106 (1941), page 416.

been a decrease in the rate, due either to the reduced number of automobiles on the streets during the depression and war years, or to the development of increasingly successful methods of accident prevention. However, the fatality rates from this cause are still higher in many cities than they were in 1915, and there should be no relaxation in the attempts to reduce them.

The federal census bureau has compiled statistics of the deaths resulting from accidents caused by motor vehicles during each year since 1915. As these reports did not include the entire country until 1933, comparative total figures are not available; therefore Table 14 gives comparative figures for the twelve largest cities of the United States, arranged in the order of population in 1940. Since 1930 New

York City shows the lowest motor-vehicle fatality rate of any of the twelve largest cities, largely because of the small proportion of cars in relation to population.

Traffic-fatality figures have also been compiled on the basis of the number of fatalities per 100,000,000 vehicle-miles and the number of fatalities per 10,000 registered motor vehicles. Such figures are indicative of the quality of driving, whereas the figures in Table 14, comparing fatalities with population, are more indicative of the safety of the citizen within the community.

The number of automobile fatalities per 10,000 registered motor vehicles, as compiled by the National Safety Council for the year 1946 for the same cities listed in Table 14, is as follows: [15]

Pittsburgh	4.3	San Francisco	7.4
Detroit	4.8	Boston	7.5
Buffalo	5.0	Los Angeles	7.7
Cleveland	5.7	Philadelphia	8.1
Baltimore	5.7	New York	9.2
St. Louis	5.9	Chicago	9.2

It will be noted that on this basis New York which, because of its relatively small automobile ownership in relation to population, ranked first in the figures in Table 14 tied with Chicago for eleventh place in the figures given above. Similar average 1946 fatality rates, by population groups, for all cities reporting to the National Safety Council were as follows: [15]

POPULATION	RATE
Over 500,000 (14 cities)	7.3
250,000 to 500,000 (24 cities)	5.5
100,000 to 250,000 (55 cities)	4.9
50,000 to 100,000 (96 cities)	4.6
25,000 to 50,000 (144 cities)	4.0
10,000 to 25,000 (342 cities)	3.7

These figures show very definitely the increased hazard as cities become larger.

Studies of traffic congestion, its causes and results, while interesting, will be profitless unless they lead to the adoption of means for relief and prevention. These may involve physical improvements to increase vehicular capacities through new or widened streets, or

[15] *Accident Facts,* 1947 Edition, National Safety Council, Chicago.

the regulation of traffic movement so that more vehicles may be accommodated on existing roadways. The former remedy is extremely costly, as the greatest congestion is usually found in the most intensively developed portions of the city, where land values are highest and buildings are likely to be most expensive. Traffic regulation is, therefore, the first remedy to be applied.

While new regulations have often been opposed, experience has shown that such opposition is usually followed by acceptance and later by commendation. A driver soon learns that, although weaving from one lane to another, U-turns in busy streets, and unregulated turns at intersections at first seem helpful to him, they become a source of delay and hazard to everyone as soon as they are generally practiced. He finds that it is better to by-pass main centers than to force one's way through them, and that regular stoppages to permit the free movement of cross traffic on intersecting streets will save time for all.

The police can regulate traffic at a single busy intersection by means of hand signals and whistle, or manually operated semaphores. Some officers become very expert at such work and can regulate the traffic, according to the needs of the moment, better than any mechanical signals, but it has been found that, where traffic must be controlled at a number of contiguous intersections, mechanically timed signals will give better results. At outlying intersections between a main thoroughfare and a secondary street carrying only occasional vehicles, a traffic-actuated signal light, operated by a plate in the approach lane of the secondary street, has proved efficient. Thus traffic on the thoroughfare is stopped only as a vehicle wishes to cross or enter it.

There are, in general, three different systems of traffic signal control: (1) synchronized, (2) limited progressive, and (3) flexible progressive. The first one results in stop-and-go traffic, and the others provide for continuous movement at a determined speed, which is usually between 16 and 22 miles per hour. In the synchronized system, all signals turn at the same time. This system was adopted for Fifth Avenue in New York City in 1918, is still in use and has met with considerable popular approval. It has, however, been found to have several disadvantages. Drivers try to pass as many intersections as possible before the lights change, and thus speeding is encouraged. The accident hazard is increased, mostly at the expense of the pedestrian. Continuous movement is not possible. Usually, long periods are permitted for movement along the main artery, causing long waiting periods for the drivers on the side streets. The willingness of pedestrians to move

cipal streets, the length of the block determining the time at which each light changes. This increases the capacity of the street and allows traffic to flow more freely. Such a system must be planned with great care and is more expensive than any of the others. It has been used successfully in Chicago, Cleveland, Los Angeles, New York, Washington, and other places. It reduces accidents and speeds up traffic.

Relatively long blocks, of 600 feet or more, are best adapted to progressive light-control

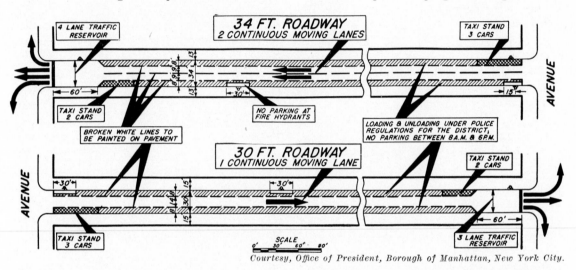

Courtesy, Office of President, Borough of Manhattan, New York City.

FIGURE 9·13. PROPOSED UTILIZATION OF 30- AND 34-FOOT ROADWAYS ON ONE-WAY EXPRESS STREETS, BOROUGH OF MANHATTAN, NEW YORK CITY, WITH RESERVOIRS AT ENTRANCES TO AVENUES

only *with* the traffic signal diminishes rapidly as the waiting period increases over about 30 seconds; hence long cycles tend to increase considerably the number of pedestrians who cross against the signal.

The progressive systems permit continuous movement on both the avenues and the cross streets. The traffic is formed into groups, or "platoons," with spaces between, so that the platoons on the cross streets go through the spaces between the moving platoons on the avenues. In the limited progressive system, all lights change at the same time, but adjacent lights are of opposite colors at the same time. This system works perfectly where all blocks are the same length, and there is an equal volume of traffic on all the streets at each intersection.

In the flexible progressive system, the lights are timed to permit uniform speed on the prin-

systems, as, where the blocks are short and traffic is heavy, the interval between changes would have to be so brief that vehicles could not keep in step with the lights. It is also desirable to have lanes marked on the pavement, or drivers will tend to weave from side to side in an effort to break loose from the platoon in which they are traveling.

In 1945 Edgar J. Nathan, Jr., then President of the borough of Manhattan, offered a seventeen-point plan to alleviate traffic congestion in midtown Manhattan, New York City. Seven proposals involved control measures affecting vehicles moving, parking, loading, or unloading, including a recommendation that strict compliance with parking regulations be adopted as the policy of the public and the police, replacing "severe spasmodic enforcement" by "reasonable continuous enforcement." Other recommendations included restoration of Traffic

Division personnel of the Police Department to its regular quota; temporary use of available city-owned property for parking; an educational campaign to acquaint citizens and visitors with parking regulations, expeditious routes, location of offstreet parking spaces, and all other facts relative to traffic; the adoption of city-aided parking garages as a public policy; and a construction program involving certain roadway widenings, expressways, a union bus terminal, and traffic islands to provide greater safety for pedestrians.

One of the control measures suggested is illustrated in Figure 9·13. This would eliminate all parking, taxicab stands, and bus stops on one-way crosstown streets for approximately 60 feet from the property line on the avenues at the ends of the blocks where traffic approaches such avenues. Such points would be designated by a painted line on the street pavement. This would establish a zone within which a considerable number of cars could wait from curb to curb during a red light. Vehicles in side lanes could turn into the avenues without disturbing the through flow of traffic. It was recommended that this be done on selected pairs of one-way express crosstown streets. On roadways 34 feet wide these painted lines would mark out two nine-foot center lanes and two eight-foot side lanes. On 30-foot street pavements the center line would be omitted, and only the eight-foot side lanes would be indicated. In this way, at the expense of a few painted lines, traffic could be made to flow more freely.

Economic Aspects of Congestion

It is now generally recognized that, when congestion reaches certain points, it makes the transaction of business difficult and brings serious economic disadvantages to a city. Yet in the early days of the motor vehicle there was a feeling among many merchants that congestion meant good business; they opposed vigorously any attempt to route traffic away from their doors. Congestion was even claimed by some eminent engineers as a reason for the prosperity of New York, Chicago, and other populous centers. Such claims were, however, probably due to thinking of congestion as mere concentration or crowding, instead of overcrowding.

The difficulty of finding any permanent relief from congestion has been pointed out as follows:

It has of course to be recognized that a degree of relief that could be described as a solution of the problem of traffic congestion is probably unattainable. There can be no finality in any project put forward as the solution of the problems of traffic and transit in the modern city, so long as the city continues to grow and changing factors continue to operate in producing new conditions. One thing that stands out clearly as a result of past experience is the need of considering the problem on broad and general lines simultaneously with the study of its local phases. The cause of congestion in a particular locality may have its origin in some defect of the plan of the city at a considerable distance from the point of congestion that can be traced only by careful investigation over wide areas. On the other hand, it may be the result of such minor causes as defective paving or bad regulation; or it may be merely a temporary ailment needing very simple treatment. Where, however, congestion is persistent and extends over a considerable period of the day, it will be found that it is likely to arise as a result of a defective street system over a wide radius, or from excessive height and bulk of buildings in a neighborhood, or from a combination of both of these things.[16]

So long as a city continues to grow, there must be constant planning in regard to all these phases of civic growth if congestion is to be kept within reasonable bounds. Mere street changes and measures of traffic control would by themselves involve prohibitive cost if they were carried to the point where they would provide any effective remedy for street congestion. Such control measures as one-way streets and parking bans are part of the price that every crowded community must pay for neglecting a comprehensive plan of communications and land uses to guide its early growth and provide adequately for the future.

Estimates made in the 1920's of the financial losses resulting directly from traffic congestion in cities are still quoted today. These were summed up by the New York Regional Plan as follows:

[16] *Highway Traffic,* Vol. III, Regional Plan of New York and Its Environs, by Harold M. Lewis, in consultation with Ernest P. Goodrich, 1927, page 59.

While no comprehensive estimates have been made, as far as known, in regard to points within the New York region, some idea can be secured with reference to probable losses by comparison with other municipalities where such estimates have been carefully made. In Worcester, Mass., detailed traffic tallies were made of all vehicles which entered the central business district, the number of each license and the time of entry and leaving being noted. From these data, and considering only those vehicles which were obviously delayed in passing through the central district, an estimate was prepared of the costs of congestion to the community. It amounted to $35,000 per day. In Cincinnati studies were made of the speed at which vehicles could traverse the central business district on each of its streets, hour by hour, throughout a business day. Rough estimates of the time which certain recommended changes in traffic regulations would save to the vehicles which, according to traffic counts, made use of the streets indicated that approximately $100,000 per day was the cost of the congestion. In Chicago certain estimates have been made with reference to the cost to the community of permitting cars to park within the "loop district," and $200,000 per day is approximately the figure reached. Judged by the total amount of traffic in these various communities compared with New York, it would seem safe to estimate the cost of congestion on Manhattan Island at $500,000 per day, and the cost in the whole Region to approximate $1,000,000 per day.[17]

Since these estimates were made, the number of motor vehicles in the United States has approximately doubled. As pointed out earlier in this chapter, traffic in downtown areas increased nearly as fast as motor-vehicle registration (see page 159). Therefore, in spite of the many highway improvements that have been made in urban areas in recent years, it is probable that the direct financial losses from congestion in American cities and metropolitan areas are now substantially greater than the figures quoted above.

By carrying out comprehensive traffic plans which separate through from local traffic and by taking at least the long-time parker off downtown streets, the economic stability of existing business centers can, in most cases, be assured.

The obstruction to moving vehicles in the outside lanes of business streets by vehicles stopping to deliver passengers or parcels cannot be entirely eliminated even where parking has been prohibited, although such stopping can be banned at certain hours of the day in

[17] *Ibid.*, pages 60–61.

strategic locations. Much can be accomplished by requiring certain large establishments to provide offstreet spaces for the loading and unloading of vehicles which serve them (see Chapter 17, Volume II). But it is not practicable to apply such requirements to prevent the occasional stopping of a vehicle at the curb in front of properties with only 20 or 25 feet of street frontage.

Although there are certain downtown areas where trucks cause most of the congestion, as in wholesale and heavy manufacturing districts, the private passenger car is the chief cause of traffic congestion in our cities. This is due to the excessive area it requires per passenger. Daniel L. Turner and J. P. Hallihan stated this as follows: "The pedestrian who occupies 10 square feet of space while moving freely in a sidewalk crowd, and approximately seven square feet as a street-car rider, consumes 135 square feet of roadway space as the average passenger in a private automobile."[18]

Need for Variety in Detailed Design

Even though the general plan for the streets and roads of a city and its environs may be sound, the streets of generous width and good alignment and skillfully located with respect to the topography, the roadways and sidewalks properly proportioned, and the underground utilities efficiently located, there are still other details of design which should be considered. Otherwise, movement along them may be seriously impeded by useless obstructions; roadway pavements may be unsuited to the character of the traffic or to the grades; injudicious tree planting or entire absence of planting may make them bare and unattractive; lamp posts and street signs may be conspicuously ugly; unlawful occupancy of the sidewalk spaces by abutting owners may interfere with pedestrians and produce a ragged and unsightly appearance; hideous billboards and gaudy façades may offend both residents and visitors; inadequate lighting at night may render the streets gloomy if not dangerous; and a riot of in-

[18] *The Relation of Individual to Collective Transportation*, Rapid Transit Commission, Detroit, Mich., 1928, page 29.

harmonious color in electric advertising signs may proclaim the bad taste and vulgar commercialism of the people. There are many details of street arrangement and design which are worthy of the most careful study.

But, when these details have been fully worked out for one street or even for one street of each class, that particular method of treatment should not be adopted for all streets, or for all streets of a certain class or width. The designer cannot complacently say: "There, that part of the city plan has been carefully worked out, and here is a design, the result of careful study, in accordance with which the streets of the city are to be laid out and constructed. Use this standard plan whenever a new street is to be improved." Yet that very course is being followed today in many cities. Long, straight streets at fixed intervals, each exactly like the others in dimensions and arrangement, lined with interminable rows of houses of similar design, material, and color, make the residential districts of our cities so much alike that without street signs and numbers many city dwellers would find it extremely difficult, if not impossible, to locate their own homes.

There has lately been something of a reaction against this monotony of treatment with a tendency in some places to go to the other extreme. An avoidance of identical treatment of different streets has not seemed sufficient to some designers, and an unsymmetrical arrangement of the same street has been urged and adopted by some distinguished authorities; not only a variation in the treatment of different parts of the same street, which is usually pleasing, but a different treatment of the two sides of the street, a single roadway being placed near one side, bordered by a narrow footway, while wide walks, shrubbery, grass and trees are placed on the other side. There are special cases, such as side-hill streets, or those where the property on one side is devoted to business and on the other side to residences, where the reason for such treatment is obvious; but where the improvement and use of the two sides of the street are similar and where no topographical conditions suggest such unsymmetrical treatment, it is difficult to understand why it was resorted to.

Sometimes trees have been set out and have grown to good size before the street has been built upon, or the houses on one side may have been set back from the street line, and a widening of such a street becomes desirable. By resorting to an unbalanced or unsymmetrical treatment such a widening of the roadway, or two roadways of different widths, can be adopted without the destruction of the trees. In such cases an irregular or unconventional arrangement is clearly advisable, even though the reason for it may not be apparent after the completion of the improvement. But where a single line of young trees occupies one side of a roadway and the sidewalks on the two sides of the street are of different widths and treated in a different manner, it appears as if the designer of the street had been guided by a passion for irregularity as strong as was the passion for sameness in those who made the plans for most American cities.

This tendency to avoid formal symmetry and geometrical pattern in the city plan is especially noticeable in the work of the German planners. On the other hand, French practice still seems to adhere to the simple dignity of classical design, the principles of which also prevail in most of the designs for civic centers and important plazas in American cities. Examples of the German tendency to irregularity are found in Essen, where the roadways are frequently placed off the center line of the street, giving sidewalks of different widths, a paved walk close to the building line on one side and generous planting spaces being provided in front of those on the other side. While this adds pleasing variety to the street, it appears to make a sharp distinction in the treatment of the two sides which must necessarily affect their desirability for residential purposes, a discrimination which would probably be vigorously resented in an American city. (See Figures 9·14 and 9·15.)

Unwin protests against the adoption of a minimum street width and the tendency to standardize street dimensions. Perhaps there is good ground for this protest, as nothing will more certainly tend to make a city monotonous or deprive it of local interest than to impose upon it many miles of streets of perfectly regular width and of uniform treatment. A like protest may well be made against standardizing the treatment of streets of the same width.

Now that the height of buildings and the proportion of the lots which they may occupy can be restricted for any particular section, a very material reduction in the required street width may be permitted, as wide streets are no longer the only means of providing light and air, and an indefinite increase in future traffic

FIGURE 9·14. THE UNSYMMETRICAL ARRANGE-MENT OF A LOCAL RESIDENTIAL STREET IN ESSEN, GERMANY

need not be provided for if building cubage is definitely limited. Similarly, if business has already gained a foothold on one side of a street and it is desired to preserve the other side for residences, a different treatment of the two sides of the street will tend to the accomplishment of this result. Several examples of such treatment are to be found in Toronto, but not to the degree indicated in the views of streets in Essen.

Some writers on city planning have attempted to prescribe the proper proportions of a "place." It is argued that a square shape should be avoided and that the place should be made oblong, the length and width bearing some definite proportion, the length, however, not being greater than three times the width. It would scarcely be safe to adopt such a rule. The picturesque features and the charm of every one of these places which are to be

found in old-world cities depend not so much upon their shape and their dimensions as upon the character of the buildings by which they are surrounded. It is quite apparent that an over-large place will dwarf the buildings around it, and that a mass of towering structures built around a place or square of limited area will rob it of its dignity. It is quite improbable that the most famous places of Europe were laid out, as they are today, for the reason that the particular size and shape which were adopted were believed to be most effective or artistic. These places were usually markets about which buildings had grown up, and it is highly probable that the dimensions and arrangement of many of them which are so much admired are the result of accident rather than design. The markets were the chief centers of activity, and the most important buildings

FIGURE 9·15. AN UNSYMMETRICAL BOULEVARD IN ESSEN, GERMANY

were naturally built about them. Good architecture and thorough work were the rule in those days, and the result has been a very happy one.

Street Adornment

There are other details of street design which may be considered primarily as street adornment intended to add to the attractiveness of the city. Some of these, such as street illumination, may also promote convenience and safety. A street may be well lighted so far as the amount of light is concerned, but this may be accomplished by the use of ugly lamp stand-

may be so meagre as to produce unsatisfactory results at night.

Very attractive and costly lamp standards have been placed on some of the older bridges

Courtesy, NEMA.

FIGURE 9·16. EXAMPLES OF MODERN STREET LIGHTING

The lower view shows the even light distribution obtained on a business street of Oconomowoc, Wisconsin; the modern type of light standard is shown on a residential street in Clarinda, Ohio (*upper left*) and on a business street in Corinth, Mississippi (*upper right*).

ards or by the suspension of the lights from overhead wires supported by poles. On the other hand, graceful lamp standards may be introduced which will be attractive by day, but they may be so placed and the illumination

and in front of public buildings, but in recent years scientific research has provided the basis for street-lighting programs. A relation has been established between traffic safety and street illumination, and recommended standards have been published by the Illuminating Engineering Society.[19] These vary from 0.2 lumen per square foot (average horizontal footcandles) with very light vehicular and pedestrian traffic to 1.2 lumens per square foot with heavy vehicular and pedestrian traffic. The recommended lamp standards are designed to provide the required height and spacing of lights in the most unobtrusive manner, and the

One of the essential though minor adjuncts of city streets are the signs bearing the names of the streets. Although they should not be obtrusive, they should be sufficiently conspicuous to attract the attention of those passing them, whether walking or riding. While not large, they should be so plain as to be easily read. These signs have been made of almost every material suitable for such use, and have

FIGURE 9·17.   USE OF SODIUM LUMINAIRES TO LIGHT AN UNDERPASS IN SACRAMENTO, CALIFORNIA

results are more artistic than some of the more elaborate designs previously used (Figure 9·16). Sodium luminaires, giving a light free from glare, have been used successfully on main highways (Figure 9·17).

The illumination of important buildings has also received much attention, and strikingly beautiful results have been obtained by indirect lighting, which received great impetus due to its successful use at the San Francisco Exposition of 1915. Some examples of the effective lighting of buildings and towers are shown in Figures 9·18 and 9·19.

[19] See *Recommended Practice of Street and Highway Lighting*, Report of Committee on Street and Highway Lighting, Illuminating Engineering Society, 1945.

been placed in every possible position. The commonest type of sign is the enamelled plate affixed to the corner of a building, white letters on a blue ground being the most easily read. The street names were formerly cut into the stone of the buildings, but they never showed distinctly and in a few years became almost illegible. It is difficult to provide signs which are readily distinguishable at night. When the old open-flame gas street lamp was in general use, street names on glass plates attached to them served the purpose. Now that electricity has displaced gas for street illumination in practically all cities, these illuminated street signs have been lost. It would be advisable to consider some form of electric illumination of street signs, especially in the business districts. In some cases it has proved effective to paint the street names on the curb near intersections where they can be readily picked up at night by drivers of automobiles (see Figure 9·26). A combined street-sign and traffic-light standard to which has also been attached a sign and push-button control for pedestrians is illustrated in Figure 9·20.

Courtesy, New York Edison Company.

FIGURE 9·18. ILLUMINATION OF TOWER OF WOOLWORTH BUILDING, NEW YORK CITY

It is difficult to realize today the problems posed by overhead wires 20 or 30 years ago. At that time, almost every street had two or three rows of poles, with wires strung on from one to twenty cross-arms. In some cases the wires almost completely covered the streets and interfered with the work of firemen. In addition to the trolley wires for street cars there were the power-feeder cables to supply the trolley wires, and power and light wires for the city street lights and for the supply of private customers. Sometimes there were municipal power lines and lines owned by two or

more utility companies, telephone and telegraph wires, police and fire-alarm systems, etc. Before 1920, city plan reports usually had a section on the "suppression of ugliness," and the first item was often "removal of poles and wires." The following quotation from one of those reports, published in 1915, is interesting:

Widespread use of the telephone and of electricity has resulted in an enormous increase of wires, particularly upon the larger thoroughfares. A multiplicity of wires and poles is extremely detrimental to the aspect of a street. Much commendable work in removing them has recently been undertaken, though it is only a beginning. In several streets . . . the wires have been buried, numerous poles removed, and combination poles for trolley wires and street lights erected. Not alone is the appearance of the street improved through the burial of the wires, but the menace of fire and shock also.[20]

New York City pioneered in the elimination of overhead wires on Manhattan Island, banning not only telephone, light, and general power lines, but also overhead conductors for street railway systems. This required the adoption of the alternative arrangement of an underground contact with a slotted rail in the center of the track. In some European cities one of the running rails is slotted instead, and the power obtained through it.

One advantage of the underground contact is that the track is necessarily more substantial and the pavement along it can be more readily maintained, although the central slotted rail involves an extra subdivision of the pavement for each track. A disadvantage is the danger of clogging with ice and snow in northern cities. The construction is also more expensive, as indicated by the relative costs of the different types of railway construction given in Table 7, page 115. This additional cost would doubtless be prohibitive in small towns or in the outlying districts of large cities where traffic is light. Standards located between the tracks with brackets from which the overhead contact wires are suspended reduce the disfigurement of the streets, but offer serious obstruction to street traffic.

While there was much discussion in other cities of methods of controlling or removing

[20] *Comprehensive Plan of Newark, N. J.,* the City Plan Commission, 1915, page 104.

Courtesy, Los Angeles County Chamber of Commerce.

Courtesy, National Capital Park and Planning Commission.

FIGURE 9·19. EFFECTIVE FLOOD LIGHTING OF PUBLIC BUILDING

Los Angeles City Hall (*upper view*); the Capitol at Washington, D. C. (*lower view*).

overhead wires, such laws were never generally adopted; yet today overhead wires are the exception rather than the rule. The economic advantage of uninterrupted service associated with underground conduits has accomplished more than all the campaigns to promote civic beauty, by law or by persuasion. However,

Courtesy, Public Roads Administration.

FIGURE 9·20.   COMBINED STREET-SIGN AND
TRAFFIC-LIGHT STANDARD

At the intersection of Massachusetts and Wisconsin avenues, Washington, D.C.

the problem still persists in many of our cities (see Figure 7·18, page 109).

There is no one other thing that tends to make a city street as attractive as planting. Well-kept grass plots and well-selected shrubs give streets a certain distinction, but nothing dignifies them so much as rows of fine, healthy trees. As C. M. Robinson said, "In the mental picture of a beautiful city or village the tree has an inseparable part." Where the streets are only wide enough to permit a single row of trees on each side, it has been the custom to place them just back of the curb. Where the buildings are on the street line, this may be necessary, but the space about the trees is so completely covered by stone or concrete flags that they have a hard struggle for exist-

ence. Even where the buildings are set back from the street line, this custom as to the location of the trees persists. In such cases, if they were placed inside the walk at or near the street line, with turf about them, not only would they thrive better, but also the street would acquire added dignity and appear wider (Figure 9·21). The details in two streets may be identical, the setback of the houses the same, the distance between curb lines the same, and the trees about the same size, yet there are a dignity and an impression of greater width where the trees are set back on the street line

FIGURE 9·21.   VIEWS SHOWING THE EFFECT OF
PLACING TREES ON THE STREET LINE INSTEAD
OF ALONG THE CURB

The two views show consecutive blocks on the same street. In the upper view the trees are located between the curb and sidewalk; in the lower view they are located back of the sidewalk along the street line, and, in addition, an irregular mall has been introduced in part of the block, taking advantage of excessively deep lots at that point.

which are lacking where they are in their usual places next to the curb.

It is unfortunate that tree planting is quite generally left to the real estate developer, who is free to carry out any scheme which seems to suit his fancy, with respect to not only the kind of trees to be used on each street, but also their location. Washington is one of the few American cities that has given this matter the attention which it deserves, a consistent scheme of planting having been worked out for each street, and this wise policy has contributed in no small degree to making Washington the beautiful city that it is. Lincoln, Nebraska, provides a good example of a medium-sized city which has developed, under municipal jurisdiction, an effective system of street trees. Although a prairie city, its trees give it a splendid appearance.

As Charles D. Lay has well said, "Tree planting cannot safely be left to individual enterprise, for a tree out of place is just as objectionable as any other misplaced object." The book by William Solotaroff devoted to this subject is well worth the careful study of those who are responsible for the planting and care of trees in city streets.[21]

The most frequent error in planting street trees is to put them too close together. They are so small when obtained from the nursery that they are too often planted only 18 or 20 feet apart. When the trees have had a few years' growth, they are found to interfere with the street lighting. The Committee on Public Lighting of the American Public Works Association recommends an average spacing of 45 feet between street trees, and no tree closer than 21 feet to a lamp standard.[22] In planning tree locations, the relation to property lines, driveway entrances, hydrants, catch basins, and other structures must receive careful consideration.

Unfortunately, trees are subject to many diseases, and many species do not thrive in the smoky atmosphere encountered in most cities. The American elm, one of the most beautiful trees, has suffered almost total extinction because of the ravages of the Dutch elm disease and other diseases. Now the Oriental plane tree is threatened. While it is advisable to use only one variety of tree on a street, as many varieties as possible should be used in each city, so that one disease does not attack all the trees in a city at one time.

The following list of trees is acceptable to the New York City Park Department and is recommended by the Municipal Art Society and the Park Association in their current campaign for more street trees in New York City: [23]

1. Oriental plane.	5. Red oak.
2. Honey locust.	6. Sweet gum.
3. Ginkgo.	7. Norway maple.
4. Pin oak.	8. European linden.

Courtesy, Public Roads Administration.

FIGURE 9·22. INFORMAL PLANTING ON A DIVIDED HIGHWAY IN MIAMI, FLORIDA

Edward H. Scanlon, City Forester of Cleveland and editor of *Trees Magazine*, has pointed out the importance of the planning and maintenance of shade trees as a phase of city planning. In addition to some of the trees mentioned above, he refers to the globe-headed elm (*Ulmus carpinifolia umbraculifera*) and Buisman elm as useful trees resistant to the diseases which attack other members of the elm family. Among the fastigiate (tall, narrow) trees which are disease resistant and free of spreading roots and will let through enough sunlight to support lawns and foundation planting, he recommends the upright sugar maple, upright American elm, upright Norway maple, black maple, red maple, and upright American linden. Among smaller types of trees which have similar advantages he lists the

[21] *Shade Trees in Towns and Cities,* by William Solotaroff, John Wiley & Sons, 1911.

[22] *Municipal Index and Atlas, 1945,* published by *The American City,* page 516.

[23] *New York Times Magazine,* March 30, 1947.

English oak, Wheately elm, upright Sargent cherry, chalk maple, and Chinese cork tree (*Phellodendron*).[24]

Location of Underground Utilities

Among the most important adjuncts of the city street are the various structures beneath the surface. Since these are out of sight and little in evidence, the importance of their location and control is not so apparent to the casual observer as are the more obtrusive but not more important structures above ground, except when the street surfaces are torn up for

to Covent Garden Market of what is now known as Garrick Street, which was completed and opened to traffic in 1861. The new construction included an arched subway 7½ feet high by 12 feet in width for gas and water mains, sewers, and other underground works. In addition there were 14 arched side passages for house-service pipes.

In spite of this early start, the total length of pipe subways in London in 1922 was less than 8½ miles. In explanation of this very limited mileage it was said that only when a new street is created or an old street is widened or straightened is any attempt made to build

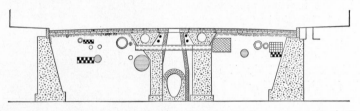

FIGURE 9·23. SUBSURFACE STRUCTURES IN A TYPICAL MAIN AVENUE IN NEW YORK CITY FREE OF A RAPID-TRANSIT SUBWAY

the repair of old or the installation of new sewers, pipes, or conduits. The work of building them is often so indifferently performed that repairs or renewals are frequently required, and their arrangement is frequently so unsystematic that the work of repair or renewal is slow, costly, and attended with great inconvenience and discomfort. A typical instance of the great number of underground structures in a large city is shown by Figure 9·23. It is often urged that the only effective remedy for this nuisance is to build subways for the accommodation of all subsurface structures and thus put an end to the constant mutilation of street pavements. The cost of doing so would be enormous, to say nothing of the great disturbance of business, and it is doubtful if such an undertaking would be justified except in connection with the creation of a new street or the widening or reconstruction of an old one.

The first subways for the express purpose of accommodating pipes and mains were built in London. In 1846 the Metropolitan Board considered the cutting through from Longacre

pipe subways, and that the expense of constructing them in existing streets simply for the accommodation of underground structures would be so great as to be out of proportion to the benefits to be derived. In three typical subways in the busiest streets of London, the inside dimensions in each case being 12 by 7½ feet, the average of the combined cross-sectional area of the pipes and conduits was found to be 6.17 square feet. At two typical sections of Broadway, New York, the average combined area of similar structures was found to be 44.05 square feet, or more than seven times as great, while at two places in Canal Street the average was 30.7 square feet, or five times as great as in the London utility subways.

In Nottingham, England, in 1862 and 1863, underground structures were built in Victoria and Queen streets. Arthur Brown, the borough engineer, in a paper read before the Incorporated Association of Municipal and County Engineers in April, 1892, said, "To show the value of such works in the street called Victoria Street, in which is situated the general post office, there are, besides the gas and water pipes and connections, no less than six pipes

24 See "Street Trees," by Edward H. Scanlon, *The American City,* March and April, 1947.

containing telegraph wires in this subway, and not one single stone was disturbed in this carriageway for twenty-five years, and in that period not one single penny was spent in repairs on the street."

One of the advantages which have been claimed for the large sewers of Paris is that in the sewers, which, besides providing for drainage, accommodate the telephone and telegraph wires, the water mains for the dual service, pneumatic tubes, and hydraulic power pipes.

Two exceptionally well-paved cities are Liverpool and Berlin, in neither of which are

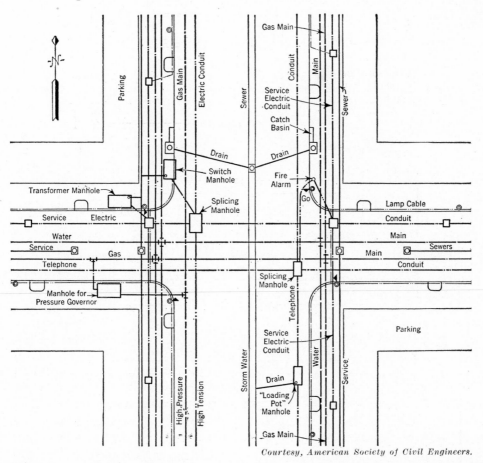

Courtesy, American Society of Civil Engineers.

FIGURE 9·24. STANDARD PLAN FOR LOCATION OF UNDERGROUND UTILITIES IN WASHINGTON, D. C.

they can accommodate the various pipes and wires which are ordinarily placed beneath the roadway, thereby avoiding the disturbance of the pavement. It was formerly the practice to place gas mains in the sewers, but owing to several explosions, attended by serious results, it was decided about 75 years ago not to admit gas pipes to the Paris sewers. These pipes, together with electric light and power conductors, are now placed under the sidewalks. The engineers in charge of the sewers say that they still consider the former practice dangerous and never permit gas pipes to be placed

to be found the evidences of frequent disturbance of the pavement surface so often seen in American cities. Yet neither of them has pipe subways. It is probable, therefore, that this condition is due to efficient administration, under which the various pipes and conduits are arranged in an orderly manner and are laid with great care, and to the fact that when openings are made the surface is promptly and thoroughly replaced. It must also be remembered that the number of openings under the same conditions would be less than in American cities.

In 1931 the City Planning Division of the American Society of Civil Engineers started a study of the location of underground utilities.

advocated an official organization, either in the city engineer's office or the city plan commission, which would keep an accurate record

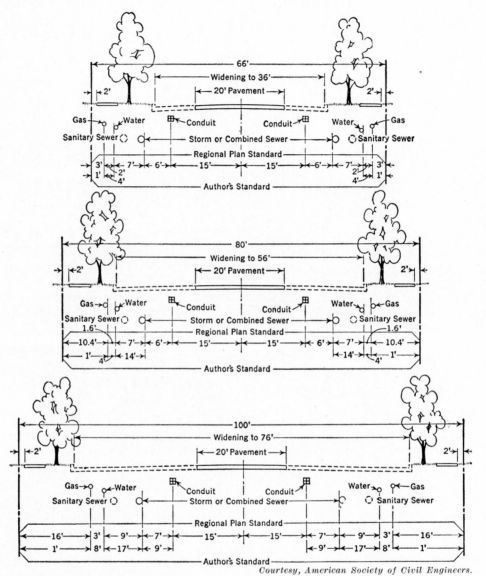

Courtesy, American Society of Civil Engineers.

FIGURE 9·25. LOCATION OF UNDERGROUND UTILITIES IN UNDEVELOPED TERRITORY, RECOMMENDED BY THE CITY PLANNING DIVISION, AMERICAN SOCIETY OF CIVIL ENGINEERS

The dimensions shown as "Regional Plan Standard" were developed by the Chicago Regional Planning Association, and those marked "Author's Standard" were recommended by the City Planning Division.

A special committee under the chairmanship of Arthur W. Consoer prepared a report which was approved in 1937 by the Executive Committee of the Division and published by the Society as one of its manuals.[25] This report

of all present underground utilities and make plans for the location of all future ones. This office would issue the permits for such work and could in this way control the location of all

[25] "Location of Underground Utilities," *Manual of Engineering Practice* 14, American Society of Civil

Engineers, 1937; also supplement entitled "Typical Plans and Forms for Use in Locating Underground Utilities."

underground utilities. Examples were given of the standard records and forms used in St. Paul, Cincinnati, and Washington, D. C. This manual of the American Society of Civil Engineers should be consulted by anyone making a plan for underground utilities. Figures 9·24 and 9·25 are reproduced therefrom.

Among the essential accessories to these underground utilities are fire hydrants and catch basins. Their efficiency is the foremost factor in their design. Fire hydrants must be readily

Courtesy, "Engineering Record."

FIGURE 9·26. A WIDE SEWER INLET IN PASADENA, CALIFORNIA, WHERE THE RAINFALL IS SOMETIMES VERY HEAVY

accessible, frost proof, and sure of operation; catch basins must take care of surface water during the heaviest storms. To attempt to make the fire hydrant a thing of beauty would probably result in making it ridiculous, and this is even more true of the sewer inlet, which has lately been made less obtrusive. The great gaping openings formerly so common were not only very ugly, but also involved a certain element of danger, and there have been instances of children falling or being washed into them; but statements that such casualties were not uncommon are gross exaggerations. There is no more utilitarian adjunct of a city street than a sewer inlet, which must do the work for which it was designed. When rainfalls of great intensity are likely to occur, these inlets must be of adequate capacity, but this can be done by making the openings longer rather than higher, as in Pasadena (Figure 9·26). The area drained by each catch basin should be de-

termined, and the maximum run-off computed. Where this exceeds the capacity of a standard inlet, a special design should be made.

Contributions of the Private Developer

The street details already considered are those over which the municipal authorities have control and which are installed by the city at public expense or by public-service corporations under a certain degree of public control. Most of them are utilitarian in purpose, and the effort to make them attractive has resulted from the higher standard of public taste which has recently been developed. Many of the most effective adjuncts of city streets have been supplied by real estate developers, some within the street lines and others on private property. Developments on an extensive scale have been undertaken where a street plan has already been adopted, but, the streets not having been taken over by the city, the owners have been able to carry out their own ideas without the approval of the public authorities. In some instances, with little or no departure from a conventional rectangular plan which may have been imposed upon the territory, they have been able, by the introduction of central parkways, the judicious planting of trees and shrubs, the erection of ornamental columns at the boundaries of the property, the imposition of setback restrictions and stipulations as to the position of buildings with respect to the lot lines, to give the neighborhood a distinctive character. As a result they have added greatly to the attractiveness of the community and materially increased its property values.

Such successful treatment of details is to be found at Forest Hills Gardens, New York, described and illustrated in Chapter 13, "Neighborhood and Community Planning," Volume II. In this development the rectangular street plan of the adjoining sections was entirely disregarded, as will be seen by reference to Figure 13·4. Another of the many examples which might be given is a suburban development at San Francisco, the entrances to which are shown in Figure 9·27.

Some of the most successful attempts to introduce attractive street details are to be found in private streets or places—that is, short streets or courts not recognized by or

9·28. The nature of the restrictions imposed by covenants between the developers and purchasers of plots is indicated by the following typical provisions applying to one of the more

FIGURE 9·27. ENTRANCES TO A SUBURBAN DEVELOPMENT ON THE OUTSKIRTS OF SAN FRANCISCO

included in the city plan and over which the developer, and after him the purchasers of the plots, retain and exercise entire control, maintaining at their own expense the roadway pavements, sidewalks, planting, etc. St. Louis is conspicuous for these places, some modest and others quite pretentious. Several views showing their arrangement are illustrated in Figure

modest places, which were furnished through the kindness of John Noyes of the Missouri Botanical Garden:

Private residences only may be erected with such stables or other subsidiary buildings as may be appurtenant, in ordinary use in St. Louis, to a private residence. Building lines are established as to all property on both sides of the street, that on one side being 17 feet and on the other 30 feet

FIGURE 9·28. VIEWS OF TYPICAL ST. LOUIS PLACES AS DEVELOPED ON PRIVATE STREETS

Upper views show entrance to Hortense Place (*right*) and the setback restrictions and double rows of trees between curb and sidewalk in this development (*left*). Lower views show entrances to Westmoreland Place (*right*) and Portland Place (*left*).

back of the street line, although porches and steps may extend seven feet beyond the building line so established in the former case, and eight feet in the latter. The inner line of the sidewalks or the edge next to the abutting property shall be 10 feet outside of the setback building line, so that these 10 feet will be added to the space in front of the houses.

In the more ambitious developments, such as Westmoreland Place, buildings must be kept 40 feet back of the street lines and may not be less than 10 feet from the rear lot line, the width of the lots on this place being about 100 feet and the depth 200 feet measured to the center line of the rear alley. In one instance there was originally a restriction against the erection of any dwelling costing less than $6,000, which has proved to be an entirely unnecessary provision, as none have been built at a cost of less than $20,000, and it is said that most of them were far more expensive. An annual assessment of not more than 50 cents per front foot is imposed upon all the lot owners to meet the cost of maintenance and care of the trees, shrubs, etc.

Conspicuous features of the St. Louis places are their ornamental entrances, several of which are shown in the illustrations. It is unfortunate from the point of view of the city as a whole that these places frequently have no direct relation to the surrounding street system. If they were the continuations of city streets, the entrances would add an attractive feature to the streets as a whole; but one of the chief purposes of the developers appears to have been the emphasis placed upon them as somewhat secluded colonies of home owners. That they have been placed somewhat off the regular street system is probably fortuitous and resulted from the location of the property available for the development; nevertheless, the fact that they are stumbled upon accidentally adds to their desirability for the particular purpose for which they were designed, although the city at large may be the loser.

Selected References

Action Program, The President's Highway Safety Conference, held in Washington, D. C., May 8, 9 and 10, 1946, Superintendent of Documents, U. S. Government Printing Office, Washington, D. C.

KELCEY, GUY: "Channelization of Motor Traffic" (with discussion), *Transactions of the American Society of Civil Engineers,* Vol. 106 (1941), pages 416–469.

LEWIS, HAROLD M., in consultation with ERNEST P. GOODRICH: *Highway Traffic,* Vol. III, Regional Survey of New York and Its Environs, 1927. Distributed by Regional Plan Association, Inc., New York.

"Location of Underground Utilities" and supplement entitled "Typical Plans and Forms for Use in Locating Underground Utilities," *Manual of Engineering Practice* 14, American Society of Civil Engineers, 1937.

Public Control of Highway Access and Roadside Development, Public Roads Administration, Washington, D. C. Revised 1947.

Recommended Practice of Street and Highway Lighting, 1945 (prepared by Committee on Street and Highway Lighting), Illuminating Engineering Society, New York, February, 1946.

Report of Traffic and Transportation Survey (Los Angeles) 1938–1939, sponsored by the city of Los Angeles and published by the Citizens Transportation Survey Committee in co-operation with the Haynes Foundation, 1940.

SIMPSON, HAWLEY S.: "Use and Capacity of City Streets" (with discussion), *Transactions of the American Society of Civil Engineers,* Vol. 99 (1934), pages 1012–1040.

Street Traffic, City of Detroit 1936–1937, prepared and published by Michigan State Highway Department, in co-operation with Detroit Police Department and WPA, 1937.

"The Freeway, A Modern Highway for General Traffic in Metropolitan Areas," *Information Bulletin* 33, Regional Plan Association, Inc., New York, December 14, 1936.

Traffic Engineering Handbook, Institute of Traffic Engineers and National Conservation Bureau, New York, 1941.

PERIODICALS

Proceedings (Annual) of the Institute of Traffic Engineers, New York.

Traffic Quarterly, the Eno Foundation for Highway Traffic Control, Saugatuck, Conn., January, 1947, to the present.

Questions

1. What observations and records are needed to permit a complete understanding of the traffic problem in a community?
2. In what terms is the vehicular capacity of a street generally measured? Sketch a curve showing variation as a function of these terms.
3. Give figures showing the variation in capacity of different types of highways, such as mixed

traffic expressways, parkways, ordinary city streets under various systems of light control.

4. Give suitable cross-sections for a main business street, a residence street in an apartment area, a residence street in a low-density one-family area, a major boulevard.

5. Show suitable cross-sections for a limited-access highway in a central urban area and in a suburban area.

6. What is meant by channelization of traffic? How does it improve street efficiency?

7. What kind of highway accident records are useful in street design? How is highway safety measured?

8. What are the advantages and limitations of the "progressive" system of traffic-light control?

9. What are some of the ways in which the capacity of an ordinary street intersection may be increased?

10. What are some of the economic losses resulting from poor street design?

11. Give examples where lack of symmetry may be desirable in street design.

12. What are some of the accessory features of street design that may contribute to the attractive appearance of a neighborhood?

13. What are some of the contributions of private developers to the design of local street systems? Give examples.

Part Three

A Pattern for Land Use

10

PARKS AND RECREATION FACILITIES

WHILE MOST CITIES HAVE HAD AS THEIR NUCLEUS some public open space where the people were wont to gather for meetings or for recreation, the creation of a system of parks or playgrounds has been quite a recent development in city building. It is true that open spaces such as we would today call parks date from the earliest times. The ancient Egyptians appear to have had in their cities certain open spaces usually treated in a formal manner and adorned with sculpture and architectural features, but these were probably little more than gardens. The Romans created some great parks which included gardens, athletic fields, and areas treated as are our formal parks with canals, fountains, and cascades.

The climax of Marc Antony's famous oration in Shakespeare's *Julius Caesar* is the reading of Caesar's will, in which he says:

Moreover, he hath left you all his walks,
His private arbours, and new-planted orchards
On this side Tiber; he hath left them you,
And to your heirs forever, common pleasures,
To walk abroad and recreate yourselves.[1]

This may have been a reference to contemporary affairs in England at the time the play was written, about 1603 to 1607. The early kings had proclaimed the rights of commoners to practice archery on certain vacant lands

around London, and Queen Elizabeth reaffirmed the previous proclamations. When speculative builders tried to enclose and build houses on some of these lands, appeals to the monarch were usually successful in preserving the open spaces for the public. James I appointed a commission to defend the rights of archers, quoting a number of provisions, acts, and proclamations from previous kings. In 1605 the status of Moorfields as public ground was firmly established when two sisters, Mary and Cathrine Finnes, bequeathed "the lower walks of Moorfields to the City for the use and enjoyment of the citizens." [2]

In the capitals of Europe some of the parks were developed during the seventeenth and eighteenth centuries as royal pleasure grounds. They were laid out on the most extensive scale and were lavishly adorned with sculpture, fountains, and other decorative features. It was in the design and construction of these great royal estates or parks that the profession of landscape architecture, as we know it, came into existence. Such parks are now either the common property of the people or, if still nominally an appurtenance of the Crown, the public has the free use of them, and the château, schloss, or palace about which they are laid out has become a picture gallery or historical museum.

[1] *Julius Caesar,* Act III, Scene 2.

[2] *London: the Unique City,* by Steen Eiler Rasmussen, Jonathan Cape, London, 1937, page 82.

The city park, laid out, acquired, and developed as a public playground, is a modern idea and is a result of the steadily increasing size of our cities. Even yet, the park system is a haphazard growth, and its place as a part of the city plan is not fully appreciated, although its title to such recognition is now fully recognized by city planners.

Estimates have been made of the percentage of a city area which should be devoted to parks or the proper number of people to each acre of parkland, but the needs of an urban community cannot be determined in this manner. A compactly built city where the individual dwellings have no open spaces about them, where the streets are narrow, and where the average number of occupants to each dwelling is large, requires a greater park space per capita and a larger space in proportion to the area of the city. On the other hand, where dwellings are detached and each has its garden, where the streets are broad and lined with trees, the need of parks is much less. The industrial town or district has a far greater need of park reservations than does the residential town or district, but it usually has less.

Present Provision of Urban Parks

The great variation which is found in the park areas in different cities in proportion to population and total area of the city is indicated by Table 15.[3] The last two columns compare the average density of population in each city with the ratio of the population to the acreage of parks within the city. On the basis of these ratios the cities, among those listed, which show the best provision of park area are Salt Lake City, Nashville, Toledo, Tacoma, and Youngstown. Among those with populations of over 500,000, Washington is far in the lead. New York City and the county of

[3] A similar table on page 132 of *The Planning of the Modern City*, by Nelson P. Lewis, included figures for a number of foreign cities. Because of interruptions and changes resulting from World War II, it was not possible to bring these up to date. Therefore, with the exception of London figures, this table is limited to statistics for cities in the United States.

London have nearly equal percentages of total land area in public parks, but New York shows up considerably better than London in its provision in proportion to population. The London figures, however, are for a date about five

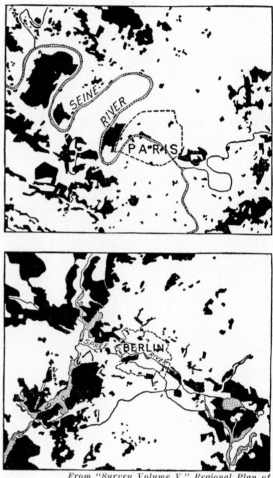

From "Survey Volume V," Regional Plan of New York and Its Environs.

FIGURE 10·1. PUBLIC PARKS AND RESERVATIONS IN THE PARIS AND BERLIN REGIONS

years earlier. In both New York and London the parks listed are supplemented by a much greater acreage outside New York City and outside the county of London but within the respective metropolitan districts. The extent to which European practice had established public parks and reservations outside city limits is shown in Figure 10·1.

Formerly one went to Europe for examples of parks and park systems, but that is no

TABLE 15

PARK STATISTICS FOR VARIOUS CITIES

| City | Population, 1940 | City Land Area, Acres, 1940 [a] | Parks | | Population | |
			Area, Acres, 1940 [c]	Percentage of Total Area	Per Acre of City	Per Acre of Park
London (Adm. County)	4,062,800 [b]	74,850 [b]	7,889 [d]	10.5	54.3	515
New York, N. Y.	7,454,995	204,982	22,054 [e]	10.8	36.5	338
Chicago, Ill.	3,396,808	132,200	6,668 [e]	5.0	25.6	508
Philadelphia, Pa.	1,931,334	81,408	7,957 [e]	9.8	23.8	243
Baltimore, Md.	859,100	50,500	3,648 [e]	7.2	17.0	235
St. Louis, Mo.	816,048	39,040	3,248 [e]	8.1	20.9	251
Boston, Mass.	770,100	28,100	3,780 [e]	13.4	27.4	204
Washington, D. C.	663,091	39,680	7,391 [e]	18.6	16.7	89.8
Minneapolis, Minn.	492,370	37,626 [f]	5,658 [f]	11.3	13	87
Kansas City, Mo.	399,178	37,500	3,701 [g]	9.9	10.7	107.6
Seattle, Wash.	368,302	43,800	2,878	6.6	8.4	127.1
Rochester, N. Y.	324,975	22,300	1,937	8.7	14.5	168
Louisville, Ky.	319,077	24,300	2,130	8.8	13.1	150
St. Paul, Minn.	287,736	33,400	2,300	6.9	8.6	125
Toledo, Ohio	282,349	23,700	5,046	21.3	11.9	56
Omaha, Neb.	223,844	24,900	2,860	11.5	9.0	78.1
Syracuse, N. Y.	205,967	16,200	1,174	7.3	12.7	175.1
Youngstown, Ohio	167,720	21,000	2,380	11.3	8.0	70.7
Nashville, Tenn.	167,402	14,100	3,587	25.5	11.9	46.7
New Haven, Conn.	160,605	11,450	2,120	18.5	14.0	75.8
Salt Lake City, Utah	149,934	33,600	6,896	20.5	4.5	21.7
Springfield, Mass.	149,554	20,300	2,017	9.9	7.4	74.2
Fort Wayne, Ind.	118,410	10,940	900	8.2	10.8	131.9
Wichita, Kan.	114,966	13,500	608	4.5	8.5	189.0
Tacoma, Wash.	109,408	29,800	1,616	5.4	3.7	67.8
Utica, N. Y.	100,518	10,100	765	7.6	10.0	131.8
Evansville, Ind.	97,062	6,210	1,092	17.6	15.6	88.8
Pasadena, Calif.	81,864	12,400	1,110	9.0	6.6	73.7
Davenport, Iowa	66,039	11,580	801	7.0	5.7	82.5
Terre Haute, Ind.	62,693	6,270	658	10.5	10.0	95.5

[a] From the United States Census, unless otherwise noted.

[b] *Statesman's Yearbook*, 1944.

[c] Areas of parks from *Municipal and County Parks in the United States*, 1940, National Recreation Association, New York, unless otherwise noted.

[d] London statistics, 1934–36.

[e] *Regional Plan Bulletin* 56, October 8, 1941, Regional Plan Association, New York, page 2. Figures for Baltimore, St. Louis, Boston, and Washington are for 1939.

[f] Board of Park Commissioners, *63rd Annual Report*, 1945.

[g] *Report of the Board of Park Commissioners, 1940–41.*

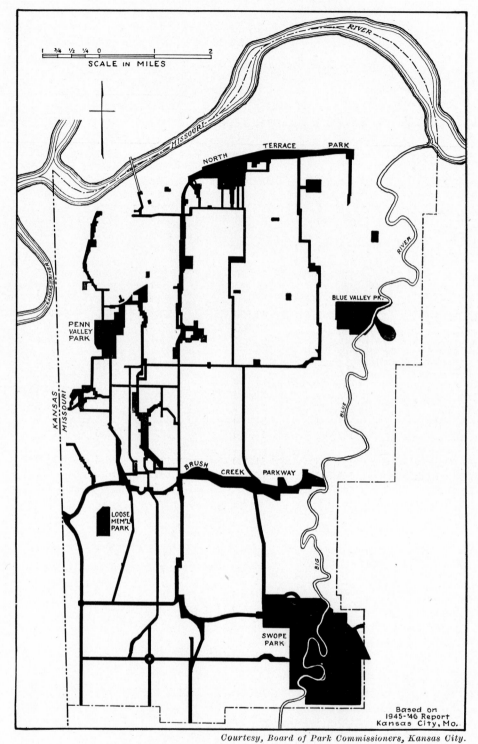

Courtesy, Board of Park Commissioners, Kansas City.

FIGURE 10·2.   PARKS, PARKWAYS, AND BOULEVARDS IN KANSAS CITY, MISSOURI longer necessary. Patrick Abercrombie, well-known British planner, has said:

A properly graded park system, into which is fitted all types of open space from the smallest

and 144 persons per acre of park about 20 years before. This city is adding to its park area from time to time and is improving its park ratio. (See Figures 10·2 and 10·3.) This

Courtesy, Board of Park Commissioners, Kansas City.

FIGURE 10·3. FLOWER GARDEN AND PATHS IN JACOB L. LOOSE MEMORIAL PARK, KANSAS CITY, MISSOURI

children's playground to the green belt of surrounding fields and the distant reserve of wild country, was first worked out in the U. S. A. We have learned much from examples such as the Metropolitan Park System of Massachusetts, which was perhaps the earliest to extend the principle throughout a whole region.[4]

Of the larger cities shown in Table 15, Washington, D. C., with less than 90 persons per acre of park in 1940, more than measured up to the generally accepted standard of one acre of park per 100 inhabitants, and its parks constituted 18.6 per cent of the city's area. Kansas City in 1940 had 9.9 per cent of its area in parks and 108 inhabitants per acre of parks, as compared with 5 per cent of its area in parks

[4] *A Plan for Plymouth,* 1943, page 98.

growth is particularly significant because of the method by which this city has bought and paid for its system of parks and parkways.[5]

Growth of the New York City Park System

Although New York is said to contain within its limits the most densely populated blocks on earth,[6] the average population per acre is less

[5] See Chapter 22, "The Economic Value of a City Plan," Volume II. See also discussion of parkway system on page 141.

[6] Many of the most congested areas lost much of their excess population in the decentralization that occurred in the decade from 1920 to 1930, as shown in Figure 4·2, page 43.

than in London (as shown in Table 15), Paris, Berlin, and other European cities. Its parks are larger in proportion to area and population but are not well distributed, as will be seen by an examination of Table 16. This shows a

of park show the futility of estimating the actual needs of a city solely in this way. A recent attempt to arrive at practical park and recreation standards is found in a preliminary report of the Committee on Park and Recrea-

TABLE 16

DISTRIBUTION OF PARK AREAS AMONG THE DIFFERENT BOROUGHS OF THE CITY OF NEW YORK IN 1920 AND 1940

Borough	Area, Acres [a]	Population		Parks				Population			
				Area, Acres		Percentage of Total Area in Parks		1920		1940	
		1920	1940	1920	1940 [b]	1920	1940	Per Acre of City [a]	Per Acre of Park	Per Acre of City	Per Acre of Park
Manhattan	14,272	2,284,103	1,889,924	1,564	2,416	11.1	16.9	163	1,460	132	785
Brooklyn	51,808	2,018,356	2,698,285	1,386	5,239	3.1	10.1	45	1,456	52	515
The Bronx	26,500	732,016	1,394,711	3,961	5,480	14.9	20.7	28	185	53	255
Queens	75,922	469,042	1,297,634	1,118	5,878	1.6	7.8	7	420	17	221
Richmond	36,480	116,531	174,441	79	3,041	0.2	8.3	3	1,469	4.8	57.3
Total, New York City	204,982	5,620,048	7,454,995	8,108	22,054 [c]	4.2	10.8	29	693	36.5	338

[a] From *Official Directory, City of New York*, 1947. The areas used for the 1920 calculations are: Manhattan, 14,038; Brooklyn, 45,326; The Bronx, 26,524; Queens, 69,101; Richmond, 36,600—as given in *The Planning of the Modern City*, Second Edition, by Nelson P. Lewis, page 134.

[b] From *Regional Plan Bulletin* 56, October 8, 1941, Regional Plan Association, New York, page 2.

[c] 479 acres were added between 1940 and 1947 (*Official Directory, City of New York*, 1947, page 7, where the total acreage is given as 22,533).

remarkable improvement in twenty years, both in the city-wide increase in park areas and in a more equitable distribution among the different boroughs. The large parks have been acquired while the land was largely undeveloped or have resulted from filling in land formerly under water. In some cases, small parks or playgrounds have been acquired by taking tax-delinquent property.

Standards of Size and Spacing for Small Parks and Recreation Facilities

As already pointed out and demonstrated by Table 15, the variations in percentage of park area and in the number of persons to an acre

tion Standards of the American Society of Planning Officials.[7] The standards given below and Figures 10·4, 10·7 and 10·10 are based on this report.

To take up first the question of total acreage, the standards of one acre per 100 population and 10 per cent of the area, both applying to parks within or adjacent to the built-up area, are satisfactory for the average city up to about 500,000 population, provided it has a population density of about 10 persons per acre. Adjustments will, however, have to be made to meet local conditions in larger or more

[7] *Planning 1943*, Proceedings of the Annual Meeting, 1943, American Society of Planning Officials, pages 106–112.

densely populated cities—possibly one acre to 200 persons as a reasonable goal in cities above 500,000, and one acre to 300 or more persons in cities above 1,000,000. Large natural park areas, reservations, or forest preserves well outside the city will help to meet the deficiency in the larger cities but should not be included in the area required by the standards.

Parks and recreational areas will be discussed under the following classifications: squares or plazas, playlots, playgrounds, playfields, neighborhood parks, large parks, bathing beaches,

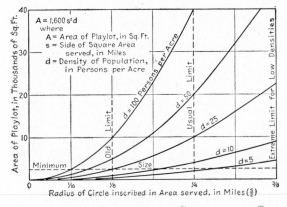

FIGURE 10·4. STANDARDS OF SPACING AND SIZE FOR PLAYLOTS

parkways, reservations, and national parks. In actual practice these uses are frequently overlapping. Playgrounds and playfields may often be combined or located within a neighborhood park, a parkway, or even a large park; likewise, a playground may include ornamental areas for passive recreation. Also the distinction between neighborhood parks, large parks, parkways, and reservations may often be difficult to determine.

Squares and plazas are ornamental areas of limited size. They normally should not be over one block in extent and may serve as the setting of a public building. There are no standards applying to either their size or their spacing. Too many small scattered areas involve a serious problem of maintenance.

Playlots are small areas suitable for the play of children less than five years of age. Such recreation areas should be provided near the homes in congested areas and in multi-family, low-cost housing developments; where possible,

they should be located within the block or superblock. The size should usually be from 5,000 to 10,000 square feet, although a minimum size of 2,500 square feet may be justified in some cases. The radius served might be $\frac{1}{8}$ mile or less in intensively developed areas, and usually not over $\frac{1}{4}$ mile; but possibly in large superblocks, where an interior playlot can be reached without crossing any street, the radius served might be as much as $\frac{3}{8}$ mile. Each child on the playlot at one time will require about 75 square feet of play space, and one-third of such children may be on the playlot at one time. The age group to be served, that is, children less than five years of age, is generally about one-tenth of the total population.

Courtesy, Department of Parks, New York City.

FIGURE 10·5. A PLAYLOT IN A CORNER OF A LARGE PARK

Illustrated by view in Central Park, New York City.

The area served will usually be one block or four contiguous blocks, and is assumed to be square in the diagram shown in Figure 10·4. This diagram shows that, when the density is less than about six persons per acre, the smallest practicable playlot would serve a radius of over $\frac{1}{4}$ mile (or a square area $\frac{1}{2}$ mile on a side). Fortunately, in residential developments of this density each family has enough open space on their own lot for this type of recreation. Where the density is less than 25 persons per acre, it would be desirable to provide such a street system that children might go

FIGURE 10·6. A PLAYLOT IN A TENEMENT AREA

Jacob Joseph Playground in the Lower East Side of Manhattan, New York City.

safely for a distance greater than ¼ mile to reach a playlot. Where the density is greater, the radius might be made less until it was ⅛ mile (or a square area ¼ mile on a side) for a

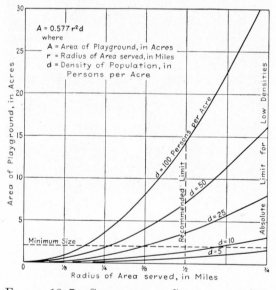

FIGURE 10·7. STANDARDS OF SPACING AND SIZE FOR PLAYGROUNDS

10,000-square-foot playlot, or 1⁄16 mile for a 2,500-square-foot playlot, at a density of 100 persons per acre.

Playgrounds should provide active recreation for children of grade and junior high school age,

usually five to 15 years. The area should be two to seven acres or more, though five acres is a desirable minimum. The spacing depends upon density of population, but a radius of ½ mile can be considered a satisfactory average. In congested areas the effective radius

FIGURE 10·8. A MODERN PLAYGROUND IN NEW YORK CITY

Corlears Hook Park and Playground, Adjoining the Franklin D. Roosevelt (East River) Drive.

FIGURE 10·9. A MODERN PLAYGROUND IN CHICAGO

At the southern end of Burnham Park on Chicago's lake front. At the far left is part of the elliptical model yacht basin. The Lake Shore Drive runs between the playground and the lake front.

should be somewhat less, but in the suburbs it might be increased. While a ¼-mile radius has been proposed by many authorities, the resulting supervision and maintenance costs required by this spacing over an entire city would be impractical.

About one-fourth of the population is children of five to 15 years of age, and one-third of them may be playing at one time. Each child on the playground will require 150 square

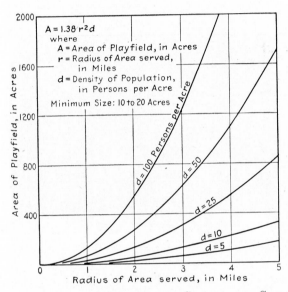

FIGURE 10·10. STANDARDS OF SPACING AND SIZE FOR PLAYFIELDS

feet of space. Assuming that the area served will be roughly circular, the area and spacing of playgrounds required under varying densities of population in persons per gross acre are shown in Figure 10·7. It will be seen that a minimum-sized playground would serve the population within ¼ mile at a density of 50 persons per acre, that is, row-house or apartment-house densities. In single-family or two-family house districts, greater service radii would have to be used to keep the costs of supervision and maintenance within reasonable limits. Where the density is less than 10 persons per acre, the radius of service might even be ⅝ to ¾ mile, but only where there were no through traffic streets in the area served by a playground.

Playfields, or athletic fields, provide active recreation for older children and adults, usually

between the ages of 15 and 24 years. The minimum size should be 10 acres, but 20 acres is more desirable, and areas up to 40 or 50 acres are found in the United States. In Germany, sports parks of 50 to 150 acres are quite common, with only one or two such parks for a city, whereas in American cities the preference is to have the playfields so distributed that no one has to travel more than a mile to reach a field. A playfield requires 600 square feet of area for each person playing at one time. The age group using such facilities constitutes about one-fifth of the total population, and one-quarter of them might be on the field at one time.

If the area served is assumed to be circular, playfield standards of spacing and size are as shown in Figure 10·10. Where the density is less than 15 or 20 persons per acre, the smallest possible athletic field will serve an area with a

FIGURE 10·11. WILLIAMSBRIDGE OVAL, BOROUGH OF THE BRONX, NEW YORK CITY

A modern playfield built on the site of an abandoned reservoir.

radius of over a mile. In suburban areas, where the density is often less than five persons per acre, an athletic field might serve an area with a radius of two or three miles, most of the players coming by automobile or public-transit lines.

Neighborhood parks are usually located to take advantage of some scenic opportunity, which cannot be included in the connected park or parkway scheme. They also serve areas not accessible to any of the larger parks. No standards in relation to population are possible, but these parks are counted in with the large parks, playgrounds, etc., in the over-all standards. They are frequently combined with one or more of the recreational facilities discussed above.

Large Parks and Bathing Beaches

Large parks are even less amenable to standards than neighborhood parks. They are usu-

large areas, such as golf, riding, boating, and bathing on beaches or possibly in swimming pools, though pools might be more appropriate in neighborhood parks or playfields.

Where *beaches* are 250 to 300 feet wide, including 50 feet of water, 50 square feet per person is uncomfortably crowded, 100 square feet per person is crowded, and 160 square feet per person is comfortable.[9] If the land back from the beach is developed for recreational use, the capacity per lineal foot of beach can

Courtesy, Toronto Park Department.

FIGURE 10·12. VIEWS IN A WILD PARK DONATED TO THE CITY OF TORONTO

ally 100 acres or more in extent, serving the city as a whole as well as the adjacent neighborhoods. As Henry V. Hubbard has said:

> The large park . . . should provide for many people, but, at least in parts of its extent, it should not be crowded by them. It may have areas where people congregate, but its essential parts are those where a person may get away from his kind, and enjoy something of the freedom of natural landscape.
>
> This means that the open areas of the park should be large enough to give some sense of extent, and self-contained, not intruded upon by the sight of buildings and other town-made structures. The open lawn in the Country Park at Franklin Park [in Boston] is 160 acres in extent; and is, besides, the foreground for a distant view. . . . The "Wilderness" [in the same park] is about 90 acres.[8]

There may be included within large parks limited areas for active recreation, as well as zoological gardens, and activities which require

be increased. There is not much information available on the need for beaches, but at New London, Connecticut,[10] it was estimated that about 4,800 people from the city of 30,000 might use the beach on a maximum day, with 11,000 coming from a 50-mile radius outside the city. This amounts to about 16 per cent of the population within five miles and one per cent of the population within 50 miles. Any city that is fortunate enough to have natural beaches should preserve as much as possible for recreational use, as they are more attractive than swimming pools and provide the most popular form of recreation.

Some of the notable large parks of the world are the Bois de Vincennes (2,270 acres) and the Bois de Boulogne (2,095 acres) of Paris, the Tiergarten (630 acres) in Berlin, the Prater

[8] "Parks and Playgrounds, Their Requirements and Distribution as Elements in the City Plan," by Professor Henry V. Hubbard, *Proceedings of the 14th National Conference on City Planning*, Springfield, Mass., 1922, page 10.

[9] *Public Recreation*, Vol. V, Regional Survey of New York and Its Environs, 1928, page 116.

[10] *Restoration, Expansion and Development of Ocean Beach, New London, Conn.*, W. Earle Andrews and A. K. Morgan, Engineers, 1938.

Gardens (1,500 acres) in Vienna, the Stadtwaldchen (about 1,000 acres) of Budapest, and Phoenix Park (nearly 2,000 acres) in Dublin.

New York City has its Central Park of 862 acres in Manhattan; Prospect Park of 575 acres, Marine Park of 1,792 acres, Shore Parkway of 827 acres, and Spring Creek Park of 618 acres in Brooklyn; Pelham Bay Park of 2,131 acres, Van Cortlandt Park of 1,146 acres, and Bronx Park of 721 acres in The Bronx; Flushing Meadow Park of 1,258 acres and Forest Park of 538 acres in Queens; and Great

Courtesy, Boston Park Department.

FIGURE 10·13. VIEWS IN THE LARGE PARKS OF THE BOSTON PARK SYSTEM

Lefthand view, the Rose Garden in the Fenway, with the Museum of Fine Arts in the background; righthand view, along Muddy River Parkway.

Courtesy, Long Island State Park Commission.

FIGURE 10·14. JONES BEACH STATE PARK, LONG ISLAND

An outstanding development serving the New York metropolitan area; West Bathhouse, with swimming pool, in foreground.

Kills Park of 1,256 acres in Staten Island. Philadelphia has its Fairmount Park of 3,316 acres, almost in the heart of the city; New Orleans its City Park (1,500 acres) and Audubon Park (365 acres). Batterson Park (1,372 acres) in Minneapolis, Swope Park (1,386 acres) in Kansas City and Golden Gate Park (1,013 acres) in San Francisco are among the other outstanding large parks in the United States. Denver owns large areas of parks in the Rocky Mountains at quite a distance from the city.

Courtesy, Metropolitan District Commission.

FIGURE 10·15.   VIEWS OF THE CHARLES RIVER WATERFRONT OF BOSTON BEFORE AND AFTER THE
CREATION OF THE CHARLES RIVER BASIN

Upper view, Back Street, Boston, as it appeared in 1904; lower view, the Charles River Basin as improved, showing a transformation of the same area.

Chicago Park District Photos.

FIGURE 10·16. VIEWS OF CHICAGO'S EXTENSIVE LAKE-FRONT PARKS

Upper view, Grant Park adjoining the loop district; lower view, Jackson Park looking south, with the Lake Shore Drive skirting the bathing beach at this point.

One of the large park improvements carried out by the city of Boston is as unusual as it is admirable, namely, the creation of the Charles River Basin. Insanitary conditions are often remedied through the costly process of buying up the blighted areas, razing the buildings, and converting the space occupied by them to some public use, but in this instance the same end was achieved, not by destroying improvements, but by creating something new on property which was previously unused and useless. The Charles River was a tidal stream the shores of which, though bordering some of the best parts of Boston on the one side and of Cambridge on the other, were unsightly and unwholesome, especially at low tide. By the building of a dam across the river with a lock to accommodate boats, the construction of quay walls and filling in behind them, and the provision of walks and drives on the reclaimed land, the shores of the river have been converted into rare beauty spots, and the stream itself has become an attractive fresh-water lake. The conditions which prevailed before the improvement was undertaken and the radical change which has been brought about are indicated by the illustrations in Figure 10·15.

The Burnham Plan for Chicago has been mentioned in Chapter 3 (page 24). One of the most spectacular parts of this plan was the extension of the park lands by filling in land under water on the shore of Lake Michigan by building bulkheads and dumping refuse and excavated material back of them. The amount of this material has exceeded the original estimates, and this project has proceeded so rapidly that the plans have been enlarged. A large part of an increase of 2,280 acres in the Chicago park system between 1920 and 1940 was obtained in this way.

Parkways and Reservations

Parkways have already been discussed in the two preceding chapters dealing with the street system (see pages 140 to 147 and page 170). Their extent and spacing are largely dependent on topography and scenery and are not subject to any definite standards, but the parkways should be as well distributed as possible and should tie the larger parks into a system. Areas for active recreation can be placed at intervals where there is more space than is needed for the roadways and their protection, and these can serve the adjacent population. As the entire area provides breathing space, it can be added to the areas of other types of parks in arriving at a figure to compare with the overall standards.

Reservations are extensive areas of natural scenery, usually well beyond the official boundaries of the main city which they serve, and may be owned by the city, a county, or a special commission under a state government; sometimes national monuments or national forests serve the same purpose. They may also include forest preserves or areas acquired primarily for the protection of public water supplies. While reservations may therefore have various names, large size, a generally wide or open character, and remote location are the distinguishing characteristics. They should have a minimum size of at least 1,000 acres. If the headwaters and flood plains of streams are in such reservations, flood prevention can be simplified. The development should be the minimum to make them accessible, and activities should be limited to those which usually cannot be enjoyed in city parks, such as overnight camping, hiking, skiing, picnicking with fireplaces, fishing, horseback riding, and golfing. The area of reservations should not be included in calculating the persons per acre in the city's parks.

National Parks

In the United States the *national parks* are playing an ever-increasing part in the recreation program. While none of the great parks is near enough to a large city for people to make a one-day excursion to it, Yosemite Park (about 750,000 acres) is so close to San Francisco and some of the other cities of California that large numbers can go there for a week-end trip of two or three days. Some of the national forests are closer to cities than the national parks and provide recreation for larger numbers of people.

The extent of the national park system under the control of the National Park Service of the United States Department of the Interior has greatly increased in the last few decades. As of June 30, 1946, it comprised 169 areas with an area close to 20½ million acres and was visited annually by over 20 million persons. While most of its units are in the wide open spaces, several of the smaller ones are close to urban areas.

A very remarkable Canadian national park, so near to centers of population that it can be made readily accessible to the people, is Strathcona Park on Vancouver Island, which covers an area of 532,000 acres in the central part of the island. It is still in large part unexplored, owing to its very rugged character, and has within its limits forests, rivers, waterfalls, canyons, glaciers, and snow-capped mountains, while fish and game are plentiful. Facilities of access to it are now very meagre, but, when they are supplied, it can readily be reached from the cities of Victoria and Vancouver and even from the towns along Puget Sound in the state of Washington.

In France, the Forest of Fontainebleau, with an area of about 42,000 acres, is close enough to Paris for one-day excursions. The same is true of the Grunewald (11,350 acres) between Berlin and Potsdam; Epping Forest of 5,560 acres in Essex County, England, is only about 15 miles from London.

Importance of a City-wide Plan

If there is to be a real park system, it must be designed comprehensively, to fit in with all the other elements of the plan, such as the transportation system, the street system, and the land-use plan, and all these must fit the topography and be designed to serve the probable future population. While it is obviously impossible to formulate as definite a plan for parks as for streets, there must be some relation between them. The parks are also part of the master plan of land use, in which the port, railroad, and industrial locations will probably have the greatest topographic limitations. At the same time, the main traffic streets must have suitable grades. These elements together will probably fix the main business center, and the residential districts will have to be related to the preceding land uses. The parks must serve the people and so must be related to the residential districts, considering the probable density of the different sections.

The land which in time will make the best parks is often passed over by the real estate developer as unsuited to his purposes: precipitous hillsides where the cost of development would be prohibitive; creek bottoms and meadows which may be subject to periodic flooding; wooded tracts somewhat off the existing lines of transit; marshes which may be suggestive of malaria and mosquitoes—any or all of these present great opportunities for effective and economical development into parks. Their actual value is small, the return from them in taxes is insignificant and to cary them until their development is needed will not be a serious burden.

Isolated parks, with nothing but business or heavy-traffic streets around them, lose much of their beauty and a large part of their possible utility. The great beauty and value of the park systems of Boston, Kansas City, and Westchester County, New York, are due in large measure to the admirable system of parkways which connect them. These parkway systems have already been described and illustrated in Chapter 8 (see pages 141 to 144).

Metropolitan and County Park Systems

Park statistics for the metropolitan park systems of seven American cities with populations of over 500,000 are given in Table 17. It will be seen that, although the New York metropolitan region has the largest park system, it has 91.7 persons per acre of park compared with a ratio of only 82.5 persons for the Chicago region. Also, while 3.8 per cent of the area of the New York region is in parks, the Boston region has 6.6 per cent and the Cleveland region has 4.2 per cent. Many of the park areas included in these systems are owned and managed by city or village park commissions or departments.

The Chicago region of 7,817 square miles has 63,450 acres of parks, most of which is in the Cook County Forest Preserve system, but it includes the Chicago city parks, acquired under 27 separate park commissions which are now combined into a single department of parks, and the parks of the other cities in the region.

Boston has exercised unusual foresight in acquiring a group of wild parks well outside the city limits, and the organization and ad-

in as natural a condition as possible. Lynn Woods, of about 1,200 acres, is owned by the city of Lynn and operated as a commercial forest for continuous timber production, but recreational uses are permitted.

The greater part of the 12,200 acres of parks in the Cleveland region belongs to the metropolitan park system of Cuyahoga County and consists of wild wooded areas well outside the central city.

TABLE 17

PARK STATISTICS FOR SEVEN METROPOLITAN DISTRICTS, 1940 [a]

Region	Acres of Parks	Population		Area of Region, Square Miles	Percentage of Region in Parks
		1940 Total	Per Acre of Park		
New York	134,282	12,308,350	91.7	5,528	3.8
Chicago	63,450	5,235,369	82.5	7,817	1.3
Detroit	6,578	2,479,002	376.8	3,250	0.3
Boston [b]	16,724	1,924,710	115.0	398	6.6
Cleveland [c]	12,200	1,217,250	99.8	453	4.2
Buffalo [d]	4,993	798,377	159.9	1,034	0.8
Cincinnati [e]	5,307	620,000	116.8	405	2.1

[a] From *Regional Plan Bulletin* 56, Oct. 8, 1941, Regional Plan Association, New York, page 2.

[b] Based on all parks under supervision of the Metropolitan District Commission in 1940 and those under the jurisdiction of the Park Department of the City of Boston in 1939.

[c] Figures for Cuyahoga County only. There are 2,300 additional acres of parks outside of the region but in the Metropolitan Park System.

[d] Figures are for that part of the region in Erie County only.

[e] That part of the region in Hamilton County only.

ministration of its system of metropolitan parks are admirable. Of the total 1940 regional system of 16,724 acres, 12,804 acres [11] belonged to the Metropolitan District Commission, and the balance to other municipalities in the district. There had been an increase in acreage of 18.5 per cent since 1930. There were 15 different park reservations and 19 parkways under the jurisdiction of the Metropolitan District Commission located in 14 cities and 23 towns, but all within a radius of about 13 miles from the State House in Boston. (See Figure 8·27, page 142). The growth of the parkway system has been described in Chapter 8 (see page 141).

In the Boston region, Blue Hills Reservation of 5,931 acres and Middlesex Fells of 2,165 acres, both owned by the Metropolitan District Commission, are wild reservations maintained

[11] By 1946, this had been increased to 12,921 acres.

The distribution by counties of the 1940 park areas in the New York region is shown in Table 18. Most of the parks in Orange and Rockland counties are properties of the Palisades Interstate Park Commission, which was established to preserve the picturesque features of the palisades along the westerly bank of the Hudson River. After this commission had been established, Mrs. E. H. Harriman gave it a tract of 10,000 acres. This great system of parks is so near New York and the neighboring cities in New Jersey that it may be considered part of their recreation grounds. The parks of Nassau and Suffolk counties are mostly properties of the Long Island State Park Commission, and most of those of Westchester County are owned by the County Park Commission, though New York City helped in financing the first of this county's park properties, the Bronx River Parkway (see Figure 8·29, page 144).

Among other duties the Westchester commission is authorized to make option agreements for acquiring real estate by purchase, to acquire real estate by purchase or condemnation, and to accept gifts, contributions, or bequests of

TABLE 18

Park Statistics, by Counties, within the New York Region, 1940 [a]

	Park Area in 1940		Total Proposed System, Acres
County	Acres [b]	Percentage of County	
New York State:			
New York City	22,054	11.6	28,538
Dutchess (part of)	406	0.5	6,081
Nassau	11,649	6.7	22,140
Orange (part of)	22,084	8.3	39,768
Putnam	3,646	2.4	11,840
Rockland	19,734	16.4	37,948
Suffolk	16,995	2.9	53,722
Westchester	17,990	6.3	24,668
Total, New York State	114,558	6.2	224,705
New Jersey:			
Bergen	2,318	1.5	31,808
Essex	4,529	5.6	6,404
Hudson	799	2.9	1,943
Middlesex	1,369	0.7	7,749
Monmouth (part of)	726	0.3	11,976
Morris	1,406	0.5	13,937
Passaic	1,568	1.3	19,653
Somerset	112	0.1	11,072
Union	4,528	6.9	8,123
Total, New Jersey	17,355	1.2	112,665
Connecticut:			
Fairfield (part of)	2,369	0.9	20,315
Total for region	134,282	3.8	357,685

[a] From *Regional Plan Bulletin* 56, October 8, 1941, Regional Plan Association, New York.

[b] Excluding all parks less than one acre in area.

money, land, or other property. (See Figure 8·26, page 141, for a map of the county park system.)

In the New Jersey part of the New York region there are six county park commissions—in Bergen, Essex, Hudson, Middlesex, Passaic, and Union counties—but most of their parks are like large city parks instead of the wild reservations usually composing the bulk of a metropolitan park system.

The proposed park system for the New York region, as shown on the Regional Plan for New York and Its Environs, consists of 357,685

acres. From 1928, when this plan was prepared, to 1940, 38 per cent of the new acreage proposed was acquired. Between 1936 and 1940 acquisitions totaled 9,396 acres, or an average of 2,349 acres per year.[12] If the same number of acres should be acquired each year, on the average, it would take 95 years to complete the system, but it is more reasonable to assume that the acquisition will be at a uniform rate based on the existing park acreage each year. From 1936 to 1940 the acquisition was at the rate of 1.8 per cent per year; at this rate it would take 54 years to complete the system.

Principles of Acquisition and Development

Public pleasure grounds may be divided into three classes: the wild park, where the natural conditions remain undisturbed as far as possible; the developed park, where by skilful treatment and planting such natural features as meadows, woods, and lakes are combined; the formal park, which is more in the nature of a garden. A city park, if of sufficient size, may pass successively through these stages. There is no greater boon to the city dweller than the opportunity to frequent a place where nature has been interfered with to the least possible degree. A few walks and roads through the woods are all that is necessary in the way of improvement. As such parks become more frequented, and as their natural beauties are much more likely to be destroyed, a greater degree of development with more strict policing may be required; gradually the wild park becomes a developed park, while portions of it may in time be treated as a formal garden. This process of evolution may cover a decade or a generation, and meanwhile other wild parks lying further out may be acquired.

If this process is followed, care must be exercised to prevent the encroachment of incongruous buildings on the park. Many taxpayers and officials consider parks vacant land, ready at any time for public or semi-public buildings,

[12] "Park and Parkway Progress and a Program for Future Regional Expansion," *Regional Plan Bulletin* 56, Regional Plan Association, New York, October 8, 1941.

such as the arsenal and Metropolitan Museum in Central Park, New York City. This park would also have provided a site for the Museum of Natural History if a campaign of popular education had not been successful in preventing it.

It is frequently argued that it is folly to select and acquire park reservations until the actual need of them is unquestionable, and that they should then be placed where that need is greatest; that the additional expense of their acquisition at the enhanced value due to the city's development, and even to the destruction of buildings if the area selected has been built upon, will be less than the carrying charges and loss of taxes if they are bought in advance of their actual need; that unimproved parks are of little value and that their development at great cost is likely to be undertaken prematurely if they are purchased at an early date. There may be instances where these arguments have proved valid, but they are the exception rather than the rule. Nevertheless, a word of caution against premature or excessive development of park area would be in order. S. D. Adshead entered his protest against the disposition to introduce so many paved walks, terracotta vases, etc., in places which would be in far better character if left like Hampstead Heath or some woodland glade. "Why," he asked, "spend so much in making beautiful fields into ugly parks?"

The unrelated and inconveniently located parks in many cities indicate quite clearly that they were selected with little regard to each other and that the most available or cheapest land which offered itself at the time was taken. Frequently the final selection was controlled to a large degree by the persistent effort of those who had property which they wished to dispose of at a good price or who had other holdings in the immediate neighborhood, which increased in value or were made marketable by the location of a park in the vicinity. The argument that a park should not be acquired unless it is at once to be improved is an unsound one.

The judicious selection of the park areas will require skill and judgment, and the advice of a competent landscape engineer or architect should be secured. To defer this step until the time comes for actual development is folly. Expert knowledge of the possibilities of the different park sites is worth far more than skill in adapting an unsuitable site to the desired purpose.

Some of London's great parks, such as Hyde, St. James, and Green Parks, Hampton Court, and Kew Gardens, are appurtenances of the Crown, but they are as fully open to the public as those which have been acquired at the city's expense. The Bois de Boulogne and Bois de Vincennes, already mentioned, were parts of the ancient forest owned by the French nation and were granted to the city of Paris on the condition that they be improved as parks, but the sale of a portion of the land was permitted as a means of paying for at least part of the cost of improvement.

All but 52 acres of the 1,386 acres of Swope Park in Kansas City was given to the city in 1896 by Colonel Thomas H. Swope. Many other parks in the United States have been donated in the same way. The park system of Birmingham, England, was started in 1856, when a 10-acre park was presented to the city and another of 31 acres was given the following year. In 1864 the city bought 50 acres for parks, and in 1873 still another park of 60 acres was presented to the Municipal Corporation. In 1863 a tract of 165 acres on the outskirts of the city was given to Toronto for a public park by one of her public-spirited citizens, and to this the city later added an equal area by purchase. This is still a wild park possessing many picturesque features (Figure 10·12). One of New York's parks was given by two women as a memorial to their father, and while its area is but a little over nine acres, it had an assessed value when presented of more than $600,000. Fort Tryon Park of 62 acres in the borough of Manhattan was presented to New York City by John D. Rockefeller, Jr., after being developed at his own expense. He also donated about 700 acres of land to enlarge the holdings of the Palisades Interstate Park Commission along the top of the palisades in New Jersey to make possible the eventual construction of a parkway to run northward from the George Washington Bridge.

Financing Park and Recreation Programs

The precise size and boundaries of a park need not be determined when the land for it is acquired. It could well be bought as acreage property, and its boundaries may be very irregular. When the street system about it is finally fixed, the park can be trimmed down to such form as is desired and to such size as the locality will probably require. Some of the land which has been acquired may be left outside the boundaries finally decided upon; it may be a few building lots or it may be several city blocks. In the latter case an admirable site for a school or a library will thus be provided which will front upon the park, or perhaps a block away there will be a convenient and not too conspicuous site for a police station or a fire-engine house. In either case there may be land left which can be sold at such an advance over its original cost and carrying charges as will materially help to pay the cost of the park. (See Figure 8·24, page 139.) As an example of this method, Glasgow bought 245 acres of land to create its Queen's Park, which was finally laid out to include 141 acres, and the remaining area is said to have been sold for residence sites for a sum sufficient to pay the entire cost of the park.

The use of benefit assessments in financing park acquisition and development and the principles of their application are discussed in later chapters.[13] This system has been used successfully in financing the Minneapolis park system.

While it is generally admitted that the establishment of a park will result in benefit to the neighborhood in which it is located and that at least a portion of the cost of its acquisition can with justice be assessed upon the district, this is not true of playgrounds. They are necessarily somewhat noisy, and the benefit resulting from their establishment will extend rather to the property which is far enough away to be free from the noise, but near enough to render them readily accessible. To assess the cost of acquiring land for playgrounds in the same manner as for parks—that is, by a graduated assessment with the highest rate on frontage, would, therefore, involve some injustice.

The method followed in the acquisition in 1912 of the 10.5-acre Betsy Head Memorial Playground in the borough of Brooklyn, New York City, was due to this consideration. The citizens of an especially congested district proposed that the city acquire four blocks and assess the cost of so doing at a flat rate over a district of such size that the expense would be about $10 for each lot unit of 2,000 square feet. This was done, the area of assessment being made approximately circular in form with a diameter of about two miles. Three of the blocks are devoted to an athletic field, baseball and football grounds, swimming pool, and other recreation facilities for larger children and grown people, while the fourth block is set aside as a recreation ground for mothers and small children.

In a study of the trend in land values around this playground over the following 15 years it was found that land values bordering the playground rose 175 per cent, and those on streets one to three blocks away rose 118 per cent, while average increases in the entire tax section were only 89 per cent. This same study concluded, however, that "it is highly probable that a small playground, located in a mixed business and residential neighborhood, has very little effect one way or another on the surrounding properties." [14]

Selected References

HANMER, LEE F., in collaboration with THOMAS ADAMS, FREDERICK W. LOEDE, JR., CHARLES J. STOREY, and FRANK B. WILLIAMS: *Public Recreation*, Vol. V, Regional Survey of New York and Its Environs, 1928. Distributed by Regional Plan Association, Inc. New York.

HUBBARD, HENRY V.: "Parks and Playgrounds—Their Requirements and Distribution as Elements in the City Plan" (with discussion), *Proceedings of the Fourteenth National Conference on City Planning*, Springfield, Mass., 130 East 22nd Street, New York, 1922, pages 1–45.

National Recreation Association, New York: *Play Space in New Neighborhoods*, 1939; *Standards for*

---

[13] See Volume II: Chapter 22, "The Economic Value of a City Plan," and Chapter 23, "Financing a City Plan."

[14] *Public Recreation*, Vol. V, Regional Survey of New York and Its Environs, 1928, page 47.

Neighborhood Recreation Areas and Facilities, 1943; *Standards: Playgrounds, Playfields, Recreation Buildings, Indoor Recreation Facilities,* 1943.

Planning for Recreation Areas and Facilities in Small Towns and Cities (prepared by J. LEE BROWN, Consultant on Community Planning), Office of Community War Services, Federal Security Agency, Washington, D. C., 1945.

Recreation Use of Land in the United States (prepared by the National Park Service), Vol. IX of the Report of the Land Planning Committee to the National Resources Board, U. S. Government Printing Office, Washington, D. C., 1938.

"Report (Preliminary) of Committee on Park and Recreation Standards" (S. HERBERT HARE, Chairman, S. R. DEBOER, RUSSELL H. RILEY), *Planning 1943,* Proceedings of the Annual Meeting held in New York City May 17–19, American Society of Planning Officials, Chicago, 1943, pages 106–112.

PERIODICALS

Yearbook (Annual) Park and Recreation Progress, National Park Service, U. S. Department of the Interior, Washington, D. C.

Questions

1. Why is the provision of public recreation facilities becoming of increasing importance?
2. What desirable standard is frequently used in determining the total amount of park area required in a municipality? Name some cities that have parks in excess of this standard.
3. List the principal types of public parks and recreation facilities that should be provided in a typical city.
4. What is the approximate radius of the area served by each of the principal types of recreation facilities?
5. What principles should be observed in the selection of areas for public parks?
6. What types of facilities can be provided in large parks within a city? In outlying wild parks and reservations?
7. What should be the relation between park sites and the plan of land uses?
8. What are the arguments for and against the acquisition of park areas some time in advance of their development?
9. Give examples of large parks donated by private individuals.

11

THE LOCATION OF PUBLIC AND SEMI-PUBLIC BUILDINGS

IN THE CLASSIFICATION OF PUBLIC BUILDINGS ARE included not only those in which the business of the nation, the state, or the city may be conducted and such buildings as public libraries and museums, which are frequented by the public, but also buildings constructed and maintained for the exercise of any of the functions performed by any public authority. In this last group are schools, penal and charitable institutions, markets, hospitals, police and fire houses, baths, structures connected with water supply and drainage, and even bridges and monuments. Efforts to so group important public buildings as to form effective civic centers will also be treated in this connection.

Under semi-public buildings are included churches and buildings used for amusement and entertainment under private as well as public management; also the various buildings and plants, many of which in European countries are maintained by the public authorities, but which in America are commonly left to public-service corporations, such as railway stations and terminals, lighting and heating plants, and financial institutions. Finally, some outstanding developments in the form of co-ordinated commercial centers will be described, and the standards and principles given which should be observed in the planning of local shopping centers.

In ancient cities individual dwellings were modest and unpretentious, while public buildings were dignified and beautiful. Palaces and castles, the abodes of reigning princes or their representatives, typified the power and dignity of the state, and nothing was too costly, no scale was too great to impress the people with their power and grandeur. The cities were rich and powerful, and their buildings were planned and adorned for the purpose of impressing their citizens and those of other cities with their power and dignity. Churches and cathedrals were the expression of the devotional spirit of the people, and their wealth or their labor was lavished on these structures. The powerful guilds built houses of beauty, and these were commonly grouped about "places" dominated by the Rathaus or the Hôtel de Ville in such a manner as to produce a charming and dignified effect.

Many American cities have profited by generous gifts from successful businessmen in the form of financing and generously endowing either public buildings, such as libraries or community centers, or semi-public institutions. Sometimes these have taken the form of more personal memorials, such as a statue or fountain. In some cases, unfortunately, the donor has prescribed limitations concerning the site or its treatment which have been the despair of the architect or sculptor charged with responsibility for the design and have prevented a harmonious relationship to adjoining structures.

There has been an awakening to the importance of the better design and grouping of both public and semi-public buildings, and a number of plans have been made for such grouping, especially in the United States, many of which attain a degree of imposing dignity and even grandeur which at least equal anything heretofore accomplished. The greatest impetus in this direction was probably the object lesson given by the wonderfully effective arrangement of the principal buildings of the Chicago Exposition of 1893, which, as already noted, gave great stimulus to the modern city-planning movement, if, indeed, it did not start the movement, at least in America.

General Principles Governing Sites of Public Buildings

As a store or theatre must be located conveniently to the people to be served, so should a public building. The public auditorium which may serve as a convention center should be near transit and transportation facilities; the courts, city hall, and offices of the tax collector and similar governmental agencies which must be visited by large numbers of people should be in the downtown areas where they are convenient to the most people, but on the edge of, and not in the center of, the main retail and commercial center; the fire and police stations and schools should be spotted to serve evenly, and with maximum convenience, large areas. The first consideration in locating any public structure must be the relative usefulness of that location for the purpose served. The second consideration should be the relationship of the function of that particular structure to other functions. The court and the jail; the water, sewer, street, and highway departments; the assessor, tax collector, and other departments dealing with real estate information— the units within each of these groups, and similarly intrarelated ones, should be convenient to each other. On the other hand, there is no important functional relationship between any of these and the public auditorium, a school, or various other cultural services for which buildings or other structures may be required. In a city of moderate size, however, where no inconvenience results from grouping buildings having unrelated functions, administration will be simplified and a more impressive effect may be obtained by such a group.

In very large cities there is a tendency toward decentralization, which is really the fundamental idea back of the so-called "garden city" movement. The location of all public buildings in one group, while it may be convenient for administration, is likely to involve congestion and annoyance to many of those who have business with the various departments of the city government. A grand climax may be all right in a city of a quarter of a million people, but when it becomes a city of several millions subcenters for government and other public activities will not only serve the public convenience, but will also add greatly to the interest and attractiveness of a large town. The segregation of places of amusement, such as theatres, has some advantages, in that, if one is unable to secure seats at one place of entertainment, he can probably be accommodated at another within a few minutes' walk; but such segregation involves long and tiresome journeys for many of those who wish to patronize the theatres or other places of amusement and is likely to result in serious congestion of traffic.

Thomas Adams has written:

The adornment of cities by the monumental treatment of centers and public buildings must continue to be one of the chief aims in city planning. Such adornment has always been the dominant consideration in the planning of capital cities by powerful rulers; but in democratic countries it is, or should be, secondary to the aim of securing healthfulness and efficiency in living and working conditions. The civic ardor that is necessary to create beautiful building in a democracy must have its roots in healthful homes, and a community that is well housed will grow in that pride and love of city that produces order and beauty in public places and in buildings devoted to art, education, and associated community life in all its forms.

The creation and preservation of beauty are possible without extravagance. Ugliness and disorder usually follow from the wrong use of money, not from saving it.

Every city gives expression to the character of its civic life in its centers. The aim should be to make these dignified and spacious, with the architecture appropriate for the functions of the buildings and embodying the distinction that comes from simple outlines and good proportions rather than from ostentatious ornament.[1]

Although important public buildings in Continental Europe are generally of good design and occupy interesting and picturesque sites, the average buildings of this kind in Great

[1] *Outline of Town and City Planning*, by Thomas Adams, Russell Sage Foundation, New York, 1935, pages 309–310.

Britain and the United States have been of inferior design and are poorly located. In the case of the Romer, of Frankfort, additional units of a design harmonizing with the ancient building have been added from time to time to meet the need of more space, and the result is admirable. Such buildings have been better designed in recent years, but the gridiron plan of most cities in the Western World does not permit them to be seen to advantage.

Where a city occupies level ground, monumental buildings can be seen to advantage only if they are approached by streets of adequate width affording a view of them from a distance. Where the site is hilly or undulating, such buildings should, if possible, be placed at the grade summits. Figure 11·1 shows the great advantage of such a location and the unfortunate effect of misplacing a monumental structure with respect to the grades of the approaches to it. An admirable example of an advantageous location is that of the Arc de Triomphe in Paris at the summit of a hill with twelve avenues leading to it. However, the Château at Versailles, which is so far back of the grade summit that only the upper part of the building can be seen by one approaching it from the gardens, is obviously misplaced. The great Palais de Justice in Brussels occupies a commanding site on a hill and can be seen from nearly all parts of the city, although there are no great avenues leading directly to it. The water front sometimes affords an excellent site for a public building in cases where a purely commercial development does not crowd too closely upon it. A good example is the Palace Monroe at one end of the water-front boulevard at Rio de Janeiro (Figure 11·2). A monumental building effectively situated on the water front at San Diego is shown in Figure 11·3.

A good example of a monumental public building which can be seen to advantage is the huge City Hall of Philadelphia, which is 486 feet 6 inches long and 470 feet wide, with an inner court 220 by 200 feet, and was erected at a cost of more than $18,000,000, exclusive of fittings and furnishings. The centers of each of the four sides are pierced by arches 18 feet wide and 36 feet high, affording access for pedestrians to and across the central court on the lines of the two intersecting streets which

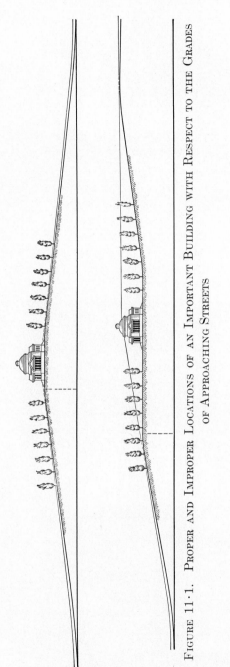

FIGURE 11·1. PROPER AND IMPROPER LOCATIONS OF AN IMPORTANT BUILDING WITH RESPECT TO THE GRADES OF APPROACHING STREETS

lead directly to it. It is located on the axes of Broad and Market streets and Fairmont Parkway. The Parkway was constructed some time after the City Hall, through a solidly built-up area, and while it is poorly designed

Courtesy, Brazilian Government Trade Bureau.

FIGURE 11·2. MONUMENTAL BUILDINGS ALONG THE WATERFRONT OF RIO DE JANEIRO

Monroe Palace (with dome), which houses the Brazilian Senate, looks out upon the beautiful harbor across Paris Square.

Courtesy, San Diego Club.

FIGURE 11·3. CIVIC CENTER BUILDING OF SAN DIEGO FRONTS ON THE HARBOR

from the standpoint of traffic intersections, its appearance and the vista terminated by the City Hall which it furnishes are impressively

mental public building with a tower located on the axes of two streets and thereby visible to advantage.

Courtesy, Pennsylvania Railroad.

FIGURE 11·4. PHILADELPHIA'S CITY HALL ON THE AXIS OF FAIRMOUNT (BENJAMIN FRANKLIN) PARKWAY

View from Logan Square with the tower of City Hall in the background.

beautiful. The axis of the parkway passes directly through the Penn statue, which surmounts the great tower of the City Hall, rising to a height of 584 feet above the level of the sidewalk. (See Figure 11·4.)

The Nebraska State Capitol, shown in Figure 2·3, page 12, is another example of a monu-

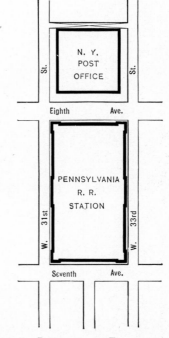

FIGURE 11·6. LOCATION OF PENNSYLVANIA RAILROAD STATION AND THE GENERAL POST OFFICE, NEW YORK CITY, WITH RESPECT TO THE STREET SYSTEM

Courtesy, Department of Parks, New York City.

FIGURE 11·5. NEW YORK PUBLIC LIBRARY AT FIFTH AVENUE AND 42ND STREET

A monumental building which cannot be seen to advantage from approaching streets.

An example of a public building which cannot be properly seen is the main building of the New York Public Library, which occupies one end of a small park, with a frontage of 460 feet on Fifth Avenue. Its beautiful façade can nowhere be seen to advantage. The illustration in Figure 11·5 shows the best view of this faces. (See Figure 11·6.) The cities of the United States are replete with such impressive buildings which cannot be seen to advantage.

The aim of city planners and architects usually is to locate public buildings, whether isolated or in groups, so that each building shall be a single unit, even though it may bear a cer-

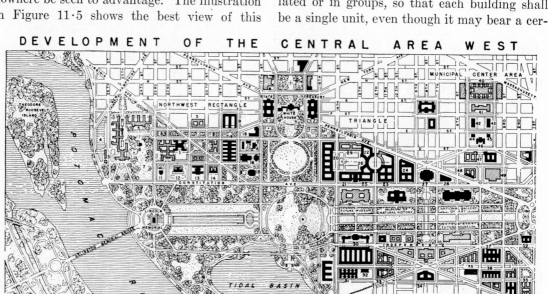

DEVELOPMENT OF THE CENTRAL AREA WEST

NORTHWEST RECTANGLE

1 WAR DEPARTMENT
2 NAVY DEPARTMENT
3 NAVAL MUSEUM
4 BASIN FOR HISTORIC SHIPS
5 SITE FOR FUTURE BUILDING
6 OLD NAVAL OBSERVATORY
  (proposed Planetarium)
7 NAVAL HOSPITAL (abandoned)
  (proposed Overlook Park)
8 RAWLINS PARK EXTENDED

9 DEPARTMENT OF THE INTERIOR (old)
10 DEPARTMENT OF THE INTERIOR
11 PHARMACEUTICAL BUILDING
12 NATIONAL ACADEMY OF SCIENCES
13 FEDERAL RESERVE BOARD
14 PUBLIC HEALTH SERVICE
15 PAN AMERICAN UNION
16 D.A.R. CONSTITUTION HALL
17 AMERICAN RED CROSS
18 CORCORAN GALLERY OF ART

TRIANGLE

20 DEPARTMENT OF COMMERCE
21 DEPARTMENT OF LABOR
22 POST OFFICE DEPARTMENT
23 INTERNAL REVENUE
24 DEPARTMENT OF JUSTICE
25 INTERSTATE COMMERCE COMMISSION
26 DEPARTMENTAL AUDITORIUM
27 NATIONAL ARCHIVES
28 FEDERAL TRADE COMMISSION
29 OLD DISTRICT BUILDING

SOUTHWEST AREA

30 DEPARTMENT OF AGRICULTURE
31 BUREAU OF ENGRAVING AND PRINTING
32 CENTRAL HEATING PLANT
33 BUREAU OF HOME ECONOMICS
34 PROCUREMENT DIVISION
35 SITES FOR FUTURE BUILDINGS
36 SITE FOR SMITHSONIAN INSTITUTION
37 SOCIAL SECURITY BUILDING
38 RAILROAD RETIREMENT BUILDING
39 FEDERAL OFFICE BUILDING № 1 (Census)

FIGURE 11·7. PLAN FOR THE PUBLIC

building which is obtainable, and it is obvious what has been lost through this poor location. Had a little more of the park been given up to this monumental building, so that it could have been set back even 100 feet further from the line of Fifth Avenue, it would have been much more effective. The Pennsylvania Railroad Station in New York suffers from the same lack of space from which to view it. Occupying two city blocks and what was formerly an intervening street, with an area of more than 8⅓ acres, it is set back only a few feet from the building line of Seventh Avenue, which it

tain relation to others. Each building is given a site of its own, with due regard for those of its neighbors. There are those, however, who strongly urge the avoidance of an appearance of isolation, even in buildings of the greatest importance, and who instance the charming effect of an apparently irregular "place" where really great buildings are seen to far better advantage when flanked by those of minor importance, or when even physically connected with them, and cases are cited where some small and relatively mean buildings have been removed with such disappointing result that they were subsequently replaced. The artistic judgment of these writers and critics will not be questioned, but these pages are frankly written from the viewpoint of the engineer; and it is the engineers who will largely control the general plan of the city, making it easy or difficult to select sites for public and semi-public

in Ghent, each standing by itself, are said to suffer from their isolation, and this view is probably correct, but no city plan likely to be made today would contemplate such locations. It is difficult to imagine anything more pleasant in its simple dignity than the New England village green, with the church, or

AND EAST OF THE CAPITOL - WASHINGTON D. C. 1941

MUNICIPAL CENTER AREA	CAPITOL AREA	EAST CAPITOL STREET DEVELOPMENT
40 GENERAL ACCOUNTING OFFICE	50 SUPREME COURT	60 FOLGER LIBRARY
41 DISTRICT COURT OF D.C.	51 SENATE OFFICE BUILDING	61 HOLMES MEMORIAL GARDEN
42 POLICE COURT	52 HOUSE OFFICE BUILDING	62 ARMY MEDICAL MUSEUM
43 MUNICIPAL COURT	53 NEW HOUSE OFFICE BUILDING	63 PROPOSED SEMI-PUBLIC BUILDINGS
44 COURT OF APPEALS	54 LIBRARY OF CONGRESS	64 PROPOSED FEDERAL OFFICE BUILDINGS
45 JUVENILE COURT	55 LIBRARY OF CONGRESS ANNEX	65 PARKING AREAS
46 OLD SUPREME COURT OF D.C	56 CITY POST OFFICE	66 EASTERN HIGH SCHOOL
47 MUNICIPAL BUILDINGS	57 GOVERNMENT PRINTING OFFICE	67 ELIOT JUNIOR HIGH SCHOOL
48 CENTRAL LIBRARY	58 FUTURE BUILDING	68 CONSTITUTION AVENUE EXTENDED
49 PROPOSED AUDITORIUM	59 BOTANICAL GARDEN	69 INDEPENDENCE AVENUE EXTENDED

70 ARMORY	
71 STADIUM	
72 SPORTS FIELD	
73 NATATORIUM	
74 TENNIS ARENA	
75 RECREATION AREA	
76 DISTRICT JAIL	
77 GALLINGER HOSPITAL	
78 PROPOSED MASSACHUSETTS AVE. BRIDGE	
79 CONGRESSIONAL CEMETERY	

BUILDINGS AREA IN WASHINGTON, D. C.

Courtesy, National Capital Park and Planning Commission.

buildings, without the costly and disheartening process of tearing down buildings and rearranging streets in order to provide such sites. If there are smaller structures on adjacent plots which will enhance the beauty of the more important buildings, they can remain; if necessary, they can be built. If competent authorities decide that they should go, they can readily be removed. The small and shabby shops which cluster about Antwerp Cathedral are held by some to enhance its beauty, by others to detract from it. The Cathedral of St. Bovan, the Church of St. Nicholas, and the old belfry

churches, and the town hall placed either in it or fronting it. They are not connected with other buildings in order to secure a picturesque effect; each has its own site; they are in many respects isolated, yet the impression they create is a very satisfactory one.

Civic Centers

The grouping of public buildings is advantageous in that it will permit the concentration of public business and facilitate the conduct of interdepartmental affairs, in addition to which

Courtesy, The National Commission of Fine Arts.

FIGURE 11·8. PUBLIC BUILDINGS AREA OF WASHINGTON, D. C., 1947, AS SEEN FROM THE WASH-
INGTON MONUMENT

Upper view, looking east toward the Capitol. Lower view, looking northwest up the Potomac; buildings in center foreground are "temporary" offices built during World War I.

such grouping will give an added dignity to the city and make a favorable impression upon visitors. This is especially true of cities of moderate size or those of several hundred thousand population. The effective grouping of public buildings to create civic centers has re-

ment of the government center as designed by the National Capital Park and Planning Commission, and Figure 11·8 shows the actual appearance of the west half of the area in 1947. The distance from the Capitol to the Lincoln Memorial on the bank of the Potomac is about

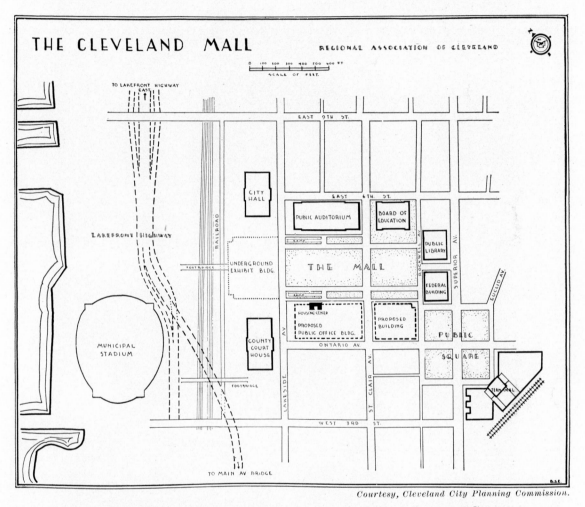

Courtesy, Cleveland City Planning Commission.

FIGURE 11·9. PLAN FOR ULTIMATE DEVELOPMENT OF THE CIVIC CENTER OF CLEVELAND

ceived much attention of late, so much so that it appears to have become a passion in American cities. Numerous towns, great and small, and many villages are now studying this problem.

Probably no such extensive grouping of monumental public buildings has ever been planned or undertaken as is proposed for Washington. Each one of these buildings is given a spacious site, so that it can be seen to advantage. Figure 11·7 shows the plan for eventual develop-

two miles. Along the easterly two-thirds of this distance, or between the Washington Monument and the Capitol, most of the public buildings have been completed; the other one-third is a beautiful park. An extensive new development is planned east of the Capitol, which will eventually result in a public buildings center extending all the way from the Potomac to the Anacostia rivers.

Throughout the plan there has been no striving after picturesque effects by placing one great building where it will show to advantage by contrast with smaller ones. While there will be sufficient harmony in their design and treatment to give a pleasing effect each will stand by itself and be worthy of its setting. This allowance of spacious sites is a conspicuous characteristic

One of the largest and furthest developed civic groups in the United States is in Cleveland and is shown in Figures 11·9 and 11·10. The original plan for this center called for the railroad station to be built at the north end of the mall, near the water front. Its final loca-

Courtesy, Cleveland City Planning Commission.

FIGURE 11·10. AIR VIEW SHOWING PRESENT DEVELOPMENT OF CLEVELAND CIVIC CENTER

of the public buildings of Washington, from the Capitol itself to the railway station, from the White House to the Senate and House office buildings, and it is consequently difficult to appreciate their great size. It has been questioned whether a monotonous, regular, low façade, resulting in long corridors and clumsy interior courtyards, is preferable to taller buildings more widely spaced, with better means of access and simpler floor plans. However, the general success of the arrangement of the government buildings in the national capital hardly can be denied.

tion off the southwest corner of the civic center proper has resulted in two connected groups rather than a single one. Another spacious design for a civic group which has reached an advanced stage of development is in St. Louis and is illustrated in Figures 11·12 and 11·13. In 1946 Los Angeles had elaborate plans for a civic center, as shown by Figure 11·16; at that time several of the buildings were built but open spaces had not yet been acquired and cleared. Funds were authorized in 1947 for the commencement of work on a civic center for the borough of Brooklyn in the city of New

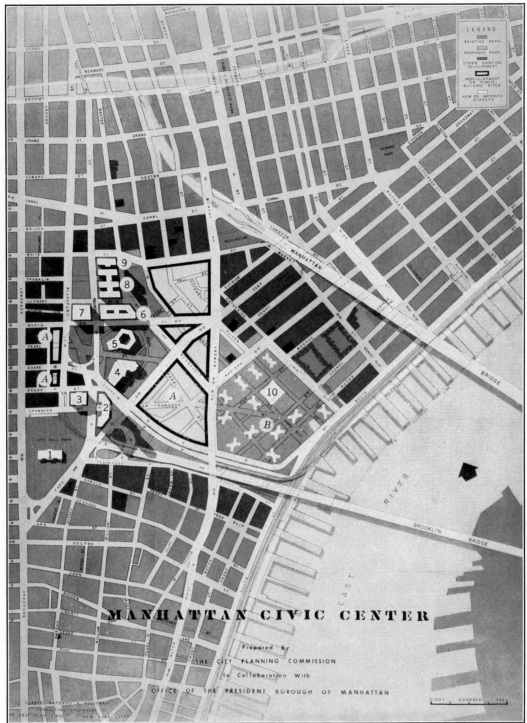

FIGURE 11·11. PROPOSED ENLARGEMENT OF THE NEW YORK CITY CIVIC CENTER AS PART OF A RE-
DEVELOPMENT PLAN

Extensive street changes would provide adequate sites for new public buildings and the redevelopment of adjoining areas.

Key for existing public buildings: 1—City Hall, 2—Municipal Building, 3—Hall of Records, 4—United States Courthouse, 5—New York County Courthouse, 6—State Office Building, 7—Departments of Health, Hospital, and Sanitation, 8—Criminal Courts Building, 9—Jail, 10—Public School 114. *A* indicates principal sites for new public buildings. *B* indicates Governor Smith Houses, a proposed public housing project.

225

York, the ultimate design of which is shown in Figure 11·17.

The city of New York has planned and partially completed an extensive civic center in lower Manhattan, which is shown in Figures 11·11 and 11·18 (page 231). To the observer on the ground the scheme appears as three sepa-

spoiled. The post office building has been removed, and the proposed removal of the courthouse, as shown in the plan, will restore this setting. Site costs in the area surrounding City Hall Park resulted in the next group of buildings being located a few blocks to the north and cleared an area of several blocks

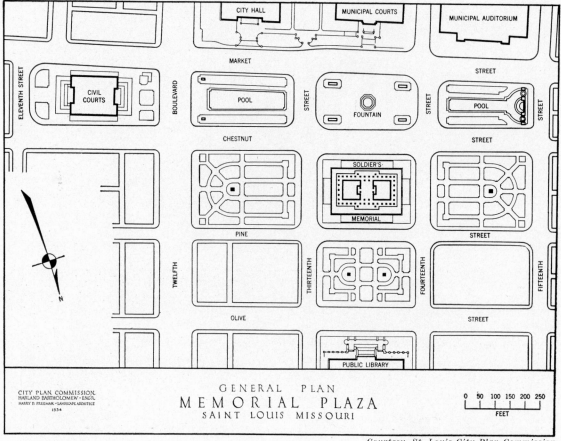

GENERAL   PLAN
MEMORIAL   PLAZA
SAINT   LOUIS   MISSOURI

CITY PLAN COMMISSION.
HARLAND BARTHOLOMEW · ENGR.
HARRY D. FREEMAN · LANDSCAPE ARCHITECT
1934

0   50   100 150 200 250
FEET

Courtesy, St. Louis City Plan Commission.

FIGURE 11·12

rate centers. The original public building in this area was the New York City Hall, which admirable two-story building was erected during the first decade of the nineteenth century in a triangular park, which has lately become an oasis in a district fast being given over to skyscrapers. The municipal authorities foolishly permitted the United States Post Office to be erected at the apex of this triangle, and then built a large courthouse directly in the rear of the City Hall. Both of these buildings were of poor design and, while the City Hall itself has been jealously preserved, its setting was

around Pearl and Centre streets of some of the worst slums in the city (see Chapter 14, Volume II). The third subdivision of this civic center area centers around the block bounded by Lafayette, Leonard, Centre, and Franklin streets, still occupied in 1947 by the old Tombs Prison (then unused), which it was proposed to demolish to form an open space.

Areas facing City Hall Park and around the end of Brooklyn Bridge are proposed for redevelopment for a more sightly appearance than the present obsolete structures which overcrowd these blocks. One of the outstanding features of this civic center development in Manhattan (not visible in the illustration) is its exceptional convenience to transit lines, there being stations on three different subways and one elevated line adjacent to or within the

thetic results are pleasing. An example of the type of civic center which may be developed in a small locality is furnished in Verona, New Jersey, which had a population of about 9,000 persons in 1940. In 1947 the existing struc-

Courtesy, St. Louis Chamber of Commerce.

FIGURE 11·13. AIR VIEW OF ST. LOUIS CIVIC CENTER

Memorial Plaza is in the foreground.

area and three bus lines crossing it, in addition to surface cars operating over Brooklyn Bridge.

In San Francisco the rather compact civic center is well developed, as shown by Figure 11·19. In Denver the United States Mint, State Capitol, city and county buildings, a public library, a Greek theatre, and a memorial have been combined in one civic center, shown in Figure 11·23 (page 236). While this layout may be criticized because structures having unrelated functions have been grouped, the aes-

tures in this group consisted of a municipal building, library, high school, and grade school (located across the mall from the municipal building). Figure 11·21 shows a study for its eventual development, which contemplates its extension across the principal street, in connection with proposed parking lots and business structures in the same general area.

Portland, Oregon, has planned an extensive civic center along the water front, with the location selected deliberately in a blighted com-

Courtesy, St. Paul City Planning Board.

FIGURE 11·14.   AIR VIEW OF STATE CAPITOL AT ST. PAUL, MINNESOTA

Courtesy, St. Paul City Planning Board.

FIGURE 11·15.   PLAN FOR MINNESOTA STATE CENTER AND WAR MEMORIAL, ST. PAUL
View looking north.

mercial area. The proposed center was planned in part as a redevelopment project which would stabilize property values in the surrounding

Veterans' Service Building, in St. Paul. An area of approximately 40 acres was to be cleared and added to the 20 acres then occupied

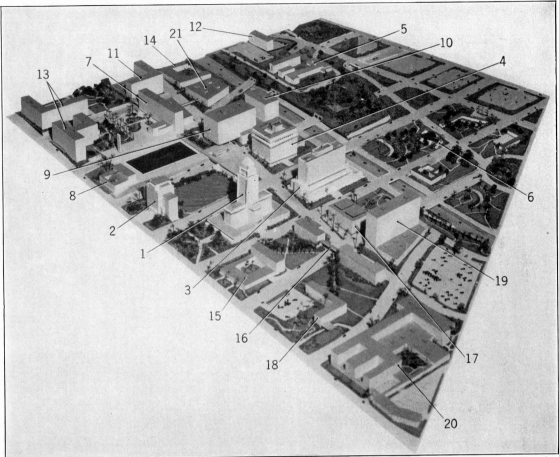

Courtesy, Department of City Planning, Los Angeles.

FIGURE 11·16. EVENTUAL DEVELOPMENT OF CIVIC CENTER IN LOS ANGELES AS PROPOSED BY THE CIVIC CENTER AUTHORITY IN 1947

Key for existing buildings: 1—City Hall, 2—California State Building, 3—Federal Office Building, 4—County Hall of Justice, 5—City Board of Education Building, 6—Plaza Church.

Key for proposed buildings: 7—County Administration Building, 8—Law Library Building, 9—Superior Courts Building, 10—Municipal Courts Building, 11—County Engineering Building, 12—County Agriculture, Forestry, Park, and Recreation Building, 13—Municipal Water and Power Buildings, 14—County Library and Education Building, 15—City Health Building, 16—County Health and Charities Building, 17—Federal Courts Building, 18—City Receiving Hospital, 19—Federal Office Building, 20—Police Administration and Traffic Courts Building.

area, which had been declining for over 20 years. The plan, shown in Figure 11·22, called for buildings to be built on terraces under which parking facilities were to be provided.

In 1945 the Minnesota State Legislature authorized the expenditure of $6,000,000 for the construction of a state center, to include a

by the Capitol Building, the State Office Building, the State Historical Building, and the State Powerhouse. Figure 11·14 shows the area as it was in 1945, and Figure 11·15 shows a perspective of the proposed development when completed. Land and buildings had been acquired in 1947, but construction was awaiting an opportunity for persons to be displaced to find other housing.

There are many other examples of civic centers throughout the country, too numerous to illustrate or even list here, and many more which as yet are only planned. All well-planned new towns and cities include civic centers, with the smaller ones usually prin-

of it in any discussion of the location of public buildings. The early efforts of the General Assembly to find a suitable headquarters site and all the studies of its Interim Committee and Headquarters Commission aimed at the establishment of a new community, in which the various buildings for public meetings and conferences would form the center, but which would

Courtesy, Hon. John Cashmore, President, Borough of Brooklyn.

FIGURE 11·17. BROOKLYN'S CIVIC CENTER, SHOWING PROPOSED LOCATIONS OF PUBLIC BUILDINGS

Based on a model prepared in 1945. *Key for Buildings:* A—Supreme Court Building, B—Covered parking, C—Welfare Center, E—Fire Headquarters, G—Montague Branch Library, H—Children's Court Building, J—Family Court Building, K—County jail, L—Public works repair shop, M—Transportation Building, N—City and Municipal Courts Building, O—Federal Building, P—High school, R—Areas suitable for redevelopment.

cipally cultural and recreational, rather than governmental.[2] The civic center perhaps is essentially a symbolic expression of the organization of society and society's pride in its achievements as a group of individuals.

The United Nations Capital

The development of a headquarters for the United Nations organization, created at the end of World War II, has been of such interest to city planners that mention should be made

[2] See Figure 8·11 (Canberra) and Figure 18·7 (Cidade Dos Motores), Volume II.

have its own business and cultural facilities and residential accommodations for at least a substantial portion of the delegates and staff. The Interim Committee on Headquarters called on city planners to appraise its alternative sites, and the staff of the Headquarters Commission was headed by an experienced planner, Howard K. Menhinick. If the kind of community first contemplated had been developed, it would have offered an opportunity to create a model of planned development which it was hoped might be as much of an incentive to better city planning as was the International Exposition at Chicago in 1893. The site finally selected raised city-planning problems in adjoining areas but is so small that its development is essentially an architectural problem of the design and grouping of the public buildings required.

An inspection group of the Interim Committee visited 14 sites in the Boston and New

tion of this site would seriously disrupt the community, no decision was made, and a Headquarters Commission was directed to make a new study of all available sites in the Fairfield County, Connecticut-Westchester County, New York, area and to recommend five alterna-

Courtesy, American Scenic and Historic Preservation Society.

FIGURE 11·18. CITY HALL PARK, NEW YORK CITY, AS PARTLY RESTORED

City Hall is in the center of the park. The Municipal Building appears in right background.

York metropolitan areas in January of 1946 and, after study of reports made for it on each site, suggested four sites to the General Assembly but recommended the site of 42 square miles in the North Stamford-Greenwich area of Connecticut, extending into Westchester County, New York. As a result of the wave of local protests on the grounds that the selec-

tive sites to be made up of one with each of the following areas: two, five, 10, 20, and 40 square miles. The staff was organized and got its work under way in July, 1946.

The Headquarters Commission of the United Nations initially estimated its site requirements, based on the establishment of a new community, as follows:

1. Official buildings area—two square miles;
2. Living facilities for all United Nations personnel, plus facilities for 30 per cent of the required service personnel—11½ square miles;
   or
3. Living facilities for all United Nations personnel and all required service personnel—17½ square miles;
4. Required park for border "insulation"—area variable.

The site was to be located not more than 1½ hours' travel time from midtown Manhattan

Plains, New York, aroused highly vocal opposition from a minority of the residents in the area who objected to being evicted from their homes, although the prospect of immediate mass evictions was slight. As a result, final decision was postponed, and during the interim the city of New York offered a 320-acre portion of Flushing Meadow Park, the site of the New York World's Fair of 1939–1940, for the official headquarters buildings, and other sites were

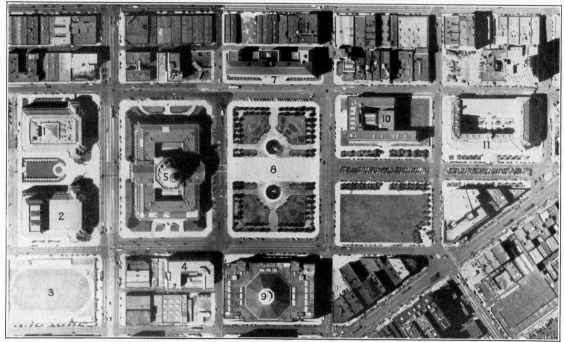

Courtesy, Department of Public Works, City and County of San Francisco.

FIGURE 11·19. AIR VIEW OF SAN FRANCISCO CIVIC CENTER, 1947

Key to Buildings: 1—Veterans Building, 2—Opera House, 3—High School of Commerce Athletic Field, 4—Health Center, 5—City Hall, 6—State Building Annex, 7—State Building, 8—Plaza, 9—Auditorium, 10—Public Library, 11—Federal Building.

by the fastest existing or potential means of public transportation and was to include, or be near to, an area suitable for development as an international air terminal.

Fifteen possible sites in the Westchester County, New York-Fairfield County, Connecticut, area were investigated, of which five sites were recommended by the Headquarters Commission, one each of the areas designated above, varying from two to 40 square miles. Tentative decision on an area lying roughly midway between Greenwich, Connecticut, and White

offered in the San Francisco, Philadelphia, and Boston areas. Less than 24 hours before the final decision was to be made, an area of six blocks in Manhattan, bounded by 42nd Street, First Avenue, 48th Street and the East River, was offered by John D. Rockefeller, Jr., and the city of New York. This area was accepted, and Figure 11·20 shows the plans for its development.

The United Nations Headquarters will be a sort of international civic center on a grand scale. While the arrangement and design of the proposed buildings are impressively beautiful, many city planners, including the author, feel that the final decision to locate on this site was not a wise one. The site, consisting of only about 28 acres, including the area of streets to

of buildings in the vast metropolis, instead of a community with the character and dignity of its own as the earlier proposals contemplated and which such a magnificent concept as the United Nations deserves.

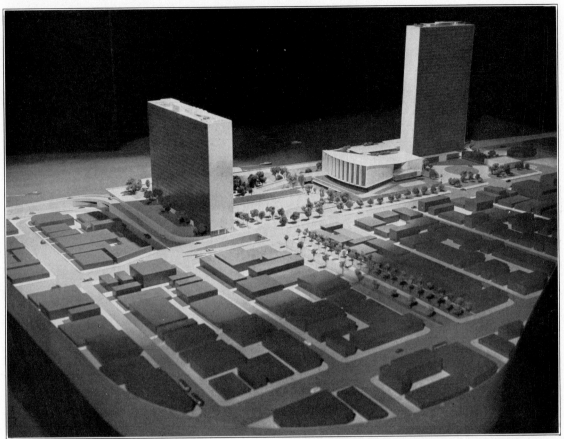

Official United Nations Photo (Department of Public Information).

FIGURE 11·20. ARCHITECT'S MODEL SHOWING PROPOSED UNITED NATIONS HEADQUARTERS IN NEW YORK CITY

be closed or decked over, is so grossly inadequate that the required working space can be provided only by constructing skyscrapers which it will be impossible to see properly, except from across the river. There is no possibility of provision on the site for housing the personnel from all countries who will work there, so that they will scatter through the city of New York, with the attendant loss of convenience to them. Future expansion of the site, if and when it is required, will be very expensive. But, most important, United Nations Headquarters will be just another group

Public Schools

The location of public schools has been neglected too often in city planning and left almost entirely to the local boards of education. School location is an important part of the city plan and must be related to the street system, the park and playground system, and the neighborhood plan (see Chapter 13, "Neighborhood and Community Planning," Volume II). The modern school plant is an expensive investment, and considerable study is merited in so planning for its location and environment as to assure maximum return for money expended. Planning for schools should be done with the most active co-operation between the planning board and the local board of education.

The size of schools varies, depending on several factors. Ray L. Hammon, Chief of

found in different localities. Other authorities have stated that 800 to 1,200 pupils is the minimum economical size, but a school of 400-pupil capacity probably may be taken as the desirable minimum in any case.

The ratio of school population to total pop-

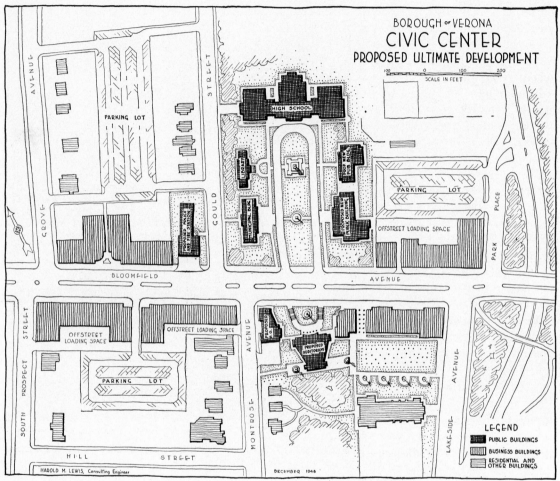

Courtesy, Planning Board, Borough of Verona, New Jersey.

FIGURE 11·21

the School Housing Section in the United States Office of Education, wrote in 1946, "There is little, if any, evidence to indicate that financial economies or educational advantages result from elementary schools larger than 700 . . . pupils. . . ." [3] However, this represents only one opinion, and different standards will be

[3] "Planning the School Plant Program," by Ray L. Hammon, *The American School and University,* Vol. XVIII, American School Publishing Corporation, New York, 1946.

ulation varies greatly and deserves most careful study in the individual community. Computations for nine cities of over 100,000 population in New York, Pennsylvania, and New Jersey in 1940 showed that school children between the ages of five and 13 represented 11 to 12 per cent of the total populations of those cities in that year, and that school children between the ages of 14 and 17 represented five to 6⅓ per cent, with totals for the two age groups ranging from 16.4 per cent in New York

City to 18⅓ per cent in Pittsburgh. However, within a particular city much wider variations will be found. Estimates made for two statistical areas in the borough of The Bronx of New York City showed school populations of 13.6 and 18.2 per cent of total populations respectively in 1940. Some indication of the school population to be expected in a given area may be found in the average number of persons per occupied dwelling unit, and there is a relationship between family income and school population. Records of the Board of Education on school attendance by districts are excellent sources of information.

For planning purposes the important figure to establish is not present but future school attendance. This introduces another variable which is of the greatest importance—that of future age groups (see Chapter 4, pages 41 to 45). Most students of population trends are of the opinion that the proportion of persons of school age in the United States will decrease at an accelerating rate in the last half of the twentieth century. This change in proportion must be estimated as accurately as possible for the various school districts in the community.

Various communities use different divisions in their education system, which have an important effect on the school plan. Some may use eight years of elementary school followed by four years of high school, whereas elsewhere there may be six years of elementary school, three of junior high school, and three of high school. The preliminary year of kindergarten is common practice in education systems today, and in many communities the pre-kindergarten nursery school is becoming increasingly popular. The maximum desirable walking distance from home to elementary school usually is considered one-half to three-quarters of a mile. The distance may be increased for junior high schools, and further increased for high schools.

Schools should be so located as to avoid the necessity of dangerous street crossings for school children in so far as is possible. The school site should be sufficiently large to accommodate playground facilities. The location of playgrounds adjacent to elementary school buildings and playfields adjacent to high school

buildings makes for more efficient use of these facilities and simplifies supervision (see Chapter 10, pages 202 and 203).

Miscellaneous Public Structures

There are many minor public buildings—far greater in number than those which are likely

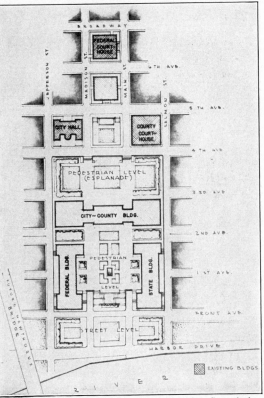

FIGURE 11·22. PROPOSED EXPANDED PUBLIC BUILDING CENTER, PORTLAND, OREGON

Plan of October, 1946, which includes a proposal for underground parking.

to be grouped in a civic center—which are commonly located in a haphazard fashion wherever the most available or the cheapest property can be acquired for them at the time they are erected. These buildings are of two classes, to which different kinds of location are best suited. One class includes the schools of various grades (discussed above), branch libraries, public comfort stations, etc., which need not be and should not be on main traffic streets. Their location will depend to a large degree upon the distribution of population, but, if certain blocks in different parts of the city were set aside for them, several could be grouped together and designed in harmony with each other, with sufficient space about them to in-

important thoroughfares, in order that the territory which they serve might be easily reached. In either case such municipal blocks would be creditable to the city, while the maintenance problem would be greatly simplified.

Photo by O. Roach.

FIGURE 11·23. AIR VIEW OF CIVIC CENTER IN DENVER

sure abundant light and air and with room for future additions, space for which, until needed, might well be devoted to playgrounds. Such a block would be peculiarly well suited to the purpose if the street system about it were sufficiently irregular not to invite traffic. The other class would include such buildings as police stations, fire-engine houses, repair shops, and municipal garages. These could also be designed to harmonize with each other and form consistent groups. They would naturally be located on or in close proximity to the more

Although an effort usually is made to adapt dwellings to climate and environment, too often little attention is paid to these considerations in the location and design of public buildings. A fine example of architecture which harmonizes with a residential environment is shown in the fire station illustrated in Figure 11·24. The post office building in Santa Barbara is also quite different from the usual type of post office to be found through the country, and is more in harmony with the prevailing architecture in the locality, while in two railway stations, the one at San Diego and the other at Barstow, the mission type of architecture, so generally found in California, has been successfully used (Figure 11·25).

While the location of a railroad station is to some extent fixed, all too often insufficient attention has been paid to its proper setting.

Courtesy, Village of Scarsdale, New York.

FIGURE 11·24. A WELL-DESIGNED FIREHOUSE IN A RESTRICTED RESIDENTIAL AREA

Since the railroad station is one of the great "traffic generators" in the city, it should be so located as to be convenient to the heart of the city and to its transit lines and traffic arteries. There should be space around it for waiting cabs, buses, etc., for automobile parking, and for adequate loading platforms, all of which

Arches, monuments, and fountains are supposed to be for purposes of adornment and should, therefore, be placed where they can be seen to advantage; but this, unfortunately, is not always done. In Paris there are many instances of the admirable location of such structures. The Brandenburg Gate across Unter den Linden at the entrance to the Berlin Tiergarten is another. The Washington Arch forms an impressive terminal at the lower end of Fifth Avenue in New York but cannot be seen to advantage for any distance from the south. A Soldiers' and Sailors' Memorial Arch has been erected at the main entrance to Prospect Park in Brooklyn, and although several important streets converge at the plaza in front of this entrance, the arch appears to have been deliberately located off the axis of every one of these streets, and its effect is thereby lost (Figure 11·28).

There are no urban structures other than great public buildings which attract more attention, and the location and design of which are of greater importance, than bridges. As bridges are parts of highways, their position will largely be controlled by the street system, while the material of which they are built, their weight, and their design will necessarily be

FIGURE 11·25. MISSION ARCHITECTURE USED SUCCESSFULLY IN TWO SANTA FÉ RAILROAD STATIONS IN CALIFORNIA

Entrance to San Diego Station (*left*); Barstow in the desert (*right*).

should be off the streets which surround it. Such space also should provide the station with a setting which will permit its architecture to be seen to advantage. The railroad stations in Washington, D. C., and Providence, Rhode Island, are examples of successful location and setting (Figures 11·26 and 11·27).

governed by the character of the foundations, the kind of traffic which is to pass over and under them, the topography of the site, and considerations of cost. Nevertheless, the planner should have a larger voice in designing approaches. It is only in very recent years that approaches to vehicular bridges have re-

FIGURE 11·26. UNION RAILROAD STATION IN WASHINGTON, D. C.

The station (*right center*) is admirably located as one of a group of public buildings.

FIGURE 11·27. RAILROAD STATION AT PROVIDENCE, RHODE ISLAND

The state capitol is in the background; the main business district is immediately behind the point from which the view was taken.

FIGURE 11·28. GRAND ARMY PLAZA, BOROUGH OF BROOKLYN, NEW YORK CITY

The memorial arch in the center of the plaza is on the axis of the park entrance, but not on that of any of the streets intersecting the plaza.

FIGURE 11·29. LONGFELLOW BRIDGE OVER THE CHARLES RIVER

View from Cambridge looking toward Boston.

ceived the careful consideration which they require if the bridge is to function efficiently as a part of the arterial traffic plan.   The Manhat-

FIGURE 11·30.   BAYONNE BRIDGE OVER THE KILL VAN KULL, PORT OF NEW YORK

Connecting Bayonne, New Jersey, with Port Richmond on Staten Island, New York City.

tan, Williamsburg, and Queensboro bridges across the East River in New York City furnish examples of inadequate consideration of

themselves were completed many months before suitable approaches were provided, during which period the public was unable to enjoy other than a very restricted use of them.   In fact, the question of their approaches was not seriously taken up until the bridges themselves were nearing completion, although, if the idea that a bridge is part of a highway is correct, intelligent planning would dictate the determination of the approaches to and connections with a bridge as a part of the original plan.   Today, every one of the bridges over the East River south of the Triborough Bridge needs more adequate vehicular approaches.   As they are, during rush hours the great volumes of traffic which use them find bottlenecks at the ends, which cause great congestion and delay.   The plans which have been made to correct this situation will be very expensive to put into execution.

No one feature of Paris is more impressive than the bridges across the Seine, the beautiful Alexandre III bridge being one of the most notable structures of its size in the world.

FIGURE 11·31.   GOLDEN GATE BRIDGE, SAN FRANCISCO

View looking north.

approaches.   When they were new, one might have thought that they were erected merely for the sake of building a bridge, as the structures

Those of London and Berlin are also interesting and dignified, while the Longfellow Bridge at Boston is a great addition to the monumental structures of the metropolitan district, of which the Massachusetts State House is the center (Figure 11·29). One of the most beautiful types of street bridge is the through arch (see Figure 11·30), which has become popular for moderately long spans in recent years. However, no bridges approach in size and impressiveness the great suspension bridges, with their appearance of grace and delicacy. Of these, probably the most beautiful total effect is produced by the Golden Gate Bridge in San Francisco (Figure 11·31), with its superb natural setting, although there are many others whose structures are equally, or more, beautiful. There are those of the opinion that no suspension bridge ever has been constructed which is more beautiful than the first major span of that type, the Brooklyn Bridge over the East River in New York (Figure 11·32).

The city has to build and maintain within its limits mechanical plants such as pumping stations, refuse destructors, and sewage-disposal works, which the residents of the district in which they may be located are likely to regard as more or less of a nuisance, and the location of which in their neighborhood they vigorously oppose, thinking that it will inevitably mean smoke, noise, bad odors, and unsightliness, with a consequent depreciation of property values. This feeling is not unnatural and is fully justified by the manner in which such plants have been commonly designed, built, and operated.

It has been found possible, however, to eliminate almost entirely these objectionable features. Reservoirs and pumping stations for water supply are now quite generally built so that they are actually an ornament to the city, as witness the Chestnut Hill Reservoir of Boston and the pumping stations of Detroit and Chicago. The sewage-pumping station on the water front of Rio de Janeiro is not at all objectionable. Even sewage-treatment plants can be made not only inoffensive but even attractive, as has been done at Essen-Nord, where such a plant was located in a well-populated district, without, it is said, any complaint of nuisance from it, and in New York City (Figure 11·33). An attractive treatment of a sewage-disposal plant in a suburban community

is shown in Figure 11·34. A chimney of a lighting plant in Dresden has been so designed that it might be taken for an ornamental tower, while in this same city the difficult problem of mitigating the ugliness of a gas holder appears to have been accomplished, not by covering it with aluminum coating, but by enclosing it in a rather attractive concrete structure.

Courtesy, Department of Public Works, New York City.

FIGURE 11·32. BROOKLYN BRIDGE, NEW YORK CITY

The pioneer of suspension bridges; view looking toward Manhattan.

Even when the city has to erect structures far beyond its limits, it is now generally agreed that they should be designed with some regard to their appearance, and that they should be in some way typical and worthy of the city which they serve. Up in the Catskill Mountains, 100 miles from the city, where New York has built a great reservoir, the aerating of the water before it begins its long journey through the aqueduct to the city, has so been done as to provide a beautiful group of fountains (Figure 11·35). At the head of this reservoir the fine road which has been built around it is carried across a ravine by an attractive bridge shown in Figure 11·36.

Commercial Centers

In large cities it sometimes happens that an area of two or more blocks is developed in a unified way by one owner as a commercial center.   While such developments may not always embody all the desirable features which

Hartford railroads in connection with the construction of the Grand Central Terminal, which was begun in 1903.   The Grand Central improvement, covering an area of about 40 acres, probably is the largest commercial center ever developed under one ownership.   It is also probably the greatest single improvement un-

Courtesy, Department of Public Works, New York City.

FIGURE 11·33.   TALLMANS ISLAND SEWAGE-TREATMENT PLANT IN BOROUGH OF QUEENS, NEW YORK CITY

Showing a park-like treatment of a large activated sludge plant.

may be achieved in a unified area, most of them represent considerable improvement over the more usual piecemeal efforts which characterize the commercial sections of cities in the United States.

The older examples of this unified commercial development occurred in connection with railroad terminal improvements, such as the Park Avenue development north of Grand Central Terminal in New York and the Union Terminal Group in Cleveland.   The former is the earlier of the two developments and was made possible by the electrification of the New York Central and New York, New Haven, &

dertaken in the city of New York since the construction of the Brooklyn Bridge, in that it transformed the area from a noisome eyesore to one of the most valuable sections in the city.

The story of the development of the Grand Central area is best told in pictures.   Figure 11·37 shows the plan of the area as it was about 1900, before reconstruction, and Figure 11·38 shows its status in 1939.   Figure 11·45 shows the open yards as they appeared in 1906 while still under steam operation; Figure 11·43 shows the same view after construction of the station and installation of electric operation, but before the yard area was covered; and

Figure 11·44 shows the area in 1939. The entire yard and train shed is completely covered by streets and buildings, including several office buildings, hotels, and apartment houses, as well as Grand Central Terminal itself. (See Figures 6·10 and 6·11 on pages 70 and 71 for plans of the terminal.) Not only was the appearance of this section greatly improved and the capacity of the station more than trebled by the development, but also the complete stoppage of cross-town traffic between 42nd and 56th streets, almost three-quarters of a mile, was reduced to only three blocks from 42nd to 45th streets, and grade separations of

Courtesy, Interstate Sanitation Commission.

FIGURE 11·34. SEWAGE-TREATMENT PLANT DESIGNED FOR A RESIDENTIAL DISTRICT

As shown by the plant of the Belgrave Sewer District, a special improvement district in the Town of North Hempstead, New York.

vehicular traffic were provided, carrying Park Avenue traffic over 42nd and 45th streets, which in effect added a major and much needed north-south traffic artery in the center of Manhattan Island. The locations of Grand Central Terminal and the New York Central Building are two of the best in the city from the aesthetic viewpoint, standing at the end of long vistas up and down Park Avenue, which is 140 feet wide.[4]

[4] For a complete discussion of this development and its history see "The Grand Central Terminal in Perspective," by William J. Wilgus, *Transactions of the American Society of Civil Engineers,* Vol. 106 (1941), pages 992–1051.

The Cleveland Terminal Group is located adjacent to the Civic Center, as shown in Figure 11·9, page 223. The general plan of the area is shown in Figure 11·42, a sectional perspective of the terminal in Figure 11·39, and a

Courtesy, Board of Water Supply, New York City.

FIGURE 11·35. AERATING FOUNTAINS IN FRONT OF ASHOKAN RESERVOIR

Here the water is aerated before passing into an aqueduct for its journey of 100 miles to New York City.

photograph of the principal entrance to the terminal group in Figure 11·40. Like the Grand Central area improvement, the Cleveland Terminal Group is built over the yards and train shed of the terminal and was made possible by electrification of the railroads

Courtesy, Board of Water Supply, New York City.

FIGURE 11·36. TRAVERS HOLLOW BRIDGE ON THE ROAD AROUND ASHOKAN RESERVOIR

through the city. While the Cleveland Group is smaller, its approach from the Civic Center is even more impressive than that to Grand Central Terminal because of the generous open space provided.

Probably the outstanding example of a commercial center not connected with railroad terminal facilities is Rockefeller Center in New York (Figure 11·41). Located between Fifth and Sixth avenues and 48th and 51st streets, in the heart of the finest part of New York's retail and office district, it had 15 buildings in

rate underground offstreet loading and unloading facilities are provided for trucks, and the entire area is connected to the Sixth Avenue subway by underground passageways.

While Rockefeller Center is probably one of the best-organized commercial centers ever built, it is questionable whether such concen-

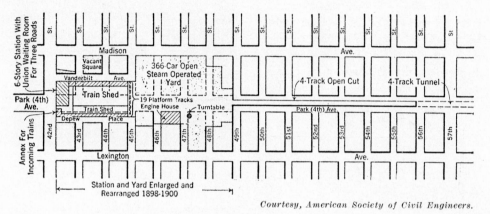

Courtesy, American Society of Civil Engineers.

FIGURE 11·37. PLAN OF GRAND CENTRAL TERMINAL AREA, NEW YORK CITY, AS OF 1900, SHOWING THE THEN-EXISTING DEPOT FACILITIES

1947, including the new Esso Building then under construction. These included three theatres, five office buildings of over 30 stories in height, dominated by the 70-story RCA Building,[5] and a parking garage with space for 800 cars. A private street (Rockefeller Plaza)

tration is desirable. Over 27,000 persons were employed there daily in 1946, and it was estimated that it was visited by an additional 125,000 daily. Its large parking garage frequently is filled to capacity by 10 o'clock in the morning, and at the evening rush hour peo-

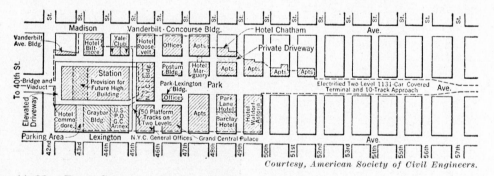

Courtesy, American Society of Civil Engineers.

FIGURE 11·38. PLAN SHOWING GRAND CENTRAL TERMINAL AND ADJACENT BUILDINGS IN 1939

All the buildings shown hatched are built over the yards and train shed.

parallel to Fifth Avenue was constructed between 48th and 51st streets. A sunken plaza, used as a skating rink in winter and an outdoor restaurant in summer, fronts on this new street between 49th and 50th streets. Elabo-

ple are lined up for 30 or more feet at each of the many turnstile entrances to the Sixth Avenue subway station at 48th Street. While surrounding areas contribute to this congestion, Rockefeller Center itself is principally responsible.

[5] Also illustrated in Figure 2·3, page 12.

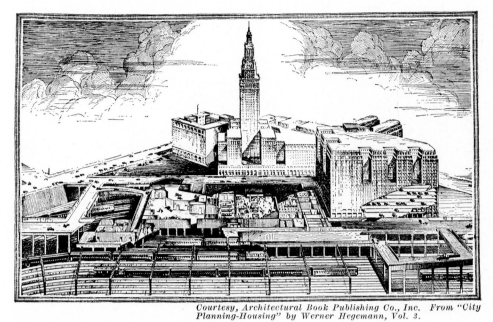

Courtesy, Architectural Book Publishing Co., Inc. From "City Planning-Housing" by Werner Hegemann, Vol. 3.

FIGURE 11·39. SECTIONAL PERSPECTIVE OF THE CLEVELAND TERMINAL

Showing the relationship of its several levels to the waiting room and concourse.

Courtesy, Cleveland Chamber of Commerce.

FIGURE 11·40. NIGHT VIEW OF THE CLEVELAND UNION TERMINAL AND PART OF THE PUBLIC SQUARE UPON WHICH IT FACES

Photo by Press Association, Inc.

FIGURE 11·41. AIR VIEW OF ROCKEFELLER CENTER, NEW YORK CITY

Local Shopping Centers

In recent years the practice of developing unified local shopping centers has become increasingly popular. Because of the need for

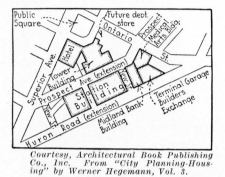

Courtesy, Architectural Book Publishing Co., Inc. From "City Planning-Housing" by Werner Hegemann, Vol. 3.

FIGURE 11·42. GENERAL PLAN OF THE CLEVELAND TERMINAL GROUP

more automobile parking facilities than are afforded by mere street frontage in business areas, such centers have been designed to provide additional space for parking, while im-

which may be expected to locate there, since the laws of supply and demand, which usually determine these factors, cannot be allowed to operate with complete freedom in these cases.

Several surveys have been made to determine how much of what kinds of business are required in relation to population (see Chapter 12, page 262). One of these studies showed that 44 per cent of the total retail business in 16 cities was located in the central business districts and the remaining 56 per cent in outlying residential areas.[6] The most recent and probably the most detailed study of business frontage was made in 1945 in the Cleveland Metropolitan District.[7] A summary of some of the cogent figures from this survey is given in Table 19. It should be noted that isolated businesses outside of shopping centers are not included in the figures presented in this table. Two sets of figures are presented for Cuyahoga County (the Cleveland Metropolitan District), one showing the entire county including the city of Cleveland, and the other showing the county outside of the city of Cleveland. A comparison

Courtesy, New York Central System.

FIGURE 11·43. THE GRAND CENTRAL TERMINAL AS IT APPEARED IN 1915

This view was taken from almost the same point as that shown in Figure 11·45.

proving the convenience and appearance of local business districts. In designing shopping centers for planned communities, where business is to be confined to predetermined areas, it becomes important to have an accurate measure of the amount and types of local business

of the respective figures will show that the reason for doing this was to indicate the relatively

[6] *Urban Land Uses,* by Harland Bartholomew, Harvard University Press, 1932, page 70.

[7] *Shopping Centers,* Howard Whipple Green, Cleveland Real Property Inventory, Cleveland, Ohio, 1945.

lower intensities of various types of business outside of the central area. The figures for Cuyahoga County outside of the city of Cleveland are more indicative of the requirements of a neighborhood shopping center than are the total county figures because the central business uses are omitted.

FIGURE 11·44. LOOKING SOUTH ON PARK AVENUE, MANHATTAN, TOWARD NEW YORK CENTRAL OFFICE BUILDING

The Grand Central Terminal lies immediately behind the office building, through which the Park Avenue roadways are carried.

Occupied business frontage in Cuyahoga County outside of the city of Cleveland amounted to 21 feet per 100 persons in 1945. Since such surveys inevitably must include businesses whose operations are marginal, an allowance of 20 feet of business frontage per 100 persons probably would be ample in planning a neighborhood shopping center in the Cleveland Metropolitan District. It must be em-

phasized, however, that such an allowance is only a general figure. The income group to be housed and the proximity of the neighborhood to other shopping areas will modify this figure. A certain minimum volume of business is required to support any given type of store. Thus, when calculations indicate that more than one store of a particular kind can be supported, one may be sufficient, but when even slightly less than one store of a particular kind is indicated, it may be impossible for such a store to be operated profitably unless subsidized to some extent by an adjustment in rent. This may be desirable in order to secure an essential service for the particular shopping center.

From the standpoint of securing maximum service to the residents of a neighborhood from their shopping center, it probably is desirable to rent or lease business space rather than sell it and to give the residents some voice in the management of the center. Where a neighborhood organization exists, this is one logical function for it. One progressive real estate developer secures the businesses desired when

FIGURE 11·45.   GRAND CENTRAL TERMINAL UNDER STEAM OPERATION IN 1906

Taken shortly before the reconstruction for electrical operation.

potential volumes of sales are insufficient to attract them otherwise by charging rentals as a percentage of gross sales, rather than at a flat rate. In the early stages of neighborhood development, when the ultimate anticipated population has not yet been reached, some such device seems to be almost a necessity if the businesses which are necessary for the convenience of the early "settlers" are to be secured.

In planning a local shopping center, certain principles should be observed. It should be

TABLE 19

INDICES OF BUSINESS DEVELOPMENT IN SHOPPING CENTERS IN CUYAHOGA COUNTY, OHIO (CLEVELAND METROPOLITAN DISTRICT) IN 1945

Type of Store	Total County Including Cleveland				County Outside of Cleveland			
	Persons per Store [a]	Average Frontage per Store [b]	Stores per 5,000 Persons [a]	Frontage per 5,000 Persons [a,b]	Persons per Store [c]	Average Frontage per Store [b]	Stores per 5,000 Persons [c]	Frontage per 5,000 Persons [b,c]
Food Group	*440*	*25*	*11.4*	*272*	*593*	*25*	*8.4*	*210*
Bakery goods	3,750	20	1.3	27	4,475	19	1.1	21
Candy and confectionery	2,800	20	1.8	35	5,400	20	0.9	18
Dairy products	13,200	30	0.4	11	9,715	35	0.5	18
Fruit and vegetable	7,300	21	0.7	15	10,300	19	0.5	9
Total groceries and meat	*700*	*25*	*6.5*	*163*	*1,015*	*27*	*4.9*	*133*
Delicatessen	5,200	20	1.0	20	6,300	20	0.8	16
Grocery stores without meat	3,200	22	1.6	35	5,670	21	0.9	19
Grocery and meat	2,000	32	2.5	81	2,360	36	2.1	77
Meat markets and sea food	3,300	19	1.5	29	4,420	19	1.1	21
Other food stores	7,450	31	0.7	21	10,600	22	0.5	11
General Merchandise Group	*3,100*	*43*	*1.6*	*58*	*5,230*	*36*	*1.0*	*34*
Department stores	25,300	75	0.2	15	42,500	44	0.1	5
Dry goods: general merchandise	5,900	25	0.9	22	13,100	27	0.4	10
Variety, 5 and 10¢, etc.	8,800	38	0.6	21	11,000	41	0.5	18
Automotive Group	*1,300*	*74*	*3.9*	*267*	*1,420*	*72*	*3.5*	*272*
Accessories, tires, batteries	9,100	33	0.6	18	17,900	27	0.3	7
Filling stations	2,300	88	2.2	192	2,330	96	2.1	206
Motor-vehicle dealers	12,150	62	0.4	25	8,500	58	0.6	34
Garages and repair shops	8,900	45	0.6	25	13,600	48	0.4	18
Other	29,600	41	0.2	7	34,000	45	0.1	7
Apparel Group	*1,150*	*22*	*4.4*	*87*	*2,085*	*15*	*2.4*	*35*
Men's and boys' clothing	7,600	26	0.7	17	21,250	21	0.2	5
Women's ready-to-wear	4,200	18	1.2	21	5,870	..	0.9	..
Shoe stores	5,100	21	1.0	20	11,000	19	0.5	..
Other apparel and furnishings	3,200	19	1.6	29	5,870	18	0.9	16
Furniture and Household Group	*1,450*	*30*	*3.5*	*99*	*2,450*	*22*	*2.0*	*46*
Furniture stores	5,100	42	1.0	42	13,600	28	0.4	10
Floor coverings, draperies, etc.	10,500	21	0.5	10	13,100	20	0.4	8
Household-appliance stores	8,600	24	0.6	14	11,300	20	0.4	9
Radio and music stores	10,950	19	0.5	9	15,500	21	0.3	7
Other	5,400	26	0.9	24	9,450	23	0.5	12
Restaurants and Other Eating Places	*735*	*27*	*6.8*	*182*	*1,465*	*28*	*3.4*	*96*
Lumber and Building Group	*3,550*	*29*	*1.4*	*37*	*4,730*	*14*	*1.1*	*15*
Lumber and building-material dealers	17,900	48	0.3	13	17,000	23	0.3	7
Electrical (without radio)	15,600	20	0.3	6	17,000	17	0.3	5
Heating and plumbing	7,600	21	0.7	14	13,100	..	0.4	..
Paint and glass stores	32,850	22	0.2	3	56,700	20	0.1	2
Other Retail Stores	*560*	*27*	*8.9*	*210*	*797*	*25*	*6.3*	*157*
Hardware	4,100	25	1.2	30	4,800	23	1.0	24
Drug	2,450	26	2.0	53	2,830	28	1.8	50
Florists	8,000	26	0.6	16	9,450	35	0.6	18
Gifts, novelties and toys	10,100	19	0.5	9	11,000	18	0.5	8
Jewelry	7,800	17	0.6	11	14,200	15	0.4	5
Office equipment, stationers	6,600	25	0.7	18	18,900	18	0.3	5
Miscellaneous	1,400	22	3.2	72	2,680	25	1.9	47
Total Retail Stores	*120*	*32*	*41.9*	*1,212*	*178*	*31*	*28.1*	*865*
Services, etc.	*380*	*22*	*13.1*	*266*	*517*	*18*	*9.7*	*189*
Barber and beauty shops	950	17	5.2	88	1,260	17	4.0	68
Cleaning and pressing	2,200	20	2.3	47	2,395	20	2.1	42
Laundries	9,700	17	0.5	9	13,600	18	0.4	7
Shoe repair, hat cleaning	2,500	16	2.0	32	4,250	15	1.2	18
Banks	9,400	37	0.5	20	10,300	28	0.5	14
Theatres	16,600	27	0.5	13	16,200	25	0.3	8
Other amusement places	7,700	26	0.7	17	22,700	30	0.2	7
Other service establishments	3,100	27	1.5	40	4,660	24	1.1	25
Grand Total: Retail Stores and Services [d]	*91*	*29*	*55.0*	*1,479*	*132*	*27*	*37.8*	*1,053*

[a] Population estimated at 1,215,000.
[b] Does not include side frontages of corner stores.
[c] Population estimated at 340,000.
[d] Does not include vacant stores or frontage.

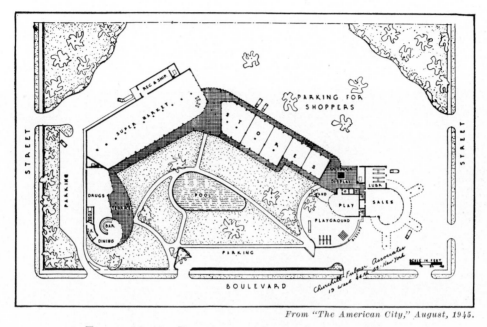

From "The American City," August, 1945.

FIGURE 11·46. DESIGN FOR A SMALL SHOPPING CENTER

Courtesy, American Community Builders, Inc.

FIGURE 11·47. SKETCH OF PROPOSED SHOPPING CENTER FOR A SATELLITE TOWN NEAR OLYMPIA FIELDS, ILLINOIS

located so as to be convenient to pedestrians, mass transit, and automobiles, which means that it almost always should be on a main highway. It should have ample offstreet parking facilities and should be so designed as to encourage the use of these facilities by the shopper. Vehicular and pedestrian circulation

An interesting example of a plan to reorganize the badly congested shopping center in Rye, New York, is shown in Figures 11·48 and 11·49. This plan proposed reorganization of vehicular circulation, closing to traffic the principal business street, providing considerable offstreet parking space, and developing the former street

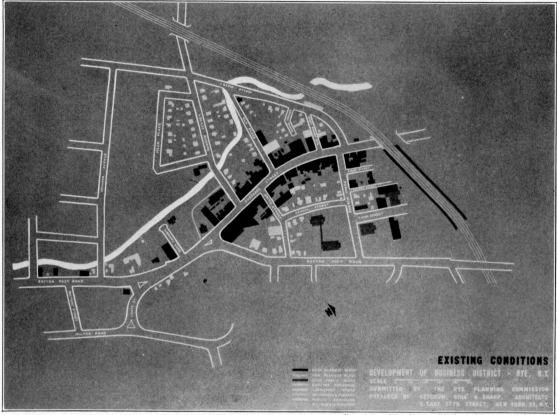

EXISTING CONDITIONS

Courtesy, Ketchum, Giná & Sharp, Architects.

FIGURE 11·48. PLAN SHOWING EXISTING DEVELOPMENT IN THE SHOPPING CENTER OF RYE, NEW YORK

should be separated as much as possible, with entrances and exits so designed as to minimize traffic congestion on the abutting streets. Deliveries to stores should be facilitated and kept separate from customer facilities whenever possible. Finally, the center should be attractive to the eye and should be insulated from abutting residential uses. Figure 11·46 shows a plan for a small shopping center which meets these requirements, and adds the desirable feature of a playground where small children can be left under supervision while the mother shops.

as a park strip. Arcaded sidewalks would conceal overhead wires and help to unify the façades of the existing business structures, most of which would be preserved. A perspective sketch of the proposed development of the closed street is shown in Figure 11·50. A bond issue authorized by referendum in June, 1948, included $500,000 for a start on this improvement by developing the parking lots essentially as shown, as part of a city-wide plan. Decision was deferred on the street changes involved, which provide an ingenious solution to a problem facing many communities today.

A plan was advanced in 1947 for a considerably larger shopping center in the borough of Queens, New York City. The 18-acre site of this project is located adjacent to a commuting railroad and the terminals of two subway lines and is the point of convergence of several local bus lines. Figure 11·51 shows a model of the proposed shopping center. In addition to the facilities shown, underground loading berths for trucks and underground moving ramps are

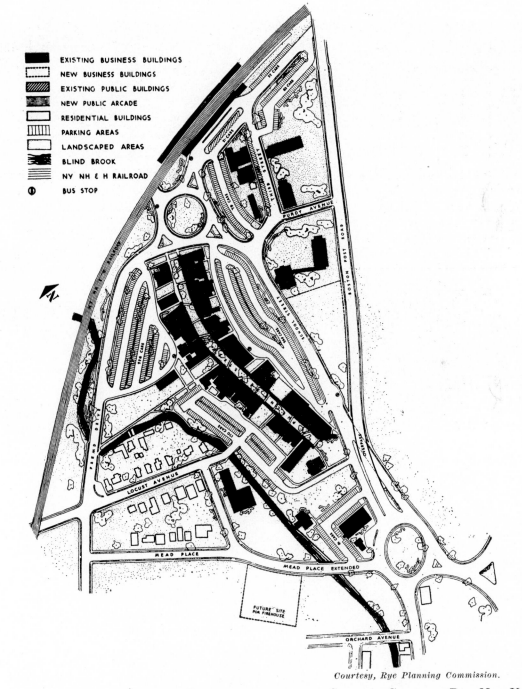

Courtesy, Rye Planning Commission.

FIGURE 11·49. PLAN OF PROPOSED REDEVELOPMENT FOR THE SHOPPING CENTER OF RYE, NEW YORK

Courtesy, Ketchum, Giná & Sharp, Architects.

FIGURE 11·50. SKETCH OF PROPOSED DEVELOPMENT AT RYE, NEW YORK

The present principal shopping street would be converted into a landscaped pedestrian way with arcaded sidewalks.

Courtesy, Lester Tichy, Architect.

FIGURE 11·51. PROPOSED NORTH SHORE SHOPPING CENTER AT FLUSHING, LONG ISLAND

Model of plan developed by Webb and Knapp, Realtors.

planned to connect all buildings in the group. Rooftop parking facilities are planned to accommodate 5,000 cars.

Selected References

A Government Center Plan for Dayton, Ohio—A Report on Civic Center Studies, prepared by the City Plan Board in co-operation with the Montgomery County Planning Commission, May, 1946.

DeBoer, S. R.: *Shopping Districts,* American Planning and Civic Association, Washington, D. C., 1937.

Green, Howard Whipple: *Shopping Centers,* Cleveland Real Property Inventory, Cleveland, Ohio, 1945.

Hegemann, Werner, and Elbert Peets: *Civic Art,* Architectural Book Publishing Company, Inc., New York, 1922.

Report of the Headquarters Commission (United Nations) to the Second Part of the First Session of the General Assembly of the United Nations, United Nations, Lake Success, New York, October, 1946.

Robinson, Charles Mulford: *Modern Civic Art,* G. P. Putnam's Sons, New York, Fourth Edition. Revised, 1918.

Wilgus, William J.: *The Grand Central Terminal in Perspective* (with discussion), *Transactions of the American Society of Civil Engnieers,* Vol. 106 (1941), pages 992–1051.

Questions

1. What are the types of public and semi-public buildings the location of which is of interest in developing a city plan?
2. What principles should govern the selection of sites for public buildings, such as municipal offices, courthouses, fire and police stations, schools?
3. How may adequate views of public buildings be assured? Give examples of good and bad locations.
4. In a capital city, should the municipal and capital centers be combined or separate? Give examples of each type of treatment.
5. To what other features of the city plan is a school site closely related?
6. What is the desirable size, as measured by the number of pupils, of an elementary school?
7. Give examples of good location and architectural treatment of miscellaneous public structures, such as post offices, monuments, railroad stations, sewage-treatment plants.
8. What effect has the Grand Central Terminal, New York City, as improved under electrification, had on the immediate vicinity?
9. What are some of the special planning features in the Rockefeller Center development in New York City?
10. What have been the main factors influencing the development of unified local shopping centers? How may the space requirements for such centers be estimated?

12

ZONING AND OTHER LAND USE CONTROLS

THIS CHAPTER WILL BE DEVOTED TO A CONSIDeration of the various measures which are designed to insure to the citizens at large the full enjoyment of all the advantages which a well-organized city should supply and to prevent such acts of the individual or such use of private property as will in any way militate against such enjoyment. The right to the free and safe use of the public streets is universally admitted. An adequate control of land use will also bring the citizens the following additional rights and advantages: freedom from obstruction of light and air by a neighboring owner; prevention of the appropriation of public property to private use; a guarantee of the preservation of the character of a district when once established by protecting it against invasion by industries, uses, and occupations inconsistent with that character; the conservation of the value of private property by an orderly scheme of development and improvement; the prohibition of the erection of structures, either permanent or temporary, which will offend the eye; the provision of facilities for sane and wholesome amusement and recreation; control of the density of population; the prevention of offensive odors or harsh and unnecessary noises, or of anything else destructive of what the English so well express by the word "amenity." In European cities these rights of the public have long been taken for granted, and the rights of the individual citizen and property owner must be subordinated to them.

Those restrictions most closely related to the city plan, and now generally considered a part thereof, are embodied in municipal zoning ordinances. There are, however, other public types of building restrictions based primarily on public safety, such as building codes, and on both safety and health, such as tenement-house laws, which will be mentioned briefly. There are also private deed restrictions imposed by the seller on the use of property by a purchaser and continuing to run with the land, usually for a specified term of years.

Varying Degrees of Acceptance of Restrictions

As already stated, the citizen is simply a small unit in what goes to make up a city. Whatever he does must be considered in its relation to and its effect upon the body of citizens whose interests, comfort, and convenience are paramount. American and, to a great extent, British cities have been slow in asserting themselves and do not appear to realize their rights as against the citizen. There is a traditional feeling among the English-speaking people, due, perhaps, to many of the provisions of the English common law, that a certain sanctity and inviolability are inherent in private property. This leads to the conclusion that its owner must be carefully protected against any act which may in the slightest degree curtail the fullest enjoyment of this property or any profit which may be derived from its use (provided such use is within the letter of the law), even though prejudicial to the comfort, convenience, and enjoyment of others.

The idea underlying this feeling is that the individual unit going to make up the city must be carefully protected against the tyranny of the city as a whole. If the owner is rich and powerful, he may take advantage of this protection for his own aggrandizement and to the serious detriment of those who are less fortunate. But it is better—so those who are passionately devoted to the sanctity of the rights of private property believe—that an injustice should be done to the general public than that the vested rights of real property should be violated. Just how private real property acquired these rights does not appear—whether through an omnipotent power which orders human affairs or whether by successive steps of aggression on the part of the land-owning class. But the right to use individual property in whatever manner seems best to the owner is a principle long accepted by many. They feel that to overturn it, or even to question it, would be subversive of public order and well-established legal procedure.

The word "restrictions," as applied to the regulations governing the use of private property, is likely to be understood in the United States and Great Britain, although in Continental Europe it is so generally recognized that the individual has no right to use his property without regard to the interest of his neighbor or of the general public that the prohibition of such use would scarcely be regarded as a restriction. The word implies public control of the use of such property in the interest of the public at large, although the right of the public to such control had yet to be conceded generally in the United States when comprehensive zoning was established in New York City in 1916.

There is still a disposition in many American cities to make use of portions of the public streets for private purposes. The exposure of goods for sale on the sidewalks in front of shops; the loading and unloading of bulky packages and barrels by means of skids extending across the sidewalks, with complete interruption of their intended use; the erection of permanent platforms on parts of the sidewalks in front of shops and warehouses handling heavy materials; the erection of storm doors, porches, steps to floors both above and below the street level; and even the storage of trucks and machinery in the streets at night—these are all common sights in many of our cities, whether the city's title to these streets is simply a public easement for street purposes or whether it is a fee absolute held in trust for the use and benefit of the whole city.

Nevertheless, the acceptance, by owners of real property in American cities, of the idea that the use of such property should be subject to a certain degree of control by the city has been surprising as well as gratifying. Owners very quickly came to understand that reasonable restrictions upon the use to which a neighbor could put his property would tend to stabilize and preserve all property values, and this idea and its enforcement have spread with astonishing rapidity.

Such regulations may have two separate and distinct purposes—(1) to improve sanitary conditions by insuring adequate light and air and avoiding damage in case of fire or accident, or (2) to add to the dignity and attractiveness of the streets. While the propriety and reasonableness of restrictions to insure better sanitation and protection from injury are now quite generally recognized, those which have for their object the mere improvement of the appearance of the street or which are based upon aesthetic considerations are very likely to be contested in the English-speaking countries. Before considering zoning as now practiced in the United States, it may be well to follow the development of similar regulations in other countries.

European Regulations

On the Continent of Europe aesthetic regulations have long been accepted as a matter of course, with the firm conviction that anything which affects the general appearance of the public streets is the concern of the entire community. In Great Britain, and more slowly in the other English-speaking countries, the feeling has grown since World War I that private rights have been unduly considered and must give way to the public interest—that is, to the interest of all the people. In large cities the social organization is so complex and the life of the individual touches thousands of others at so many points that the same freedom of action cannot be permitted which is unquestioned in a rural community.

In 1911 the greatest number of cities which had regulations designed to improve sanitary conditions was found in Germany. These regulations were applied in connection with the

in solid blocks was also permitted, and this district was commonly built up to a fairly uniform height. Outside this inner city there were other zones, in which the allowable height of buildings progressively diminished. Manufacturing districts were so located as to afford convenient transportation and to insure that the prevailing winds would blow the smoke away from the

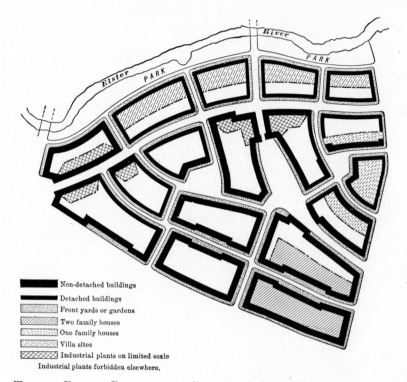

■■■ Non-detached buildings
▬ Detached buildings
▒ Front yards or gardens
▨ Two family houses
▧ One family houses
▤ Villa sites
▩ Industrial plants on limited scale
Industrial plants forbidden elsewhere.

FIGURE 12·1. TYPICAL PREWAR REGULATIONS GOVERNING THE USE AND CHARACTER OF BUILDINGS IN LEIPZIG, GERMANY

zoning system already generally adopted by German cities; this was first advocated by Baumeister in the seventies, but was not actually put in force anywhere until 1884 in Altona, when Franz Adickes was mayor. In 1891 Adickes, who had become the chief executive of Frankfort-on-the-Main, introduced it there, and it was soon taken up by the German and Scandinavian cities.[1]

In these early German regulations the older or inner city was naturally the first zone where the highest buildings were allowed. Building

[1] See report of F. B. Williams, *The German Zone Building Regulations,* made to the Heights of Buildings Commission of New York City and printed as an appendix to the report of that Commission in 1913.

residential districts. In some cases residences were entirely prohibited in the factory districts. In Munich and Karlsruhe classes of streets were established with different regulations for each class, Karlsruhe having created 16 classes of streets by ordinances adopted in 1912.

In Leipzig there was a tendency to decrease the cost of street construction and maintenance on those streets which would be confined to residences by allowing a width of only 11 meters. To compensate for this decreased width, setbacks were required, the area in front of the buildings being treated as gardens (see Figure 12·1). The planners favored a city plan which afforded artistic viewpoints, closed street pictures, variety in types of buildings, censorship of plans for the façades of buildings on prominent streets, and the preservation of natural beauties and village characteristics in outlying areas.

The proportion of the lot which could be covered with buildings was controlled by elaborate regulations in Berlin and at least six other German cities. Each city appears to have worked out its solution of this problem in a different way. All are worthy of careful study, and the fact that they were respected and followed indicates acceptance of the principle that the citizen must in the public interest submit to these limitations upon the free use of his property.

In zoning, as practiced in Great Britain, the regulations governing the proportion of the lot which must be left free are much less precise, and there is a greater similarity between those in force in different cities. The open spaces in the rear of dwellings are usually related to the heights of the buildings. A method of indirectly regulating the proportion of plots which may be built upon has been applied through the operation of the general town-planning law or was voluntarily adopted in many of the so-called garden-city developments which became so popular in England around the beginning of the twentieth century and which are treated in Chapter 18, Volume II. This method involves limiting the number of houses to the acre, such limitations, however, applying to subdivisions some acres in extent and covering an average number per acre, so that in one part of the subdivision the free space about buildings may be much less than in other parts.

The German cities did not hesitate to impose rigid height limitations on buildings. For example, in Berlin the height of buildings could not exceed the width of the street upon which they fronted, measured between building lines; in Frankfort-on-the-Main buildings on streets less than nine meters wide could not exceed 11 meters in height, but in the center of the city and in the factory district buildings on wider streets could exceed the street width in height by two meters, but could in no case be more than 20 meters high; in Hamburg buildings in so-called city divisions could not exceed 30 meters in height, while in outer or suburban divisions much stricter height provisions (expressed in number of stories) applied, and in some districts houses with more than a ground floor were not permitted. Whether these German height restrictions have gone too far is a debatable question.

Although in Great Britain considerable attention has been paid to the securing of better housing conditions, the regulations affecting the heights of buildings are quite meagre, although limitations of this character are likely to be imposed in connection with town-planning schemes. Birmingham early limited its buildings to 100 feet in height, and Sheffield to the width of the streets on which they front, with a possibility of greater height by special permission of the corporation.

While Edinburgh was the birthplace of the skyscraper, the high buildings in that city are perched on the steep hillsides. An Edinburgh lady, in conversation with the original author, severely criticised the tall station hotels at either end of the beautiful garden on Princes Street. When he reminded her that the skyscraper originated in her city, she in reply pointed out that the proper place for towers or castles was on the hilltops, where they can be seen to advantage and serve to accentuate the topography, but when placed in valleys their effect is to fill up the low places and detract from the beauty and dignity of the surrounding hills; and the force of her argument will be admitted.

Prezoning Restrictions in North America

Before the adoption of comprehensive zoning in 1916, a number of cities in the United States had enacted regulations governing the portions of lots which might be built upon. In no case had they been worked out in as great detail as in the German cities. These regulations were generally contained in city building codes, health regulations, factory and labor laws, and city ordinances. For example, in New York City tenement houses, or houses accommodating three or more families, could cover 90 per cent of corner lots having an area of not more

than 3,000 square feet, but if located on interior lots over 90 feet but not exceeding 105
feet in depth, only 70 per cent of the lot could
be covered. In Chicago tenement houses could
not be built nearer than 10 feet to a rear lot
line, except that when there was a rear public
alley, they could come within 16 feet of the
opposite side of the alley. In Philadelphia no
building for dwelling purposes could have a
frontage of less than 14 feet, and at least 144
square feet of the lot had to be kept open. In
each of these cities modern zoning ordinances
have supplemented or superseded these regulations.

As previously noted, regulations governing
the portions of building plots which may be
occupied are not likely to be opposed, as their
necessity is obvious. Those which are designed
to limit the height to which buildings may be
carried or to improve the appearance of the
city are not always accepted as reasonable.
Offices on the highest floors of American skyscrapers rent more readily than any others.
Why, then, both owner and tenant are likely to
ask, attempt to limit building heights for the
sake of the general appearance of the city, and
thereby limit the earning capacity of a building and the value of the ground and make it
impossible for those who wish comfortable
offices on the twenty-fifth or fortieth floor to
secure what they want?

A few cities in the United States had height
regulations before the era of zoning. Although
in New York City the labor, tenement house,
and other special laws imposed a virtual limit
upon the height of certain classes of buildings,
no direct limit was prescribed, except to restrict
buildings used as dwellings to a height of one
and a half times the width of the widest abutting street. Office buildings could be carried
to any height, and one 792 feet high had been
erected.

In Chicago tenements or dwelling houses
were limited to one and one-half times the
width of the widest street on which they
fronted, with greater height permitted where
buildings were set back from the street line.
Fireproof buildings for office and business purposes could be 200 feet high at the street line,

In Boston buildings in the business section
could not exceed two and one-half times street
width, or 125 feet, in height. In other parts of
the city the limit of height was 80 feet.
Wooden dwellings were limited to three stories
or 45 feet. Charleston, New Orleans, Cleveland, Fort Wayne, Buffalo, and Rochester in
the United States, and Toronto in Canada, also
had height limitations.

What was then considered a more radical
step in these early American regulations was
the attempt to restrict the use of property outside of street lines by specifying the uses to
which it might be put. While for many years
the conduct of certain noxious trades or occupations had been quite generally prohibited
within city limits or had been restricted to
certain districts where they would not affect
values or discourage other use of neighboring
property, the division of an entire city into districts, in each of which is prescribed the use to
which private property may be put, came into
practice in the United States only in the first
two decades of the twentieth century. In accordance with a procedure similar to that described for the early American area and height
limitations, the area of a municipality was divided into districts which were restricted to
business, residential, manufacturing, or mixed
occupancy. The factory districts were naturally those located along lines of rail or water
transportation, but their location was sometimes determined by the direction of prevailing
winds, in order that smoke and odors might not
become a nuisance in the business and residential districts.

Although a number of American cities had
adopted such regulations as to district use before 1916, none of them went as far as Los
Angeles. By an ordinance enacted in 1909 the
entire city, with the exception of two suburbs,
was divided into industrial and residential districts. There were 25 types of industrial districts but only one type of residential district.
Within the latter there were "residence exceptions" in which business was permitted subject
to certain conditions. Under the provisions of
this ordinance the municipal authorities sum-

marily ejected a number of small businesses from the residential district, and in one case a brickyard, established before the district in which it was located became a part of the city and operated for seven years before the law was enacted, was compelled to remove kilns, buildings, and machinery. This action was carried to the Supreme Court of the United States and sustained in one of the most sweeping decisions used in support of modern zoning —Hadacheck *v.* Sebastin (239 U. S. 394, 36 Sup. Ct., R. 143).

Seattle adopted a building code in 1913 which imposed restrictions upon the use to which property within the city might be put, and the state legislature of Maryland, by a special law, regulated the use of property in certain parts of the city of Baltimore. In 1912 the Massachusetts legislature amended the general municipal law to permit any city or town in the state to regulate the height, area, location, and use of buildings and other structures. The state of New York in 1913 authorized the municipal legislative body in any city of the second class, on petition of two-thirds of the property owners, to establish residential districts within which no buildings other than single- or two-family dwellings might be erected. Minnesota, in 1913, authorized the cities of Minneapolis, St. Paul, and Duluth to establish residential and industrial districts when petitioned for by a majority of the property owners. Wisconsin, in the same year, conferred quite similar power upon eight of the principal cities of the state after the city of Milwaukee had adopted an ordinance establishing a business section and excluding certain industries anywhere within the corporate limits.

The provincial legislature of Ontario authorized the councils of cities having a population of more than 100,000 to enact by-laws restricting the erection of buildings of certain classes to designated parts of the city, and Toronto, acting under the provisions of this law, prescribed the uses to which property might be put in a considerable portion of the city. Under this enactment apartment houses and garages were excluded from most of the residential streets.

New York City's Adoption of Comprehensive Zoning

This was the situation when New York City initiated in 1913 its pioneer effort in comprehensive regulation of use, height, and area which culminated in the New York City Zoning Resolution, adopted July 25, 1916, and giving the first legal status to the term "zoning." This term has since been generally accepted in the United States as applied to the establishment of regulations limiting the use to which property may be put, the proportion of the lot area which may be covered, the height to which buildings may be carried, and the density of population in residential areas.

It has been pointed out that the ideas that the municipal authorities had a distinct responsibility for the manner in which cities developed, that the general public had a right to protection from unsightly and offensive development, and that the individual property owner was entitled to guaranteed permanance of the character of the district in which he located his home or business, had already taken a firm hold in the United States and Canada. The New York City charter then gave the Board of Estimate and Apportionment, with approval of the Board of Aldermen, power to limit the height of buildings, but it did not appear to permit the designation of different limits for different streets or districts. The same height limit had to be imposed upon the financial and apartment house districts of Manhattan Island, the local business centers of other portions of the city, and the modest residential sections of Staten Island and the borough of Queens on Long Island. This did not begin to solve the problem.

Early in 1913 the Board of Estimate and Apportionment created a special committee of three of its members which was authorized to appoint an advisory committee to aid it in making a thorough study of all phases of the regulation of the height, size, and arrangement of buildings in different districts or zones. It was directed to examine into the practice and comparative experience of other cities in the United States and abroad and to report on the legal right of the city to regulate building construction in the manner proposed.

The advisory committee of nineteen, of which Edward M. Bassett was chairman, included in its membership lawyers, engineers, architects, builders, real estate developers, merchants, and experts on taxation, housing, and finance. A staff of investigators, statisticians, and draftsmen was organized under the general direction of George B. Ford. A great number of public hearings were held, at which representatives of every interest that would be affected appeared and presented their views. A special investigation was made of the results of the districting methods employed in Europe, and a final report submitted in December, 1913, which is a valuable contribution to the literature of the subject.[2] The report strongly emphasized the need and reasonableness of establishing districts both for height and use, and also for the area of yards, courts, and other open spaces on the lot. A few paragraphs of this report are worth quoting:

Manhattan with its skyscrapers is comparatively undeveloped. It is a fact that a large proportion of the area of lower Manhattan is now so poorly developed that the existing improvements are reckoned of no value for purposes of purchase or sale. The bare value of the land is all that is considered. This means that a large portion of the land of Manhattan is very inadequately utilized. Where space is so scarce, this inadequate utilization is a great social and economic loss. . . . A considerable percentage of the land, even in what are considered built-up districts, is either vacant or very inadequately utilized. . . . The natural result of a poor utilization of its land area by a city is high rents for occupiers and low profits for investors. It may seem paradoxical to hold that a policy of building restriction tends to a fuller utilization of land than a policy of no restriction; but such is undoubtedly the case. The reason lies in the greater safety and security to investment secured by definite restrictions. The restrictions tend to fix the character of the neighborhood. The owner therefore feels that if he is to secure the maximum returns from his land, he must promptly improve it in conformity with the established restrictions. . . .

Anything that will tend to preserve the character of a particular section for a reasonable period of years, will tend to bring about the uniform improvement of the section. A large proportion of the

[2] *Report of the Heights of Buildings Commission to the Committee on the Height, Size and Arrangement of Buildings of the Board of Estimate and Apportionment of the City of New York,* December 23, 1913.

land of New York City that is now unimproved or poorly improved is in that condition because the owners feel that the character of the section is changing, is bound to change in the near future or that the character of the section is unknown. If restrictions were imposed so that the general character of particular sections could be forecasted with reasonable certainty for a period of years, owners who had been holding back on account of the uncertainties of the situation would find it clearly to their advantage to improve their holdings. The result would be that these restricted sections would be more quickly built up with buildings of similar type and use. This should have the effect of improving living conditions, reducing the cost of living, and maintaining real estate values.

Any growing city that fails to control building development must inevitably suffer enormous loss due to building obsolescence. Obsolescence . . . results from changed conditions and surroundings that render the building an inappropriate improvement for the particular location. . . .

The need for the creation of special restrictions for special districts is most clearly exemplified in the case of suburban residence districts. Here real estate developers have often found it profitable to secure control of large areas in order by restrictive covenants to insure to intending purchasers of homes the creation and maintenance of a residence section of a certain desired type. The surroundings and neighborhood are all important in securing desirable home conditions. . . .

While its recommendations were chiefly in the nature of suggestions, the commission strongly urged that the state legislature be asked to grant to the city the power to establish districts and to impose for each district limits not only as to height and area which might be built upon but also to prescribe the use to which the property in each district might be put. Drafts of two proposed amendments to the city charter, in the form of grants of police power from the state to the city, were submitted with the report and were enacted into law by the state legislature. This law authorized a commission to recommend the boundaries of districts and appropriate regulations for each.

No time was lost in the appointment of the new commission, which included most of the members of the first commission and had the same chairman. The commission began work promptly and, although the undertaking was a formidable one requiring an immense amount of investigation, tentative plans were ready for discussion at the beginning of 1916. The question was whether the idea of imposing city-wide restrictions of this kind upon the use of real property would meet with popular support. Those most concerned were the owners of real estate, but they had begun to appreciate that any restriction placed upon the use of the individual owner was more than compensated for by a regulation which would prohibit an adjoining owner from doing something objectionable. Perhaps no one thing was of greater assistance to the commission in securing sympathetic interest than the steps taken by a group of real estate owners, merchants, manufacturers, bankers, hotels, and clubs in the Fifth Avenue district. In the daily papers of March 5, 1916, there appeared a full-page advertisement bearing the signature of 13 retail merchants, with the endorsement of 54 others, headed with the words: "Shall we save New York?—Shall we save it from unnatural and unnecessary crowding, from depopulated sections, from being a city unbeautiful, from high rents, from excessive and illy distributed taxation? We can save it from all of these, so far at least as they are caused by one specified industrial evil—the erection of factories in the residential and famous retail section." They then served notice that they would give the preference in their purchases to firms whose manufacturing plants were located outside a specified zone which included most of the high-class shops and hotels and many of the finest residences. The movement was successful, and a new garment center has been established on Seventh Avenue north of the Pennsylvania Railroad Station.

A tentative report and maps were prepared by the Commission and submitted on March 10, 1916; public hearings were held from then through the month of April. Surprisingly little opposition developed. Where opposition had been expected, there was either indifference or positive approval. The Commission submitted its final report on June 2.[3] The ordinance, accompanied by maps and defining the various districts, was adopted on July 25, 1916, and took effect immediately.

[3] *Commission on Building Districts and Restrictions —Final Report,* Committee on City Plan, Board of Estimate and Apportionment, City of New York, June 2, 1916.

Zoning Trends in the United States since 1916

Any new policy must be judged by its results. That these were prompt and effective was shown by a statement on what zoning had done for New York City, made in December, 1921, by E. M. Bassett, who was chairman of both commissions. His statement is briefly abstracted as follows:

It has checked the infiltration of hurtful industries in business and residence localities; it has entirely excluded public garages and service stations from residence districts and, except in special cases, from business districts; new stores cannot be placed at will in residence districts but must be confined to business streets where rental values are consequently improved; old established residence districts will continue as such and home-owning citizens can stay there; while not specifically forbidding apartment houses the area restrictions have prevented their invasion of districts where only a small proportion of the lot areas may be built upon; a new type of business and office building has been evolved which allows light and air to reach the streets; additional open space on building lots has made the structures more habitable and sanitary; there is a tendency to distribute population instead of concentrating it, rendering the transit problem less difficult of solution; owners of attached houses are maintaining them in better condition as the menace of invasion by business or apartment houses has passed and property values generally have been stabilized.

In the second edition of *The Planning of the Modern City,* Nelson P. Lewis deemed it necessary to list a large number of examples of use, height, and area regulations, mostly European, to prove the legality of zoning. That is no longer necessary, since the decision of the Supreme Court of the United States on November 22, 1926, in the case of the village of Euclid, Ohio, *v.* Ambler Realty Company,[4] established beyond a doubt the constitutionality of comprehensive zoning, including regulation of the use of both buildings and land.

The zoning idea has spread with extraordinary rapidity, and it may safely be stated that there is no aspect of city planning which is now attracting more attention. The danger is that it may be considered a substitute for city planning and that, a zoning plan having been adopted, enthusiasm and interest may die out. Zoning is not a substitute for a city plan; it is

[4] 272 U. S. 365, 47 Sup. Ct., R. 114 (Ohio).

an essential part of a comprehensive plan. Although the first thing to be done is to determine the general framework or structure of the city, the details cannot be intelligently worked out except in connection with the zoning plan or after the use districts, at least, shall have been determined.

In the first few years following the adoption of the New York City Zoning Resolution, the regret was frequently expressed that the restrictions had not been carried somewhat further, especially those as to height, and that provision was not made for both light- and heavy-industry districts. The members of the commission, especially its chairman, felt that the zoning idea would be on trial, that cases would inevitably be carried to the courts, and that if the plan and resolution were not upheld as reasonable and free from confiscatory provisions, other cities would not be encouraged to undertake zoning. The New York resolution has been sustained in every instance, and the extent to which the idea has been taken up and pushed is indicated by the long list of cities and towns in every part of the country which have either adopted zoning or have it under consideration.

A canvas made in 1922 indicated that city-wide zoning plans had then been adopted by 85 cities and towns in 21 different states. By January 1, 1926, the number had increased to 427 municipalities. The last nation-wide survey, made in 1936, listed 1,322 cities, towns, and villages in 47 states and the District of Columbia with zoning ordinances.[5] Since that time Detroit and an unknown number of smaller municipalities have adopted such ordinances. It was estimated that in 1946 over 1,500 zoning ordinances were in effect in the United States.

Not all zoning has been good zoning. In some cases ordinances have been copied arbitrarily from those from other communities (a dangerous procedure), and maps have been carelessly drawn, resulting in certain provisions which might be called discriminatory, or with an assumption by the municipality of

police power not actually delegated by the state. These defects have resulted in some adverse decisions, but these have almost universally applied to the application of the ordinance to a particular piece of property and not to zoning as such.

The national government helped to promote the cause of zoning through the appointment by then Secretary of Commerce Herbert Hoover of an Advisory Committee on Zoning. This committee was created in connection with the effort of the Secretary of Commerce to relieve the shortage of housing facilities by encouraging the adoption of zoning plans which would protect residential districts, in the belief that, with such protection assured, real estate owners would be more likely to resume the building of houses. It prepared a statement of what zoning is which, if kept in mind by those responsible for preparing zoning plans, may go far to preserve the integrity of such plans when adopted. The definition is substantially this: [6]

Zoning is the application of common sense and fairness to the public regulations governing the use of private real estate. It is a painstaking, honest effort to provide each district or neighborhood, as nearly as practicable, with just such protection and just such liberty as are sensible in that particular district. It avoids the wrong of trying to apply exactly the same building regulations to every part of a city, or town, regardless of whether it is a suburban residence section or a factory district, or a business and financial center. . . . Zoning gives everyone who lives or does business in a community a chance for the reasonable enjoyment of his rights. At the same time it protects him from unreasonable injury from neighbors who would seek private gain at his expense.

Zoning enabling legislation and the context of a municipal zoning ordinance will be discussed in more detail in Chapter 20, "City Planning Legislation," Volume II.

One of the difficult problems in zoning has been to determine the amount of business area that will be needed in a community. The first comprehensive study of the problem was made by Clarence Arthur Perry for the Committee on a Regional Plan of New York and Its Environs. From an analysis of retail business statistics and populations in seven cities, Perry found

[5] "Status of City and County Planning in the United States," *Circular X*, National Resources Committee, May 15, 1937.

[6] *A Zoning Primer*, by the Advisory Committee on Zoning, Department of Commerce, 1926, page 1.

that there were then two stores (50 feet of frontage) for each 100 residents "under average urban conditions." [7] Coleman Woodbury, in a study of 40 outlying municipalities in the Chicago region, found from 40 to 55 front feet of retail business per 100 persons of the city population.[8] However, these figures represent a greater amount than actually is necessary for profitable business, since all marginal stores are included, and there had been a tendency to overzone for business uses, thus encouraging overdevelopment. After considering all these studies and all the additional information that he could find, Perry in 1939 decided that one store per 100 population was the best available guide for allocating business frontage in an urban neighborhood community.[9] This figure checks closely with the results of a survey made in the Cleveland Metropolitan District in 1945 (see Chapter 11, page 246).

A book of fundamental importance in the development of zoning is the research on urban land uses made for the School of City Planning in Harvard University.[10] This analyzed the areas of different urban land uses in 16 typical self-contained cities and six satellite cities. Considerable variation was found in the relative amounts of specific uses in the different cities. The 16 self-contained cities, which varied in population from 8,697 to 307,808, had an average of 39.8 per cent of their total city area in vacant land. The average use distribution in the 60.2 per cent of developed area was as follows:

Use	Percentage
Single family	36.1
Two family	2.1
Multiple family	1.1
Commerce	2.4
Light industry	3.2

[7] *Neighborhood and Community Planning*, Vol. VII, Regional Survey of New York and Its Environs, 1929, pages 76–83.

[8] "The Size of Retail Business Districts in the Chicago Metropolitan Region," *Journal of Land and Public Utility Economics*, Vol. 4, February, 1928, pages 85–91.

[9] *Housing for the Machine Age*, by Clarence Arthur Perry, Russell Sage Foundation, New York, 1939, page 228.

[10] *Urban Land Uses*, by Harland Bartholomew, Harvard University Press, 1932.

Use	Percentage
Heavy industry	2.7
Railroad property	5.5
Streets	33.6
Parks	6.3
Public and semi-public	7.6

The commercial area was found to be the most uniform of all urban land uses, but its total was small. It was found that the average self-contained city had approximately 63.7 linear feet of commercial frontage per 100 persons, with about 28 linear feet per 100 persons in the central business district and the remainder in secondary and neighborhood business districts.

In the preface to the report, Theodora Kimball Hubbard said:

The practice of zoning has spread so rapidly in this country in the last dozen years, and municipalities have in so many cases adopted zoning ordinances based on inadequate and far from comprehensive or logical considerations that the time has come to pause in advocating merely zoning as such and to promote a wider understanding of zoning rationalized and related to sound economic policy. It is clearly impossible that all the land in a community should be developed for the uses which the individual land owner might imagine would be most profitable to him, were there no economic laws of supply and demand which must inevitably govern the amounts of land needed for the various purposes and the types of activities engaged in by citizens of any community.

. . . this volume will have an immediate value, both in planning new developments and in the revision of zoning ordinances found defective in operation.

A great help to scientific zoning for commercial districts has been the United States Census of Distribution, taken for the first time in 1929 and repeated in 1939. This gives the number of stores, the kinds of stores, and the sales, by minor civil divisions and by wards for the larger cities. There are wide differences between cities, and these data help the zoner in determining the individual needs of a particular city.

Need of Rezoning

Zoning techniques and standards have improved as the zoning process has been accepted by the courts, the municipal officials, realtors, and the public at large. As a practical necessity, zoning in its early stages involved many compromises, and many municipalities did not have the knowledge of local conditions and future trends that is now available. A better job can be done today than was possible 15 or 20 years ago.

Realizing this, a number of cities have been revising their zoning ordinances and maps.

this would increase the value of their holdings. An occasional owner may have profited, as against many who suffered from invasion of a one-family neighborhood by scattered apartments. A bulletin of the Regional Plan Association pointed out in 1938 that apartment zones are, in general, larger than necessary, partic-

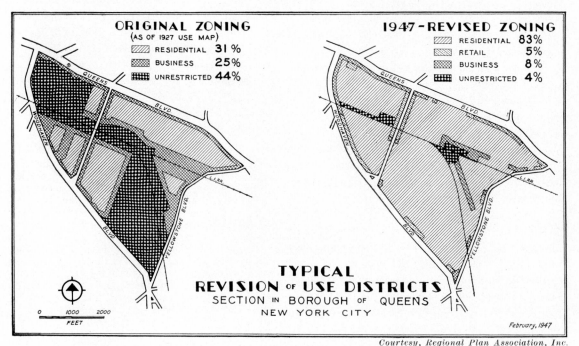

ORIGINAL ZONING
(AS OF 1927 USE MAP)
RESIDENTIAL 31 %
BUSINESS 25 %
UNRESTRICTED 44%

1947-REVISED ZONING
RESIDENTIAL 83%
RETAIL 5%
BUSINESS 8%
UNRESTRICTED 4%

TYPICAL
REVISION of USE DISTRICTS
SECTION IN BOROUGH OF QUEENS
NEW YORK CITY

February, 1947

Courtesy, Regional Plan Association, Inc.

FIGURE 12·2

These revisions have usually been along two lines: (1) reduction in the areas zoned for business and industry, and (2) provision of density regulations in residential areas.

When the first zoning ordinances were adopted, the city councils were faced with determined opposition from the owners of property on main streets. They had to choose between permitting business on all such property or running the chance of legal suits which might endanger the whole ordinance. As a consequence, most of the early ordinances included too much area for business and industry. These large areas zoned for business remained undeveloped. The expansion of business was very slow, and no new residences were built in these business zones.

There was pressure from some property owners in early zoning to have their property put in multi-family districts, as they believed that

ularly in view of the expected decline in rates of population growth, and stated:

Especially in suburban communities there is no justification, from the viewpoint of availability of space, for large multi-family districts. Not only is it improbable that these areas will ever be absorbed by their allotted use, but single-family residences will tend to avoid sections so zoned. The resultant spotting of apartments over a large area invariably leads to blight.

Contrary to popular belief, the apartment in unsuited locations does not create values, but actually exploits and capitalizes on the openness of adjoining single-family residences. From the community standpoint the apartment pays in taxes per square foot of land approximately three times as much as the single-family dwelling. However, when related to taxes per family, the apartment brings in only about one-half the amount paid by the single-family dwelling, yet the same municipal services including schools are provided for both.[11]

[11] "Need for Rezoning Found in New York and Its Environs," *Information Bulletin* 43, page 6, Regional Plan Association, Inc., October 31, 1938.

Where apartments were permitted, a density of occupancy much above modern standards was often allowed. Development of such buildings was generally in small units, whereas it is now the practice to have large-scale developments of groups of buildings on large sites, often combining in a single project various types of dwelling accommodations. The two-story or 2½-story garden apartment is replacing the three-story tenement and, in many cases, even the six-story elevator apartment. Such low apartment buildings, under proper restrictions, make better neighbors for one-family districts than the older kind of apartment. A greater flexibility in zoning ordinances to permit such buildings on suitable sites is often a desirable part of rezoning.

Most of main highway frontages were originally zoned for business, have been held by the owners for that purpose, and in many cases have been taxed upon such a future use. Much of such frontage has been rezoned for residence, and the business areas have been concentrated at strategic locations, but the problem is often a difficult one. Property adjoining new parks and parkways should generally be rezoned to more restrictive uses for protection of the parkway borders (see Figure 12·3).

The principal criticisms, already mentioned, of the original New York City zoning regulations have been largely remedied by supplementing the business districts by retail districts (added in 1929), restricted retail districts (added in 1927), and local retail, retail-1, and business-1 districts (added in 1940). There were also added in 1940 manufacturing districts to supplement the former unrestricted districts. The height and area regulations were considerably strengthened in 1944. The Resolution has become very involved, particularly because of the way in which some of the recent amendments were worded, and is badly in need of complete revision and simplification. Although this was one of the principal tasks urged by civic associations upon the City Planning Commission when it was established in 1938, it still remained to be done in 1947, although the height, use, and area maps for certain sections of the city had been overhauled and brought up to date.

There are other situations which call for rezoning. Inconsistencies may occur at the boundary lines of adjoining zoned communities; for example, one may have zoned vacant areas for future business or industry, while abutting areas in the other community have been de-

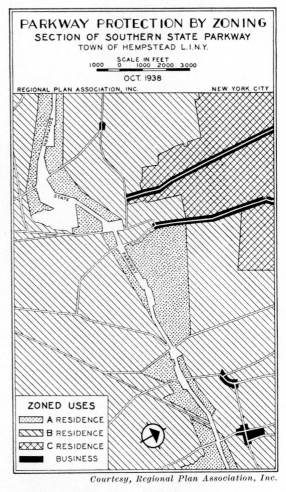

Courtesy, Regional Plan Association, Inc.

FIGURE 12·3

veloped and zoned for high-class residences. An early zoning ordinance may seriously conflict with a master plan which was developed at a later date. Single-family residences may not be sufficiently protected from two-family and multi-family districts. The need for offstreet parking of motor vehicles may have been overlooked. A grouping into logical neighborhoods may alter the distribution of both retail business and residence. Deflated ideas of population growth and a greater realization of the advantages of light and air and the lack of any

Courtesy, Regional Plan Association, Inc.

FIGURE 12·4. INFLUENCE OF ZONING ON ARCHITECTURE IN NEW YORK CITY

View in upper left shows the New York Life Building (with tower) compared with adjacent prezoning buildings; view in upper right, 40 Wall Street Building (*center*) and other buildings on its right compared with prezoning buildings on its left; lower view, hotels in the vicinity of 57th Street, Manhattan (*center and left*), compared with the prezoning Hotel Plaza (*right*).

necessity for overcrowding open the door to higher zoning standards.

There is also need for better administration of zoning and clearer definition in zoning ordinances of the duties and rights of zoning boards of appeals. Bassett has warned against unlawful zoning, pointing out that many boards of appeals are taking action which should be handled as amendments of the zoning ordinance by the legislative body. He stated:

The board of appeals is not a legislative body, and it cannot amend the law. It can do two things to help out property owners and must not go beyond them. It can make variances in cases of *practical difficulty* or *unnecessary hardship*. This does not mean changes. A wise judge in the early days of zoning said it means variations in the *application* of the words of the ordinance. The other place where the board can act is when the ordinance provides specifically for an exception—as, for instance, the provision for exceptions in the New York City ordinance, which states that in a business district the board of appeals may permit a new public garage in a street between two intersecting streets where a garage existed before the ordinance passed. These two are the only cases where the board can act in a valid manner.[12]

New Trends in Municipal Zoning

Certain significant trends appear in recent municipal zoning ordinances. These will be briefly mentioned.

Most of the zoning ordinances adopted before 1930 controlled population density indirectly by height and area requirements. It is now the practice to control population density directly, generally by a land-per-family requirement in residential districts.

Multi-family districts are being made subject to greater yard and lesser height requirements. Where these are designed for garden-type apartments, already referred to, ordinances frequently limit the height to 2½ stories, the coverage to 25 per cent and the density to 25 families per acre.

Special zoning around airports is being given increasing attention, although it is recognized that the owners of property within runway approaches have the right to a reasonable use of

[12] "A Warning as to Unlawful Zoning," by Edward M. Bassett, *The American City,* January, 1947, page 119.

the air space over their land, and that where such use might interfere with the safe use of an airport, the airport must purchase such air rights as it needs. The subject of controlling the area around airports is discussed in more detail in Chapter 16, "The Airport and the City Plan," Volume II.

It is customary to have a greater number of use categories than formerly, particularly for residential use. Unfortunately these have seldom been laid out in conformity with a sound physical pattern for the community, and confusion has resulted. Use districts must be designed to bear a relationship to each other, as well as to their physical environment, if zoning is to achieve its basic aim.

Specific requirements for offstreet parking space for automobiles are being established as accessory to certain types of business use, places of assembly, and multi-family residences. Closely related are requirements for offstreet truck-loading and unloading space, as accessory to certain types of business and manufacturing (see Chapter 17, "Motor-vehicle Parking," Volume II).

Special provisions are being included to facilitate large-scale development and provide a greater flexibility to the developer. In some cases these provisions authorize that, subject to approval of the Planning Commission, a developer may vary the use and height provisions of the zoning ordinance, provided the average density on the site will not exceed that required for the district or districts in which it lies and that he will develop it in accordance with a building plan made a part of the agreement. These provisions are generally applicable only to holdings exceeding a minimum area, such as 15 or 25 acres.

Neighborhood business districts restricted to retail shopping and small service establishments and with heights of buildings limited to 2½ or three stories are being created to supplement central business districts and provide a type of development that will not be harmful to abutting residential areas. In some cases the excess business areas along main highway frontages are being rezoned for a highly restricted type of light industrial district.

Billboards and advertising signs are being subjected to greater control. This is sometimes done by a separate municipal ordinance but is frequently handled through zoning. Many communities have adopted a complete ban of the advertising billboard. In many others they are permitted only in certain types of business areas, with their size and location strictly regulated; loud speakers, flood lighting, and flashing lights are frequently banned. Even large cities are tightening up on these forms of control, as illustrated by the following provisions added to the New York City Zoning Resolution in 1945:

No advertising sign shall hereafter be erected, placed, or painted, nor shall any existing advertising sign be structurally altered, in any use district within 200 feet of an arterial highway shown as a "principal route," "parkway," or "toll crossing" on the "Master Plan of Arterial Highways and Major Streets," provided such arterial highway has been designated by the City Planning Commission as an arterial highway to which the provisions of this section shall apply, or within 200 feet of a public park of one-half acre or more in area, if such advertising sign is within view of such arterial highway or park.

The municipal control of billboards has been supplemented by state control of signs along state highways. Massachusetts pioneered in this field, and its regulations were approved by the State Supreme Court in January, 1935, in a decision which recognized the use of the police power for aesthetic purposes.[13]

County Zoning

In many states, particularly those on the eastern seaboard, every part of the state lies within a city, borough, village, town, or township authorized under state enabling acts to prepare and adopt its own zoning ordinance. In some states there are large unincorporated areas which have only the county as a local governmental agency; in such cases it is only through some form of county zoning that these rural areas can have such protection as zoning affords.

The 1936 survey of planning agencies, already referred to, reported seven counties with comprehensive zoning ordinances and 23 counties with ordinances controlling only the use of land.[14]

Wisconsin heads the list of states with 23 county use zoning ordinances, one comprehensive county zoning ordinance, and two county ordinances in preparation. The comprehensive zoning ordinance is for Milwaukee County and is an extension of the municipal zoning of the city over the whole county. The 23 use zoning ordinances are for counties in the cut-over forest lands of the northern part of the state. The ordinances divide the area into agriculture and forest zones. In the agriculture zone all kinds of agriculture and year-round residence are permitted. In the forest zone only forestry and forest agriculture are permitted, and year-round residence is prohibited. The idea is to prevent scattered developments where schools, roads, and other services are prohibitively expensive. In some counties a third type of district, called the recreation zone, is included. In these, year-round residences for the caretakers of expensive summer camps are permitted. These ordinances are drawn up by a county agency but are operative only in those townships which adopt them by official action. They therefore are really a form of township zoning under county sponsorship.

California reported six counties with use zoning ordinances and four with comprehensive zoning ordinances. Most of these counties contain cities or a number of small villages, and the ordinances are to control the expansion of urban planning rather than to control agricultural development, as in Wisconsin.

All the counties surrounding the District of Columbia have zoning ordinances. The Montgomery and Prince Georges County zoning ordinances in Maryland are typical urban ordinances extending over an area much of which will never be urban. In Virginia the Arlington County area is small, and all of it is subject to urban development, so that the usual urban type of ordinance is appropriate.

[13] General Outdoor Advertising Co. v. Dept. of Public Works (289 Mass. 149, 193 N. E. 799).

[14] "Status of City and County Planning in the United States," *Circular X,* National Resources Committee, May 15, 1937.

In Fairfax County, Virginia, an attempt was made to provide an ordinance which would preserve land for agricultural uses until it was ripe for residential development, but the people were mainly interested in preventing the spread of hot-dog stands and filling stations along the main roads into the city of Washington.

Henrico County, Virginia, was reported to have a county zoning ordinance, but it appears that the county administers the local zoning ordinances of its villages. This is the county surrounding the city of Richmond.

Three counties in Colorado have been reported as recently adopting zoning ordinances. That for El Paso County, a semi-urban area outside Colorado Springs, was adopted April 15, 1942, and contained some novel provisions. In a dry-land farming district residences are required to have 10 acres of land. There is a forestry and recreation district, an airport farm district, and a roadside service district. Required highway setbacks run as high as 70 to 110 feet. In some areas the removal of non-conforming uses of *land* is required by the end of three years.

There seems to be a need in this country for a new type of county zoning, based on the model which has been developed in England, but not yet adopted very extensively. There the counties can zone their areas into "urban development zones" and "rural zones." The urban development zones are intended to be large enough to provide for the probable urban growth for five years, and at five-year intervals the situation must be restudied and these areas enlarged to provide for the next five years. Petitions can be filed at any time if the urban expansion requires more area. Sewers, water mains, and similar services are installed only in these areas. In the rural zones permits for the building of new residences are granted only where the lot is five acres or more in extent—large enough to provide safe water supply and sewage disposal on the individual lot.

Bergen County, New Jersey, furnishes an example of the help which a county planning board can give in achieving what is, in effect, a county zone plan. There 56 out of a total of 70 municipalities had adopted zoning or-

dinances by 1938, due largely to the educational campaigns conducted by the county planning board. The planning board has also plotted the zoning plans of all the separate communities on a large map of the county, which shows how the different plans do or do not agree. This map is taken to conferences and public meetings and has helped to reconcile differences of opinion regarding the zoning at the boundary lines of the different municipalities.

Related Building Restrictions

As has been pointed out, there are various other types of building restrictions, most of which preceded zoning, but from the point of view of city planning may be considered supplementary to it.

Based, like zoning, on the police power of the state delegated to its municipalities, are building codes and various sanitary, housing, and tenement-house codes. The building code is based primarily on structural safety, specifying in detail the kind and weight of materials that may be used in structures of various kinds and, therefore, subject to different loads. The preparation of such codes is a specialty in which engineers and architects have the leading parts. Much progress has been made in recent years toward their standardization and the provision of sufficient flexibility to enable the builder to make effective use of new materials. The sanitary, housing, and tenement house codes are designed for the protection of the health of the occupants of residential buildings. They deal with minimum space requirements, sanitation features, and fire protection and apply to all such buildings regardless of where they are located in the municipality.

The power of condemnation is the basis for other building restrictions. These include the purchasing of easements for utility rights of way, building setbacks for future street widenings, or pedestrian arcades within buildings. Recent redevelopment laws have permitted the employment of condemnation powers to acquire private land for the clearance of slums or other blighted areas for redevelopment in those cases where the owner refuses to sell. (See Volume II: Chapter 15, "Redevelopment of Blighted Areas," and Chapter 20, "City Planning Legislation.")

Private developers have frequently utilized deed restrictions more severe than those prescribed by the city in order to give a distinctive character to their development. This is equivalent to selling less than the full rights in the property. While such restrictions are frequently adopted in the interest of better fire protection and health, they more and more tend to prevent unsightliness, such as the provisions that side walls visible from the street must be finished to the same degree as the front and that painting in garish colors is forbidden.

In some German cities it was the custom to issue no permit for the erection of a building on any street which was classed as unfinished unless the plans for such building were first approved by some public officer. This power was frequently exercised in an autocratic fashion. For example, a piece of curbing might be deliberately left out on a certain block, and the street consequently called "unfinished." If the design of a building which a citizen desired to erect did not meet with the approval of the officer who had to issue the permit, he could say that the street was unfinished and refuse the permit. If, however, the design was so modified as to meet his approval, the permit would be issued.

There are almost no limitations on the kind or extent of restrictions which can be inserted in deeds, except that the courts have generally held that they cannot be perpetual. No public officials are responsible for the enforcement of such restrictions. The original owner, his heirs, or purchasers of lots who are subject to the same restrictions have to appeal to the courts for enforcement. Carefully drawn restrictions have been used for a large number of the best-designed subdivisions in the United States, and they have increased the value of the individual lots (see page 192). In such cases the part of the rights sold proved more valuable than the whole.

Control of Architecture of Buildings

While poor planning can lead to ugliness and monotony of appearance, these characteristics more often result from poor architecture or lack of any architectural design. The extent to which the architecture of buildings can be effectively controlled has become of increasing interest to city planners.

The progress in such control and in establishment of its legal basis was discussed in papers presented by Charles H. Cheney and Elvon Musick at one of the National Conferences on City Planning.[15] At that time Cheney said:

Architectural control and the architectural program of the city are as definite and inseparable a part of a comprehensive city plan as zoning, the major traffic street plan, the unification of rail lines and terminals, rapid transit, the park, playground, and school system or the grouping of civic centers and public buildings—the recognized parts of a complete city plan. It is astonishing that, with the marked progress in municipal planning and government in this country, some of our chief authorities overlook this important matter—the architecture, the biggest, the closest mass on the horizon of every city and of every life in it. Cities consist of buildings and their sites, commonly called architecture, although really only a small part of the buildings can be accurately dignified by that term.

The two general methods of exercising control are by private means, either through deed restrictions or voluntary associations of property owners, or by the extension of municipal powers to provide public control. In some cases there may be an effective combination of the two. The machinery should preferably involve an architectural jury, commission, or board of review. To be effective such an agency must be of high-caliber personnel and properly financed.

There have been many good examples of effective provisions in deed restrictions by progressive real estate developers, as in Roland Park, Maryland, Forest Hills, New York, and Palos Verdes Estates, California. The Palos

[15] "Progress in Architectural Control," by Charles H. Cheney, and "Legal Authority for Architectural Control," by Elvon Musick, *Planning Problems of Town, City and Region, Proceedings of the 19th National Conference on City Planning*, Washington, D. C., 1927, pages 248–286.

Verdes restrictions controlled an area of 3,225 acres and were carried out though a permanent art jury with a substantial endowment. The restrictions require that:

No building, fence, wall, sidewalk, steps, awning, tent, pole, or other structure, improvement, utility, parking, sculpture, or planting shall be erected, constructed, altered, or maintained upon, under, or above any portion of said property or of any property at any time within the jurisdiction of the Art Jury or of Palos Verdes Homes Association unless plans and specifications therefor, including the exterior color scheme, together with a block plan indicating location, shall have been submitted to, approved in writing by the Art Jury and a copy of such plans, specifications, and block plans as finally approved, deposited for permanent record with the Art Jury.

In Washington, D. C., voluntary control of architecture has been accomplished by an Architects' Advisory Council, which was organized by the Washington chapter of the American Institute of Architects and serves without fees, the architects giving their services for the good of the city as a whole.

In many communities good architecture has been stimulated by the award of certificates or other form of recognition, through local chambers of commerce or real estate boards, for the outstanding business, apartment, or other residential building erected each year.

Direct municipal control of the architecture of *public buildings* and structures has been practiced successfully in many cities for several decades. Outstanding successful examples are the New York City Art Commission and the Philadelphia Art Jury, but similar agencies have long functioned in Baltimore, Boston, Los Angeles, Milwaukee, Pittsburgh, and other cities. The federal Fine Arts Commission serves in a similar capacity in Washington, D. C.

The municipal control of *private buildings* has made slower headway but seems a logical step to expect. It was established in Santa Barbara, California, in 1925, following the destruction caused by a serious earthquake. An Architectural Board of Review of five members was appointed by the City Council, and all applications for building permits were required to be referred to them. If they approved the plans for a private building, the Inspector of Buildings was authorized to issue a permit; if they disapproved, their report was referred to the City Council, which could take final action only after a public hearing. All plans for public buildings required approval of the Architectural Board of Review.

After eight months of successful functioning, during which the board passed on some 2,000 applications, politics intervened, and the board was abolished, but it left a record of accomplishment which did much to create the present charm of Santa Barbara. In the Montecito section of the city architectural control was again established in 1927 by a voluntary agreement in the form of a protective covenant signed by several hundred property owners.

New Orleans has successfully prevented the modification, alteration, or construction of any façade out of architectural harmony with its surroundings in the Vieux Carre, or old French quarter, of the city.

All public control of architecture must, as in zoning, be based on the police power.

Relation to Land Use Master Plan

The basic part of any city plan relates to the development of the pattern of land use. This is generally based upon a survey and mapping of existing uses, such as has been described in Chapter 4 (see pages 45 to 50).

A more detailed survey of uses of land and buildings must precede the preparation of a zoning ordinance. A typical survey of this type for a suburban community obtained the following classifications, based on a survey from an automobile supplemented by one on foot in the business centers:

Business uses
  Business building, store, office, restaurant, etc.
  Gasoline filling station.
  Garage.
  Billboard.
Residential uses
  Closely developed with one-family dwellings.
  Scattered one-family dwellings.
  Two-family dwelling.
  Multi-family dwelling.
Industrial uses
  Clay or gravel pit, open storage.
  Manufacturing or covered storage.
Miscellaneous uses
  Public park, historical reservation.
  Fire house.

Miscellaneous uses
   School.
   Hospital.
   Other institution.
   Golf club.

prove valuable as an aid in zoning. Such a series is shown in Figure 12·5.

From the more elementary land use survey, a general pattern of the character of future

FIGURE 12·5. EXISTING LAND USES IN THE UPLAND SECTION OF THE TOWN OF KEARNY, NEW JERSEY, 1943

Prepared as a basis for a zoning ordinance.

   Church, cemetery.
   Nursery.
   Greenhouse.
   Fraternal organization, club, etc.
   High-tension electric line.

In more urban communities a series of maps, each showing a single use classification supplemented by one showing vacant lands, will

public and private development is prepared and may be adopted by a planning commission as part of its master plan. It would obviously be a more general and less detailed plan than that adopted by the legislative body as the building-zone map accompanying, and part of, the zoning ordinance. Yet the importance of the close relationship between the two is apparent. Only when both are worked out concurrently can there be assurance that the zoning is sound.

Selected References

BARTHOLOMEW, HARLAND: *Urban Land Uses,* Vol. IV, Harvard City Planning Studies, Harvard University Press, Cambridge, Mass., 1932.

BASSETT, EDWARD M.: *Zoning—The Laws, Administration and Court Decisions during the First Twenty Years,* Russell Sage Foundation, New York, Second Edition, 1940.

COMEY, ARTHUR C.: *Transition Zoning,* Vol. V, Harvard City Planning Studies, Harvard University Press, Cambridge, Mass., 1933.

FORD, GEORGE B.: *Building Height, Bulk and Form,* Vol. II, Harvard City Planning Studies, Harvard University Press, Cambridge, Mass., 1931.

METZENBAUM, JAMES: *The Law of Zoning,* Baker, Voorhis and Company, New York, 1930.

MONCHOW, HELEN C.: "The Use of Deed Restrictions in Subdivision Development," *Studies in Land Economics, Research Monograph* 1, The Institute for Research in Land Economics and Public Utilities, Chicago, 1928.

"Progress in Highway Protection Secured through County and Town Zoning," *The Roadside Bulletin,* National Roadside Council, New York, December, 1946.

Report (Final) of the Commission on Building Districts and Restrictions (New York City), Board of Estimate and Apportionment, City of New York, June 2, 1916.

Report of the Heights of Buildings Commission (New York City) to the Committee on the Height, Size and Arrangement of Buildings of the Board of Estimate and Apportionment, City of New York, December 23, 1913.

"The Preparation of Zoning Ordinances—A Guide for Municipal Officials and Others in the Arrangement of Provisions in Zoning Regulations," *Building and Housing Publication BH* 16, U. S. Department of Commerce, Washington, D. C., 1931.

WILLIAMS, FRANK B.: *The Law of City Planning and Zoning,* The Macmillan Company, New York, 1922.

Zoning in New York State—A Guide to the Preparation of Zoning Ordinances, State of New York Department of Commerce, Albany, N. Y., September, 1946.

Questions

1. What advantage will an adequate control of land use bring to the citizens of a community?
2. How has the general approach to land use control in the United States and Great Britain differed from that in the continental countries of Europe?
3. Where and when did the zoning of land by a municipality originate?
4. What were some of the types of regulations governing the use of land and the heights of buildings in effect in the United States before comprehensive zoning was initiated here?
5. Under what circumstances were the heights of buildings first controlled in New York City? What effect was produced on the architecture?
6. What has the federal government done to advance the progress of zoning?
7. On what power is zoning based? What are its principal objectives?
8. Why is the rezoning of many communities now essential?
9. Give a classification of districts in a zoning ordinance suitable for a suburban community of about 25,000 population.
10. What is the function of a zoning board of appeals? What pitfalls should it avoid?
11. What are some of the new trends in zoning practice?
12. What types of zoning have been done by counties?
13. What is the fundamental difference between a building code and a zoning ordinance?
14. How may private deed restrictions supplement zoning?
15. To what extent have municipalities controlled the architecture of public buildings? Of private buildings?
16. What types of information concerning land use are needed as a basis for a zoning ordinance?